Middle School 2-1
중간고사 완벽대비

KB084797

적중100

영어 기출 문제집

중2
미래 | 최연희

Best Collection

구성과 특징

교과서의 주요 학습 내용을 중심으로 학습 영역별 특성에 맞춰 단계별로 다양한 학습 기회를 제공하여
단원별 학습능력 평가는 물론 중간 및 기말고사 시험 등에 완벽하게 대비할 수 있도록 내용을 구성

Words & Expressions

Step1   Key Words 단원별 핵심 단어 설명 및 풀이
         Key Expression 단원별 핵심 숙어 및 관용어 설명
         Word Power 반대 또는 비슷한 뜻 단어 배우기
         English Dictionary 영어로 배우는 영어 단어

Step2   실력평가 단원별 수시평가 대비 주관식, 객관식 문제풀이

Step3   서술형 대비 학업성취도 및 수행능력평가 대비 서술형 문제풀이

Conversation

Step1   핵심 의사소통 소통에 필요한 주요 표현 방법 요약
         핵심 Check 기본적인 표현 방법 및 활용능력 확인

Step2   대화문 익히기 교과서 대화문 심층 분석 및 확인

Step3   교과서 확인학습 빈칸 채우기를 통한 문장 완성 능력 확인

Step4   기본평가 시험대비 기초 학습 능력 평가

Step5   실력평가 단원별 수시평가 대비 주관식, 객관식 문제풀이

Step6   서술형 대비 학업성취도 및 수행능력평가 대비 서술형 문제풀이

Grammar

Step1   주요 문법 단원별 주요 문법 사항과 예문을 알기 쉽게 설명
         핵심 Check 기본 문법사항에 대한 이해 여부 확인

Step2   기본평가 시험대비 기초 학습 능력 평가

Step3   실력평가 단원별 수시평가 대비 주관식, 객관식 문제풀이

Step4   서술형 대비 학업성취도 및 수행능력평가 대비 서술형 문제풀이

Reading

Step1   구문 분석 단원별로 제시된 문장에 대한 구문별 분석과 내용 설명
         확인문제 문장에 대한 기본적인 이해와 인지능력 확인

Step2   확인학습A 빈칸 채우기를 통한 문장 완성 능력 확인

Step3   확인학습B 제시된 우리말을 영어로 완성하여 작문 능력 키우기

Step4   실력평가 단원별 수시평가 대비 주관식, 객관식 문제풀이

Step5   서술형 대비 학업성취도 및 수행능력평가 대비 서술형 문제풀이
         교과서 구석구석 교과서에 나오는 기타 문장까지 완벽 학습

Composition

|영역별 핵심문제|

단어 및 어휘, 대화문, 문법, 독해 등 각 영역별 기출문제의 출제 유형을 분석하여 실전에 대비하고 연습할 수 있도록 문제를 배열

|단원별 예상문제|

기출문제를 분석한 후 새로운 시험 출제 경향을 더하여 새롭게 출제될 수 있는 문제를 포함하여 시험에 완벽하게 대비할 수 있도록 준비

|서술형 실전 및 창의사고력 문제|

학교 시험에서 점차 늘어나는 서술형 시험에 집중 대비하고 고득점을 취득하는데 만전을 기하기 위한 학습 코너

|단원별 모의고사|

영역별, 단계별 학습을 모두 마친 후 실전 연습을 위한 모의고사

교과서 파헤치기

- **단어Test1~3** 영어 단어 우리말 쓰기, 우리말을 영어 단어로 쓰기, 영영풀이에 해당하는 단어와 우리말 쓰기
- **대화문Test1~2** 대화문 빈칸 완성 및 전체 대화문 쓰기
- **본문Test1~5** 빈칸 완성, 우리말 쓰기, 문장 배열연습, 영어 작문하기 복습 등 단계별 반복 학습을 통해 교과서 지문에 대한 완벽한 습득
- **구석구석지문Test1~2** 지문 빈칸 완성 및 전문 영어로 쓰기

Lesson 1

Great Things about Yourself

 의사소통 기능

- 능력 표현하기
  I'm good at jumping rope.
- 확신 표현하기
  I'm sure it's going to rain soon.

 언어 형식

- 주격 관계대명사
  - She told me about her coworkers **who** had special talents.
  - She rides a super scooter **which[that]** can fly.
- 때를 나타내는 접속사
  - **While** I was walking home, I saw a woman on a scooter.
  - **After** I got home, I began to write a new graphic novel.

Words & Expressions

교과서

Key Words

- **activity**[æktívəti] 명 활동
- **actually**[ǽktʃuəli] 부 실제로, 정말로
- **adventurous**[ædvéntʃərəs] 형 모험성이 강한, 모험을 즐기는
- **awesome**[ɔ́:səm] 형 경탄할 만한, 엄청난
- **bake**[beik] 동 (빵을) 굽다
- **become**[bikʌ́m] 동 ～이 되다
- **cafeteria**[kæfətíəriə] 명 카페테리아, 구내식당
- **cartoon**[ka:rtú:n] 명 만화, 만화 영화
- **cartoonist**[ka:rtú:nist] 명 만화가
- **character**[kǽriktər] 명 성격, 등장인물
- **cheerfully**[tʃíərfəli] 부 기분 좋게, 쾌활하게
- **cloudy**[kláudi] 형 흐린, 구름이 잔뜩 낀
- **cookbook**[kúkbùk] 명 요리책
- **coworker**[kóuwə̀:rkər] 명 함께 일하는 사람, 동료
- **danger**[déindʒər] 명 위험
- **decide**[disáid] 동 결정하다, 결심하다
- **drawing**[drɔ́:iŋ] 명 그림, 데생
- **enough**[inʌ́f] 부 ～에 필요한 정도로, ～할 만큼 (충분히)
- **fun**[fʌn] 명 재미 형 재미있는, 즐거운
- **funny**[fʌ́ni] 형 우스운, 웃기는
- **graphic novel** 만화 소설
- **hit**[hit] 동 때리다, 치다 명 인기 작품, 히트
- **husband**[hʌ́zbənd] 명 남편
- **janitor**[dʒǽnitər] 명 문지기, 수위
- **joke**[dʒouk] 명 우스개, 농담
- **jump rope** 줄넘기를 하다
- **listener**[lísnər] 명 듣는 사람, 청자
- **model**[mádl] 동 모델로 하다 명 모델, 모형

- **nervous**[nə́:rvəs] 형 불안해[초조해/두려워] 하는
- **novel**[návəl] 명 소설
- **once**[wʌns] 부 한 번, 언젠가
- **outside**[áutsáid] 부 밖에(서)
- **pause**[pɔ:z] 명 (말이나 행동 등의) 멈춤
- **per**[pər] 전 각[매] ～에 대하여, ～당[마다]
- **practice**[prǽktis] 동 연습하다
- **president**[prézədənt] 명 대통령, 회장
- **push-up**[pʌ́ʃʌ̀p] 명 엎드려 팔굽혀펴기
- **ranger**[réindʒər] 명 공원[삼림] 관리원
- **real**[rí:əl] 형 진정한, 진짜의
- **recycle**[ri:sáikl] 동 재활용[재생]하다
- **role model** 역할 모델, 모범이 되는 사람
- **scooter**[skú:tər] 명 스쿠터(소형 오토바이)
- **skill**[skil] 명 기량, 기술
- **skip stones** 물수제비뜨다
- **someone**[sʌ́mwʌn] 대 어떤 사람, 누군가
- **speaker**[spí:kər] 명 연사, 말[이야기]하는 사람
- **speech**[spi:tʃ] 명 연설, 담화
- **super**[sú:pər] 형 대단한, 굉장히 좋은
- **superhero**[sjú:pərhìərou] 명 슈퍼히어로
- **sure**[ʃuər] 형 확신하는, 확실히 아는
- **talent**[tǽlənt] 명 재능, 탤런트
- **tooth**[tu:θ] 명 이, 치아, 이빨
- **travel**[trǽvəl] 동 여행하다
- **unique**[ju:ní:k] 형 유일무이한, 독특한
- **vote**[vout] 동 투표하다
- **wrong**[rɔ́:ŋ] 형 틀린, 잘못된

Key Expressions

- **at last** 마침내, 드디어
- **be afraid of** ～을 두려워하다
- **be good at** ～을 잘하다
- **be good for** ～에 좋다
- **do a good job** (～을) 잘하다
- **fall asleep** 잠들다
- **give away** 거저 주다, 나누어 주다
- **Guess what?** 있잖아, 알겠니?, 맞혀 봐!

- **I guess so.** 그렇다고 생각한다.
- **make one's day** ～을 행복하게 만들다
- **out of** ～으로, ～에 의해
- **say hello to** ～에게 안부 전하다
- **such as** ～와 같은
- **take a look at** ～을 보다
- **watch out** 조심하다
- **Why don't you ~?** ～하지 그래?

Word Power

※ 동사에 -er, -or, -ist를 붙여서 행위자를 나타내는 단어

- □ **speak** (말하다) → **speaker** (연사)
- □ **listen** (듣다) → **listener** (듣는 사람)
- □ **write** (쓰다) → **writer** (작가)
- □ **paint** (그리다) → **painter** (화가)
- □ **invent** (발명하다) → **inventor** (발명가)
- □ **act** (연기하다) → **actor** (배우)

- □ **direct** (감독하다) → **director** (감독)
- □ **visit** (방문하다) → **visitor** (방문객)
- □ **art** (예술, 미술) → **artist** (예술가, 미술가)
- □ **science** (과학) → **scientist** (과학자)
- □ **cartoon** (만화) → **cartoonist** (만화가)
- □ **novel** (소설) → **novelist** (소설가)

English Dictionary

- □ **attend** 참석하다
  - → to be present at a meeting or event
  - 회의나 행사에 참석하다
- □ **cartoonist** 만화가
  - → a person whose job is to draw cartoons for newspapers and magazines
  - 신문과 잡지의 만화를 그리는 일을 하는 사람
- □ **cafeteria** 카페테리아, 구내식당
  - → a restaurant where you choose your food from a counter and take it to your table after paying for it
  - 당신이 카운터에서 음식을 선택하고 그것에 대해 지불한 후에 테이블로 가져가는 레스토랑
- □ **coworker** 함께 일하는 사람, 동료
  - → the people you work with, especially people on the same job or project as you
  - 당신이 함께 일하는 사람들, 특히 당신과 같은 일이나 프로젝트를 하는 사람들
- □ **janitor** 문지기, 수위
  - → a person whose job is to look after a building
  - 직업이 건물을 관리하는 사람
- □ **joke** 농담, 우스개
  - → something that is said or done to make you laugh, for example a funny story
  - 예를 들면 우스운 이야기처럼 당신을 웃게 하기 위해 말하거나 행해진 것
- □ **nervous** 불안해[초조해] 하는
  - → frightened or worried about something that is happening or might happen
  - 일어나고 있거나 또는 일어날 수 있는 일에 대해 두려워하거나 걱정하는
- □ **novel** 소설
  - → a long written story about imaginary people and events
  - 상상의 사람들과 사건에 대해 쓴 긴 이야기

- □ **pause** (말이나 행동 등의) 멈춤
  - → a short period when you stop doing something before continuing
  - 무언가를 계속하기 전에 하는 것을 멈추는 짧은 시간
- □ **recycle** 재활용[재생]하다
  - → to process things that have already been used, such as bottles or sheets of paper so that they can be used again
  - 병이나 종이와 같이 이미 사용된 것을 다시 사용될 수 있도록 처리하다
- □ **scooter** 스쿠터(소형 오토바이)
  - → a small light motorcycle which has a low seat
  - 좌석이 낮은 작고 가벼운 오토바이
- □ **speech** 연설, 담화
  - → the ability to speak or the act of speaking
  - 말하는 능력 또는 말하는 행위
- □ **speaker** 연사, 말[이야기]하는 사람
  - → a person who is making a speech or giving a talk
  - 연설을 하거나 이야기를 하는 사람
- □ **second** (시간 단위인) 초
  - → one of the sixty parts that a minute is divided into
  - 1분이 나뉘어진 60개의 부분 중의 하나
- □ **tooth** 이, 이빨
  - → the hard white object in your mouth, which you use for biting and chewing
  - 당신이 물고 씹는 데 사용하는 당신의 입안에 있는 딱딱한 하얀 물체

01 다음 중 단어의 성격이 <u>다른</u> 하나는?

① writer
② scooter
③ speaker
④ painter
⑤ listener

02 다음 빈칸에 알맞은 말이 바르게 짝지어진 것은?

- He was standing in front _____ me in the line.
- Eating too many snacks is not good _____ your health.

① of – at
② of – for
③ at – in
④ at – with
⑤ to – over

03 다음 영영풀이에 해당하는 단어로 알맞은 것은?

to go from one place to another, often to a place that is far away

① stay
② spend
③ carry
④ travel
⑤ dwell

서답형

04 다음 짝지어진 단어의 관계가 같도록 빈칸에 알맞은 말을 쓰시오.

boy : girl = husband : _____

05 다음 우리말에 맞게 빈칸에 알맞은 것은?

그들은 서로 인사한다.
➡ They say hello _____ each other.

① to
② of
③ at
④ for
⑤ with

서답형

06 다음 영영풀이에 해당하는 단어를 쓰시오.

the possibility that someone may be harmed or killed

➡ _____

서답형

07 다음 우리말에 맞게 빈칸에 알맞은 말을 쓰시오.

나는 무엇을 입을 것인지 결정할 수가 없어.
➡ I can't _____ what to wear.

08 다음 빈칸에 공통으로 알맞은 것은?

- The man is afraid _____ the mouse.
- There is a lot _____ water in the bottle.

① in
② of
③ up
④ about
⑤ at

01 다음 짝지어진 두 단어의 관계가 같도록 빈칸에 알맞은 말을 쓰시오.

(1) listen : listener = act : _____

(2) art : artist = cartoon : _____

(3) invent : _____ = write : writer

02 다음 우리말에 맞게 빈칸에 알맞은 말을 쓰시오.

(1) 바이러스들은 독감과 같은 질병을 일으킨다.

➡ Viruses cause diseases _____ _____ the flu.

(2) 나는 Erica가 잘할 거라고 믿는다.

➡ I think that Erica will _____ _____ _____ _____.

(3) 제가 가서 그 집을 한 번 보면 어떻겠습니까?

➡ Why don't I just go take _____ _____ _____ the house?

03 다음 빈칸에 들어갈 알맞은 말을 〈보기〉에서 골라 쓰시오.

┌─ 보기 ─┐
per   give   fun   unique
└────────┘

(1) We had a lot of _____ at Sarah's party.

(2) He will _____ an important speech tomorrow.

(3) That will be 50 dollars _____ day.

(4) Everyone's fingerprints are _____.

04 다음 괄호 안의 단어를 문맥에 맞게 고쳐 쓰시오.

(1) The next night was dark and _____. (cloud)

(2) She felt _____ on her wedding day. (nerve)

(3) Some robots do _____ jobs for humans. (danger)

05 다음 빈칸에 알맞은 말을 〈보기〉에서 골라 쓰시오.

┌─ 보기 ─┐
fall asleep   good for
give away   good at
└────────────┘

(1) Tom is _____ singing.

(2) Milk is _____ your health.

(3) I think he will _____ food to hungry people.

(4) He used to _____ after drinking a glass of beer.

06 다음 영영풀이에 해당하는 단어를 주어진 철자로 시작하여 쓰시오.

(1) h_____: the man a woman is married to

(2) d_____: to choose to do something, usually after you have thought carefully about the other possibilities

Conversation

교과서

1 능력 표현하기

> **A** What are you good at? 넌 무엇을 잘하니?
> **B** I'm good at skipping stones. 나는 물수제비뜨기를 잘해.

■ be good at은 '~을 잘하다, ~에 능숙하다'라는 의미로 at 뒤에는 명사 혹은 동사에 -ing를 붙인 동명사가 온다. be good at 대신 조동사 can을 쓸 수도 있다.

- I am good at playing basketball. 나는 농구를 잘해.
  = I can play basketball well.

■ be not good at ~은 어떤 일을 할 능력이 없는 것을 표현할 때 사용하는 표현이다. be poor at이나 조동사 can't[cannot]를 쓸 수도 있다.

- I'm not good at playing chess. 나는 체스를 잘 못해.
  = I'm poor at playing chess.
  = I can't play chess well.

■ 상대방의 능력 여부를 묻는 표현으로 'how+to부정사'의 구문을 쓰기도 하며 '~하는 법'의 뜻이다.

- Do you know how to ride a bike? 너는 자전거를 탈 줄 아니?
  = Can you ride a bike?

- A: Do you know how to grow these plants? 이 식물들을 어떻게 키우는지 아세요?
  B: No, I don't. 아니요.

핵심 Check

1. 다음 우리말과 일치하도록 빈칸에 알맞은 말을 쓰시오.

(1) **A**: I'm making gimbap. (난 김밥을 만들고 있어.)

   B: Wow! You're _____ _____ making gimbap. (와! 너 김밥 잘 만드는구나.)

(2) **A**: Can you show me _____ _____ use computers?

   (컴퓨터 사용하는 법을 내게 알려 줄래?)

   B: I'm sorry. I'm _____ _____ using computers. (미안해. 난 컴퓨터 사용이 서툴러.)

(3) **A**: Do you know _____ _____ _____? (너는 수영할 줄 아니?)

   B: No, I don't know. (아니. 몰라.)

2 확신 표현하기

> **A** It's so cloudy. 날씨가 아주 흐려.
>
> **B** I'm sure it's going to rain soon. 곧 비가 올 것이 틀림없어.

■ I'm sure ~.는 '나는 ~을 확신한다.'라는 의미로, 어떤 일이나 상황에 대해 확신하고 있음을 나타낼 때 사용하는 표현이다.

비슷한 표현

- It's certain that he is ill. 그가 아픈 것이 확실해.
- Certainly[Surely], Ann will succeed. 분명히 Ann은 성공할 거야.
- It's obvious that she is an actress. 그녀가 배우인 것은 명백해.
- There's no question about that. 그것에 대해서는 의심할 것이 없어.

■ 상대방이 확신하고 있는지의 여부를 물을 때는 Are you sure?로 물으며, 확신하고 있으면 Yes, I'm sure.로, 확신하고 있지 않으면 No, I'm not sure.로 답할 수 있다.

- A: What am I doing? 내가 무엇을 하고 있게?
  B: I think you're cleaning the window. 나는 네가 창문을 닦고 있다고 생각해.
  A: Are you sure? 확실해?
  B: Yes. I'm sure that you're cleaning the window. 응. 나는 네가 창문을 닦고 있다고 확신해.

비슷한 표현

- Are you certain? 확실하니?
- Are you serious? 정말이니?

- A: What am I doing? 내가 무엇을 하고 있게?
  B: I think you're singing a song. 나는 네가 노래를 부르고 있다고 생각해.
  A: Are you sure? 확실해?
  B: Yes, I'm sure. / No, I'm not sure. 응. 확실해. / 아니. 확실하지 않아.

핵심 Check

2. 다음 우리말과 일치하도록 빈칸에 알맞은 말을 쓰시오.

(1) **A:** I hope my mom will get better. (우리 엄마 건강이 좋아지시면 좋겠어.)

   B: Don't worry. I _____ _____ your mom will get better.

   (걱정하지 마. 틀림없이 너의 엄마 건강이 좋아지실 거야.)

(2) **A:** _____ you _____ that he'll win the game? (그가 그 게임에 이길 거라고 확신하니?)

   B: Yes, I am. (응. 그래.)

Listen & Speak 1 A-1

B: ❶What are you doing, Nami?

G: ❷I'm making a smart phone case out of my old jeans.

B: Wow! ❸You're good at recycling old things.

G: Thanks. I like recycling. ❹It's fun, and it's also good for our Earth.

B: 나미야, 뭐 하고 있니?

G: 오래된 청바지로 스마트폰 케이스를 만들고 있어.

B: 와! 너 오래된 것들을 재활용하는 것을 잘하는구나.

B: 고마워. 나는 재활용하는 것을 좋아해. 그것은 재미있고, 우리의 지구에도 좋아.

❶ 의문사로 시작되는 진행형 의문문: '의문사+be동사+주어+-ing ∼?'의 구문을 취한다.

❷ out of: ∼으로

❸ be good at+동명사: ∼을 잘하다

❹ It은 인칭대명사로 앞에 나오는 recycling을 받는다. be good for: ∼에 좋다

Check(√) True or False

(1) The boy is good at recycling old things.   T ☐ F ☐

(2) Recycling is good for our Earth.   T ☐ F ☐

 Listen & Speak 2 A-1

B: Hi, Cindy. ❶Is something wrong?

G: ❷I have to give a speech in front of the whole school. I'm so nervous.

B: Don't worry. You're a very good speaker. ❸I'm sure you'll do a good job.

G: Thanks, Minho. I feel much better now.

B: 안녕, Cindy. 무슨 일 있니?

G: 학교 전체 학생들 앞에서 연설을 해야 해. 아주 긴장이 돼.

B: 걱정하지 마. 넌 말을 아주 잘하잖아. 분명히 잘할 거야.

G: 고마워, 민호야. 이제 기분이 훨씬 좋아졌어.

❶ 상대방이 기분이 좋지 않아 보일 때 묻는 표현으로 What's the matter (with you)?로 바꿔 쓸 수 있다.

❷ have to: ∼해야 한다 / give a speech: 연설하다 / in front of: ∼ 앞에서

❸ I'm sure (that) ∼.: 나는 ∼을 확신해. / do a good job: 잘하다

Check(√) True or False

(3) The girl doesn't look so nervous.   T ☐ F ☐

(4) The girl speaks very well.   T ☐ F ☐

Listen & Speak 2 A-2

G: Tomorrow is my mom's birthday. ❶What should I do for her?

B: ❷Why don't you bake a cake for her? You're good at baking.

G: That's a good idea. ❸I hope my mom will like my cake.

B: I'm sure your mom will love it.

G: 내일은 우리 엄마의 생일이야. 내가 그녀를 위해 무엇을 해야 할까?

B: 너의 엄마를 위해 케이크를 굽는 건 어때? 넌 빵을 잘 굽잖아.

G: 좋은 생각이야. 엄마가 내 케이크를 좋아하셨으면 좋겠다.

B: 너의 엄마는 분명히 아주 좋아하실 거야.

❶ should: ∼해야 한다

❷ Why don't you ∼?: ∼하지 그래?(제안을 나타내는 표현) / bake a cake: 케이크를 굽다

❸ I hope (that) ∼.: 나는 ∼하기를 바란다.

Check(√) True or False

(5) Tomorrow is the girl's mother's birthday.   T ☐ F ☐

(6) The boy is good at baking.   T ☐ F ☐

Listen & Speak 1 A-2

B: Hello, everyone. I'm Kim Yujin. ❶I want to be your class president. ❷I'm a good listener and always try to help others. ❸I'm also good at planning fun school activities. ❹I'll work hard for our class, so please vote for me. ❺Thank you for listening!

❶ want to: ～하기를 원하다
❷ I'm a good listener = I'm good at listening / try to: ～하기 위해 애쓰다 / others = other people
❸ fun: 재미있는
❹ so: 그래서, 그러니까 / vote for: ～에 찬성하는 투표를 하다
❺ Thank you for -ing: ～해 주어서 감사합니다

Communicate: A. Listen and Answer

Yuri: What are you doing, Jaden?
Jaden: ❶I'm drawing cartoons.
Yuri: Really? ❷Can I take a look at them?
Jaden: ❸No, not yet.
Yuri: ❹Why not? ❺You can show me a few, can't you?
Jaden: ❻Well, I guess so.
Yuri: (pause) Ha, ha, ha! Awesome! I like your cartoons. You're really good at drawing.
Jaden: ❼Do you think so? ❽I want to be a cartoonist, but I don't think my drawing skills are good enough.
Yuri: Your cartoons are really funny, and you have unique characters. I'm sure you'll be a great cartoonist.
Jaden: Thank you, Yuri. ❾You just made my day.

❶ be동사+-ing: 현재진행형
❷ take a look at: ～을 보다
❸ No, not yet.=No, you cannot take a look at them yet.
❹ Why not?=Why can't I take a look at them?
❺ a few=a few cartoons / can't you?: 그렇지 않니?(확인을 위한 부가의문문)
❻ I guess so.=I guess I can show you a few.
❼ Do you think so?=Do you think that I'm good at drawing?
❽ want to: ～하기를 원하다 / are good enough: enough는 부사로 형용사를 수식할 때는 그 뒤에 위치한다.
❾ make one's day: ～을 행복하게 만들다

Communicate: B. Make Your Own Dialogue

A: ❶Why don't you join our musical theater club? ❷You're good at singing.
B: ❸Well, I'd like to, but I don't think I'm good at acting or dancing.
A: Don't worry. We can teach you. ❹I'm sure you'll learn fast. Just join us.
B: O.K. I'll think about it.

❶ Why don't you ～?: ～하는 게 어때?(상대방에게 제안을 하는 표현) ❷ be good at+동명사: ～을 잘하다 ❸ I'd like to = I'd like to join your musical theater club ❹ I'm sure (that) ～.: 나는 ～을 확신한다.

Progress Check 1

B: What are you doing?
G: ❶I'm making pizza for dinner.
B: Wow! ❷You're really good at cooking!
G: Thanks.

❶ for dinner: 저녁 식사를 위해
❷ You're really good at cooking!=You can cook really well!

Progress Check 2

B: ❶Is something wrong?
G: ❷I have to give a speech in English. ❸I'm so nervous.
B: Don't worry. ❹Practice your speech in front of your family. ❺I'm sure you'll do a good job.
G: Thank you. ❻I'll try.

❶ Is something wrong? = What's the matter (with you)? ❷ give a speech in English: 영어로 연설을 하다 ❸ nervous: 불안해 하는, 초조해 하는 ❹ 동사원형으로 시작하는 명령문 ❺ I'm sure (that) ～.: 나는 ～을 확신해. ❻ I'll try.: 그렇게 해볼게.

Progress Check 3

W: ❶Everybody is good at something. ❷Some people are good at drawing. ❸Other people are good at singing. ❹What are you good at?

❶ everybody는 부정대명사로 단수동사로 받는다.
❷, ❸ Some people ～. Other people ...: 어떤 사람들은 ～한다. 또 어떤 사람들은 …한다
❹ 의문대명사 What이 전치사 at의 목적어이다.

● 다음 우리말과 일치하도록 빈칸에 알맞은 말을 쓰시오.

Listen & Speak 1 A. Listen and Check

1. **B:** _____ are you _____, Nami?

   G: I'm _____ a smart phone case _____ of my old jeans.

   B: Wow! You're _____ at _____ old things.

   G: Thanks. I like _____. It's _____, and it's also _____ for our Earth.

2. **B:** Hello, _____. I'm Kim Yujin. I want to _____ your class _____. I'm a good _____ and always _____ to help others. I'm also _____ at planning _____ school activities. I'll _____ hard for our _____, so please _____ for me. Thank you for _____!

해석

1. B: 나미야, 뭐 하고 있니?
   G: 오래된 청바지로 스마트폰 케이스를 만들고 있어.
   B: 와! 너 오래된 것들을 재활용하는 것을 잘하는구나.
   G: 고마워. 나는 재활용하는 것을 좋아해. 그것은 재미있고, 우리의 지구에도 좋아.

2. B: 여러분, 안녕하세요. 저는 김유진입니다. 저는 여러분의 반 학급회장이 되고 싶습니다. 저는 남의 말을 잘 경청하고 항상 다른 사람들을 도우려고 노력합니다. 저는 재미있는 학교 활동 계획도 잘합니다. 저는 우리 반을 위해 열심히 일하겠으니 저에게 투표해 주세요. 들어주셔서 감사합니다!

Listen & Speak 2 A. Listen and Check

1. **B:** _____, Cindy. Is something _____?

   G: I _____ to give a speech in _____ of the whole school. I'm so _____.

   B: Don't _____. You're a very good _____. I'm _____ you'll do a good _____.

   G: _____, Minho. I feel much _____ now.

2. **G:** Tomorrow is my mom's _____. What _____ I do for her?

   B: Why _____ you bake a cake _____ her? You're _____ at baking.

   G: That's a good _____. I _____ my mom will _____ my cake.

   B: I'm _____ your mom will _____ it.

1. B: 안녕, Cindy. 무슨 일 있니?
   G: 난 학교 전체 학생 앞에서 연설을 해야 해. 아주 긴장이 돼.
   B: 걱정하지 마. 너는 말을 아주 잘하잖아. 분명히 잘할 거야.
   G: 고마워, 민호야. 이제 기분이 훨씬 좋아졌어.

2. G: 내일은 우리 엄마의 생일이야. 내가 엄마를 위해 무엇을 해야 할까?
   B: 너의 엄마를 위해 케이크를 굽는 건 어때? 넌 빵을 잘 굽잖아.
   G: 좋은 생각이야. 엄마가 내 케이크를 좋아하셨으면 좋겠다.
   B: 너의 엄마는 분명히 아주 좋아하실 거야.

Communicate A. Listen and Answer

1. **Yuri:** _____ are you _____, Jaden?

   Jaden: I'm drawing _____.

   Yuri: Really? _____ I take a _____ at them?

   Jaden: No, not _____.

   Yuri: Why _____? You can _____ me a few, _____ you?

   Jaden: Well, I _____ so.

   Yuri: (*pause*) Ha, ha, ha! Awesome! I like your _____. You're really _____ at _____.

   Jaden: Do you think _____? I want to _____ a cartoonist, but I don't _____ my drawing skills are good _____.

   Yuri: Your cartoons are really _____, and you have _____ characters. I'm _____ you'll be a great _____.

   Jaden: _____ you, Yuri. You just made my _____.

2. **A:** Why _____ you join our _____ theater club? You're good at _____.

   B: Well, I'd _____ to, but I don't _____ I'm _____ at acting or dancing.

   A: Don't _____. We can _____ you. I'm _____ you'll learn fast. Just _____ us.

   B: O.K. I'll _____ about it.

Progress Check

1. **B:** What are you _____?

   G: I'm _____ pizza for dinner.

   B: Wow! You're _____ good _____ cooking!

   G: Thanks.

2. **B:** Is something _____?

   G: I have to _____ a speech _____ English. I'm so _____.

   B: Don't _____. _____ your speech in _____ of your family. I'm _____ you'll do a good _____.

   G: Thank you. I'll _____.

3. **W:** Everybody is good at _____. _____ people are good _____ drawing. _____ people are _____ at singing. _____ are you good at?

1. 유리: 너 뭐 하고 있니, Jaden?
   Jaden: 만화를 그리고 있어.
   유리: 정말? 내가 그것들을 봐도 되니?
   Jaden: 아니, 아직은 아니야.
   유리: 왜 안 되는데? 몇 개 보여줄 수 있지, 안 그래?
   Jaden: 음, 그럴 수 있지.
   유리: (멈춤) 하, 하, 하! 대단해! 너의 만화가 마음에 들어. 넌 그림을 정말 잘 그리는구나.
   Jaden: 그렇게 생각하니? 나는 만화가가 되고 싶지만, 내 그림 그리는 기술이 충분히 능숙하지 않다고 생각해.
   유리: 네 만화들은 정말 재미있고, 독특한 캐릭터를 가지고 있어. 나는 네가 훌륭한 만화가가 될 거라고 확신해.
   Jaden: 고마워, 유리야. 넌 날 행복하게 해줬어.

2. A: 우리 뮤지컬 연극 동아리에 가입하는 게 어때? 노래를 잘하는구나.
   B: 음, 그러고 싶지만, 연기나 춤을 잘 못해.
   A: 걱정하지 마. 우리가 가르쳐 줄 수 있어. 나는 네가 빨리 배울 거라고 확신해. 그냥 우리와 함께 해.
   B: 좋아. 생각해 볼게.

1. B: 너 뭐 하고 있니?
   G: 저녁으로 피자를 만들고 있어.
   B: 와! 넌 요리를 정말 잘하는구나!
   G: 고마워.

2. B: 무슨 문제 있어?
   G: 영어로 연설을 해야 해. 아주 긴장이 돼.
   B: 걱정하지 마. 가족 앞에서 연설을 연습해 봐. 넌 분명히 잘할 거야.
   G: 고마워. 그렇게 해볼게.

3. W: 모든 사람은 잘하는 것이 있습니다. 어떤 사람들은 그림을 잘 그립니다. 또 어떤 사람들은 노래를 잘 부릅니다. 당신은 무엇을 잘합니까?

01 다음 대화의 빈칸에 들어갈 말로 알맞은 것은?

> **A:** Are you _____ at skiing?
> **B:** No, I'm not. But I can skate very well.

① bad   ② good   ③ well
④ fine   ⑤ better

02 다음 두 문장이 공통으로 의도하는 것은?

> • I'm sure that you're cleaning the window.
> • Surely, Ann is playing the piano.

① 확신하기   ② 허락하기
③ 변명하기   ④ 충고하기
⑤ 사과하기

03 다음 두 문장의 뜻이 같도록 빈칸에 알맞은 것은?

> musical instrument 악기

> Peter can play musical instruments well.
> = Peter _____ playing musical instruments.

① is well with   ② is better to
③ is good at   ④ is as well as
⑤ is good for

04 다음 대화의 빈칸에 알맞은 것은? (2개)

> **A:** What am I doing?
> **B:** I think you're singing a song.
> **A:** _____
> **B:** Yes. I'm sure that you're singing a song.

① Are you sure?   ② Are you right?
③ Are you certain?   ④ Are you wrong?
⑤ Are you satisfied?

01 다음 대화를 의미가 통하도록 알맞게 배열한 것은?

> (A) Wow! You're good at recycling old things.
> (B) What are you doing, Nami?
> (C) I'm making a smart phone case out of my old jeans.
> (D) Thanks. I like recycling. It's fun, and it's also good for our Earth.

① (A) – (D) – (B) – (C)
② (B) – (C) – (A) – (D)
③ (C) – (D) – (B) – (A)
④ (D) – (B) – (C) – (A)
⑤ (D) – (C) – (B) – (A)

 02 다음 문장과 바꾸어 쓸 수 있는 말은?

> Do you know how to use this machine?

① Are you using this machine?
② Why do you use this machine?
③ Can you use this machine?
④ May I use this machine?
⑤ Did you use this machine?

서답형
03 다음 우리말에 맞도록 빈칸에 알맞은 말을 쓰시오.

> 너는 그것이 네 개의 다리를 가지고 있다고 확신하니?
> ➡ Are you _____ that it has four legs?

서답형
04 다음 대화의 밑줄 친 말을 주어진 표현을 이용하여 영작하시오.

> A: Can you play the guitar?
> B: No, 나는 기타를 잘 못 쳐. (be good at)

➡ _____

 05 다음 〈보기〉의 문장과 의미가 같은 것은?

> ┤ 보기 ├
> I'm sure that he is alive.

① I think that he is alive.
② I don't know if he is alive.
③ I know where he lives.
④ It's certain that he is alive.
⑤ I've heard that he is alive.

06 다음 짝지어진 대화 중 어색한 것은?

① A: Can you fly?
　 B: Sure. I am good at flying.
② A: Are you sure that Jake is honest?
　 B: Of course. He never lies.
③ A: Sally drinks ten glasses of milk every day.
　 B: That's surprising!
④ A: You play the violin so beautifully!
　 B: I don't know how to play the violin.
⑤ A: Did you paint this?
　 B: Yes, I am good at painting.

[07~11] 다음 담화문을 읽고, 물음에 답하시오.

> B: Hello, everyone. I'm Kim Yujin. I want ⓐto be your class president. ⓑI'm a good listener and always try to help others. I'm also good ___ⓒ___ planning fun school activities. I'll work hard for our class, so please vote for me. Thank you for ⓓlisten!

07 위 담화문의 밑줄 친 ⓐ와 용법이 같은 것은?

① He has made a promise to help me.
② You are foolish to believe the rumor.
③ They sent some people to live on the planet.
④ We decided to go fishing in the river.
⑤ I awoke to find myself lying on the floor.

08 위 담화문의 밑줄 친 ⓑ와 같은 뜻이 되도록 다음 문장의 빈칸에 알맞은 말을 쓰시오.

> I _____ to others _____

09 위 담화문의 빈칸 ⓒ에 알맞은 것은?

① to   ② at
③ of   ④ for
⑤ with

10 위 담화문의 밑줄 친 ⓓ를 알맞은 형으로 고치시오.

➡ _____

11 위 담화문의 내용으로 알 수 없는 것은?

① 김유진은 반 학급회장이 되기를 원한다.
② 김유진은 남의 말을 잘 듣는다.
③ 김유진은 남을 돕기 위해 애쓴다.
④ 김유진은 공부를 열심히 한다.
⑤ 김유진은 자신을 반 학급회장으로 뽑아 달라고 말하고 있다.

[12~14] 다음 대화를 읽고, 물음에 답하시오.

> B: Hi, Cindy. ⓐIs something wrong?
> G: I have to ___ⓑ___ a speech in front of the whole school. I'm so nervous.
> B: Don't worry. You're a very good speaker. ⓒI'm sure you'll do a good job.
> G: Thanks, Minho. I feel much better now.

12 위 대화의 밑줄 친 ⓐ와 같은 뜻이 되도록 다음 문장의 빈칸에 알맞은 말을 쓰시오.

> What's the _____ _____ you?

13 위 대화의 빈칸 ⓑ에 알맞지 않은 것은?

① give   ② make
③ take   ④ deliver
⑤ bring

14 위 대화의 밑줄 친 ⓒ를 우리말로 옮기시오.

➡ _____

01 다음 괄호 안에 주어진 단어를 이용하여 우리말을 영어로 옮기시오.

(1) 그는 중국어를 잘한다. (good)

➡ _____

(2) 나는 방에 두 명의 소년이 있다고 확신해.
(sure, there)

➡ _____

(3) 너 쿠키를 어떻게 만드는 줄 아니?
(how, make, cookies)

➡ _____

02 다음 대화의 밑줄 친 우리말을 영어로 옮기시오.

> A: Do you know how to make gimbap?
> B: 나 요리 잘 못해.

➡ _____

03 다음 대화를 의미가 통하도록 알맞게 배열하시오.

> (A) Thanks.
> (B) What are you doing?
> (C) Wow! You're really good at cooking!
> (D) I'm making pizza for dinner.

➡ _____

04 다음 우리말과 일치하도록 괄호 안에 주어진 단어를 사용하여 문장을 완성하시오.

> A: Are you sure?
> B: Yes. 나는 그가 시험에 합격할 거라고 확신해.
> (sure, that, exam)

➡ _____

[05~07] 다음 대화를 읽고, 물음에 답하시오.

> G: Tomorrow is my mom's birthday. What should I do for her?
> B: ⓐWhy don't you bake a cake for her? You're good ____ⓑ____ baking.
> G: ⓒThat's a good idea. I hope my mom will like my cake.
> B: I'm sure your mom will love it.

05 위 대화의 밑줄 친 ⓐ를 다음과 같이 바꿔 쓸 때 빈칸에 알맞은 말을 쓰시오.

> How _____ _____ a cake for her?

06 위 대화의 빈칸 ⓑ에 알맞은 전치사를 쓰시오.

➡ _____

07 위 대화의 밑줄 친 ⓒ가 가리키는 것을 우리말로 쓰시오.

➡ _____

Grammar

① 주격 관계대명사

> • She told me about her coworkers **who** had special talents.
> 그녀는 내게 특별한 재능을 가지고 있는 자기 동료들에 대해 말했다.
>
> • This is the book **which** changed my view of life. 이것은 나의 인생관을 변화시킨 책이다.
>
> • Hold the door open for someone **that** is behind you.
> 여러분 뒤에 있는 사람을 위하여 문을 열어 두세요.

■ 관계대명사는 선행사인 명사를 대신하는 일종의 대명사이면서 이 대명사가 이끄는 절을 접속시킨다는 점에서 「접속사+대명사」의 기능을 동시에 갖는다. 관계대명사가 이끄는 관계사절에 의하여 수식받는 명사·대명사를 선행사라 하며 이때 관계사절은 선행사인 명사를 수식하므로 형용사절이다. 관계대명사는 선행사에 따라 which, who, that 등을 쓴다.

선행사	주격	소유격	목적격
사람	who	whose	whom / who
사물	which	whose / of which	which
사람, 동물, 사물	that	-	that

■ 주격 관계대명사는 관계대명사가 주어의 역할을 하는 경우에 쓰이며, 뒤따르는 동사는 선행사의 수에 일치시킨다.

• The boy **who** is wearing a blue shirt is my little brother. 파란색 셔츠를 입고 있는 소년은 내 남동생이다.
• This is a restaurant **which** is famous for pizza. 이것은 피자로 유명한 식당이다.

■ **주격 관계대명사 who, which, that**: 관계대명사가 이끄는 문장에서 주어 역할을 한다. 사람을 설명할 때는 「사람+who+동사」의 형태이고, 사물이나 동물을 설명할 때는 「사물[동물]+which+동사」의 형태이다. that은 사람, 사물, 동물에 모두 쓰인다.

• Mrs. Parker is a teacher **who[that]** is from Canada. Parker 씨는 캐나다에서 오신 선생님이다.
• Look at the robots **that[which]** are playing soccer. 축구를 하고 있는 로봇들을 봐.

cf. 선행사 앞에 all, every, no, any, the same, the only, the+최상급/서수 등이 올 경우, 보통 that을 사용한다.

• Jake is the only student **that** can speak Korean. Jake는 한국어를 말할 수 있는 유일한 학생이다.

핵심 Check

1. 다음 괄호 안에서 알맞은 것을 고르시오.

(1) Do you know the lady (who / which) is sitting on the bench?

(2) This is the smart phone (who / which) was made in Korea.

(3) The man (who / which) I met on the street is Mina's father.

(4) This is a novel (who / which) was written in easy English.

(5) Mr. White is a teacher (who / which) teaches English.

② 때를 나타내는 접속사

- **While** I was walking home, I saw a woman on a scooter.
  나는 집에 걸어가는 동안 스쿠터를 탄 여인을 보았다.

- **After** I got home, I began to write a new graphic novel.
  나는 집에 도착한 후에 새로운 만화 소설을 쓰기 시작했다.

- You should come back **before** it gets dark. 너는 어두워지기 전에 돌아와야 한다.

■ while

while은 '~하는 동안'의 뜻으로 뒤에는 상태를 나타내는 동사나 진행형이 올 때가 많다. while이 이끄는 부사절은 주절의 앞이나 뒤 어느 쪽에도 올 수 있다.

- **While** I'm out, be careful of the wolf. 내가 없는 동안 늑대를 조심하렴.
- I often sing **while** I'm taking a shower. 나는 샤워를 하는 동안 종종 노래를 부른다.

■ when

when은 '~할 때'의 뜻으로 while과 비슷한 의미를 나타낸다. when이 이끄는 부사절도 주절의 앞이나 뒤 어느 쪽에도 올 수 있다.

- It was snowing **when** I got up. 내가 일어났을 때 눈이 오고 있었다.
- **When** my aunt was young, she was rich. 나의 이모는 젊었을 때 부자였다.

■ before, after

before와 after는 때를 나타내는 접속사로 문장의 순서를 바꿔 같은 의미를 나타내기도 한다.

A before B: B하기 전에 A를 하다 (A가 먼저 → B가 나중)

A after B: B한 후에 A를 하다 (B가 먼저 → A가 나중)

- I eat breakfast **before** I go to school. 나는 학교에 가기 전에 아침밥을 먹는다.
- **After** I washed the dishes, I watched TV. 나는 설거지를 한 후에 텔레비전을 보았다.
- I washed my hands **before** I had dinner. 나는 저녁을 먹기 전에 손을 씻었다.
- I had dinner **after** I washed my hands. 나는 손을 씻은 후에 저녁을 먹었다.

■ 전치사로 쓰이는 before, after

- Take a bath **before** you go to bed. [접속사] 잠자리에 들기 전에 목욕을 해라.
  = Take a bath **before** going to bed. [전치사]

- I went to bed **after** I took a bath [접속사] 나는 목욕을 한 후에 잠자리에 들었다.
  = I went to bed **after** taking a bath. [전치사]

핵심 Check

2. 다음 괄호 안에서 알맞은 것을 고르시오.

(1) A man visited Ms. White (if / while) she was out.

(2) I'm going to go to the party (before / after) I put on this pretty dress.

(3) (Before / After) he goes to bed, he brushes his teeth.

01 다음 두 문장을 한 문장으로 만들 때 빈칸에 알맞은 말을 쓰시오. (that은 쓸 수 없음.)

>> stage 무대
necklace 목걸이

(1) I know the girl. She is dancing on the stage.

➡ I know the girl _____ is dancing on the stage.

(2) This is the necklace. I got it from Mike.

➡ This is the necklace _____ I got from Mike.

(3) My uncle lives in a house. It has a beautiful garden.

➡ My uncle lives in a house _____ has a beautiful garden.

(4) The boy is wearing a blue shirt. He is my little brother.

➡ The boy _____ is wearing a blue shirt is my little brother.

(5) Turkey is a country. It has many interesting things.

➡ Turkey is a country _____ has many interesting things.

02 다음 우리말과 일치하도록 빈칸에 알맞은 말을 쓰시오.

>> hurt 다치다
free 한가한
enter ~에 들어가다

(1) 나는 어제 축구를 하는 동안 다쳤다.

➡ I hurt myself _____ I was playing soccer yesterday.

(2) Jenny는 한가할 때 책을 읽는다.

➡ Jenny reads books _____ she has free time.

(3) Kirk는 숙제를 마친 후 네게 전화할 거야.

➡ Kirk will call you _____ he finishes his homework.

(4) 나는 방에 들어가기 전에 신발을 벗는다.

➡ I take off my shoes _____ I enter the room.

03 다음 괄호 안에서 알맞은 것을 고르시오.

>> water 물을 주다
flow 흐르다

(1) Look at the girl (who / which) is watering a flower.

(2) Those are the dolls (who / which) were made by my grandmother.

(3) I have a friend (which / who) lives in China.

(4) Kathy is the girl (that / which) is playing curling.

(5) The Thames is the river (who / which) flows through London.

01 다음 빈칸에 들어갈 말이 바르게 짝지어진 것은?

• I was late _____ the bus broke down.
• You can go swimming _____ I'm having lunch.

① when – if
② when – as
③ if – because
④ because – though
⑤ because – while

02 다음 대화의 빈칸 ⓐ, ⓑ에 들어갈 말이 순서대로 짝지어진 것은?

A: Do you know the girl ____ⓐ____ is sitting next to Mr. Brown?
B: Yes. She is Kevin's sister. Her hobby is ____ⓑ____ pretty dolls.

① who – collecting
② whom – collecting
③ which – to collect
④ whose – collecting
⑤ whose – to collect

03 다음 두 문장이 같은 뜻이 되도록 빈칸에 알맞은 것은?

Somebody knocked on the door before I finished the shower.
= I finished the shower _____ somebody knocked on the door.

① before
② while
③ because
④ until
⑤ after

서답형

04 다음 밑줄 친 부분을 어법상 바르게 고쳐 쓰시오.

(1) He's the boy <u>which</u> broke the window.
➡ _____

(2) This is the biggest dog <u>whom</u> I have ever seen.
➡ _____

05 다음 밑줄 친 ①~⑤ 중 어법상 어색한 것은?

You ①should ②come here ③before ④it ⑤will get dark.

① ② ③ ④ ⑤

[06~07] 다음 문장의 빈칸에 알맞은 것을 고르시오.

06

Do you know the man _____ is running after a dog?

① how
② who
③ whom
④ which
⑤ whose

07

This is the building _____ was built in 1790.

① who
② how
③ what
④ which
⑤ where

08 다음 중 빈칸에 while[While]이 들어가기에 적절한 문장은?

① _____ you do your homework, you can play.
② The girl plays the guitar _____ she is lonely.
③ _____ it rains tomorrow, we will stay home.
④ _____ it was very warm, she didn't take off her coat.
⑤ Would you clean my room _____ I'm out?

09 다음 빈칸에 알맞은 말이 순서대로 짝지어진 것은?

• Susan is the girl _____ will go to Europe with me.
• The dolls _____ are on the sofa are my sister's.

① who – which
② whom – that
③ which – who
④ which – which
⑤ whose – that

10 다음 중 밑줄 친 부분의 쓰임이 나머지와 <u>다른</u> 것은?

① Some people have long hair <u>while</u> others have short hair.
② <u>While</u> I was sleeping, I heard some strange sounds.
③ You can use my computer <u>while</u> I am out.
④ <u>While</u> I was in Rome, I visited some museums.
⑤ I was very happy <u>while</u> I was playing baseball.

11 다음 빈칸에 공통으로 알맞은 것은?

• My dad bought me a bag _____ was black.
• She would like to have a job _____ uses her talents.

① what
② who
③ whom
④ where
⑤ which

12 다음 두 문장의 의미가 같도록 빈칸에 알맞은 것은? (2개)

The bus goes to the station. It comes every fifteen minutes.
= The bus _____ goes to the station comes every fifteen minutes.

① who
② that
③ what
④ which
⑤ where

13 다음 우리말을 영어로 바르게 옮긴 것은?

내가 코트를 입는 동안 내 가방을 들고 있어 줘.

① Please hold my bag during I put on my coat.
② Please hold my bag if I put off my coat.
③ Please hold my bag though I put on my coat.
④ Please hold my bag while I put off my coat.
⑤ Please hold my bag while I put on my coat.

서답형

14 다음 문장에서 어법상 어색한 부분을 찾아 바르게 고쳐 쓰시오.

> Look at the boy and his dog which are running in the park.

_____ ➡ _____

15 다음 빈칸에 공통으로 알맞은 것은?

> • The flower died _____ I was away on a trip.
> • Mr. White likes golf, _____ his wife likes tennis.

① as   ② while
③ when   ④ since
⑤ whether

16 다음 〈보기〉의 밑줄 친 부분과 쓰임이 같은 것은?

> ┤ 보기 ├
> I know a man that works in a famous restaurant.

① They can't go that far.
② I'm afraid that he will not come.
③ The climate of Korea is similar to that of Germany.
④ There is a cat that is sleeping on the bench.
⑤ It was really nice weather that day.

서답형

17 다음 문장에서 어법상 어색한 부분을 바르게 고쳐서 문장을 다시 쓰시오.

> I will ask him about it when he will come home.

➡ _____

18 다음 중 밑줄 친 부분의 쓰임이 나머지 넷과 다른 것은?

① I'll call you after I arrive.
② She takes a walk after breakfast.
③ After I called my mom, I went to bed.
④ Tim and I always play tennis after school is over.
⑤ Apply this lotion on your body after you take a shower.

19 다음 중 어법상 어색한 것은?

① Do you know the boy which is running in the park?
② The woman is the only person that loves me.
③ Look at the trees which stand in front of the house.
④ We remember the typhoon that hit the island last year.
⑤ The girl who danced with you is my sister.

20 다음 중 밑줄 친 부분의 쓰임이 〈보기〉와 다른 것은? (2개)

> ┤ 보기 ├
> Frank plays computer games when he's not busy.

① I don't know when he will come.
② It was snowing when I got up.
③ Monday is the day when I wash clothes.
④ I cook for my father when my mother is out.
⑤ He was watching television when I called him.

01 다음 두 문장을 한 문장으로 만들 때 빈칸에 알맞은 말을 쓰시오.

> The cat has a long tail. It is lying over there.
> ➡ The cat _____ is lying over there has a long tail.

02 다음 문장에서 먼저 일어난 일을 밑줄로 표시하시오.

(1) I went shopping before he called me.
(2) After I had dinner, I read a book.
(3) They closed the door after it started to rain.
(4) Before he crosses the street, he looks around.

03 다음 빈칸에 공통으로 알맞은 말을 쓰시오.

> • Hajun has some photos _____ I took.
> • I know the woman _____ is playing the violin.

04 다음 문장에서 어법상 어색한 부분을 바르게 고쳐 문장을 다시 쓰시오.

> I will call you when I will arrive.
> ➡ _____

05 다음 두 문장을 괄호 안의 관계대명사를 이용하여 한 문장으로 바꿔 쓰시오.

(1) The young lady is sitting on the bench. She is our music teacher. (who)
➡ _____
_____

(2) We found a dog. It was running toward us. (which)
➡ _____

(3) This is the firefighter. He saved the baby from the burning building. (that)
➡ _____
_____

(4) This is the only story. It is interesting to read. (that)
➡ _____

06 다음 빈칸에 알맞은 말을 〈보기〉에서 골라 쓰시오. (문장의 앞에 오는 경우 대문자로 쓰시오.)

> ┤ 보기 ├
> when   while   after   before

(1) You must wash your hands _____ you eat.
(2) What do you usually do _____ you have free time?
(3) Mary and I always play tennis _____ school is over.
(4) We slept _____ they were working.

07 다음 두 문장을 관계대명사를 사용하여 한 문장으로 만드시오.

(1) I know the woman. She is standing by the car.

➡ _____

_____

(2) Did you see the car? It has only two doors.

➡ _____

(3) This is a restaurant. The restaurant is famous for its spaghetti.

➡ _____

_____

(4) The lady is my English teacher. She lives next door.

➡ _____

_____

08 다음 우리말과 일치하도록 주어진 단어를 바르게 배열하시오.

우리가 저녁을 먹는 동안, 엄마는 전화로 통화를 했다.
(dinner / having / we / while / are)

➡ _____, my mother talked on the phone.

09 다음 우리말을 영어로 바꾸어 쓸 때 빈칸에 각각 알맞은 말을 쓰시오.

어제 발생한 교통사고는 끔찍했다.
➡ The traffic accident _____ happened yesterday _____ terrible.

10 다음 주어진 문장을 괄호 안의 지시에 따라 바꿔 쓰시오.

After they finished dinner, they washed the dishes. (before를 사용하여)

➡ _____

_____

_____

11 다음 문장에서 어법상 어색한 부분을 찾아 바르게 고쳐 쓰시오.

Could you hold the line before my mom is taking off her shoes?

_____ ➡ _____

12 다음 주어진 단어를 이용하여 우리말을 영어로 옮기시오.

나는 야구를 좋아하는 의사를 알고 있다.
(know)

➡ _____

13 다음 우리말을 괄호 안의 단어를 이용하여 영어로 쓰시오.

그들은 그녀가 그곳에 도착한 후에 파티를 했다.
(have a party, arrive)

➡ _____

_____

Reading

Lunch Lady Begins

My name is Hojin, and I like to make graphic novels. While I was
walking home from school last week, I saw a woman on a scooter. She
looked really cool, and her scooter was very unique.

"Are you going home, Hojin?" she said to me suddenly.

"Yes, but do I know you?" I asked.

"Of course," she answered. "I see you at the school cafeteria every
day."

Surprisingly, she was one of the cafeteria workers at school.

"Amazing! She looks so different outside the school," I thought. "I
should write a graphic novel about her."

After I got home, I began to write a new graphic novel, *Lunch Lady
Begins*. In it, Lunch Lady is a superhero. She rides a super scooter
that can fly. She saves people from danger around the world. She
also makes 100 cookies per second and gives them away to hungry
children.

---

graphic 그래픽[도표]의

novel 소설

scooter 스쿠터(소형 오토바이)

unique 유일무이한. 독특한

surprisingly 놀랍게도

amazing 놀라운

different 다른

outside ~ 밖에서

superhero 슈퍼히어로

ride 타다

save 구하다

danger 위험

per ~당[마다]

give away 거저 주다

hungry 배가 고픈

📎 **확인문제**

● 다음 문장이 본문의 내용과 일치하면 T, 일치하지 않으면 F를 쓰시오.

1 Hojin likes to write romantic novels. ☐

2 The woman on a scooter works at the school cafeteria. ☐

3 Hojin never saw the woman at the school cafeteria. ☐

4 *Lunch Lady Begins* is Hojin's graphic novel. ☐

5 Lunch Lady rides a super scooter that can fly. ☐

A few days later, I showed my graphic novel to my friends.
며칠 후에   = showed my friends my graphic novel

"Awesome! I love this superhero. She's so cool," said all my friends.
awe(경외감)+some(형용사 어미)

"Guess what? I modeled her on Ms. Lee, one of our cafeteria
있잖아   동격 관계

workers," I told them.

I showed my book to Ms. Lee. She loved it, too. She also told me
= showed Ms. Lee my book   = my book

about her coworkers who had special talents. Ms. Park, another
주격 관계대명사   또 다른, 또 하나의

cafeteria worker, won a dancing contest. Mr. Kim, the janitor at our
win의 과거형 win—won—won   동격 관계

school, was once an adventurous park ranger.
한때, 예전에   adventure(모험)+ous(형용사 어미)

"I'd like to write superhero stories about them. Do you think they'll
= would like to: ~하고 싶다

like that?" I asked Ms. Lee.
그들에 대한 슈퍼히어로 이야기를 쓰는 것

"Of course they will," she said cheerfully. "Let's go and say hello to
~하자   ~에게 인사하다

our new superhero friends."

awesome 경탄할 만한, 엄청난

cool 멋진

guess 추측하다

worker 근로자, 직공

coworker 함께 일하는 사람, 동료

special 특별한

talent 재능, 탤런트

janitor 문지기, 수위

adventurous 모험성이 강한, 모험을 즐기는

ranger 공원[삼림] 관리원[경비 대원]

cheerfully 기분 좋게, 쾌활하게

확인문제

● 다음 문장이 본문의 내용과 일치하면 T, 일치하지 <u>않으면</u> F를 쓰시오.

1 Hojin showed his graphic novel to his friends. ☐

2 Some of Hojin's friends didn't like his novel. ☐

3 Ms. Lee didn't read Hojin's novel. ☐

4 Ms. Lee's coworkers had special talents. ☐

5 Ms. Park once won a dancing contest. ☐

6 Hojin wrote a new superhero story about Ms. Lee's coworkers. ☐

● 우리말을 참고하여 빈칸에 알맞은 말을 쓰시오.

1 My _____ is Hojin, and I _____ to make graphic _____.

2 _____ I was walking _____ from school last week, I saw a _____ on a scooter.

3 She _____ really cool, and her scooter was very _____.

4 "Are you _____ home, Hojin?" she said to me _____.

5 "Yes, _____ do I know you?" I _____.

6 "Of _____," she answered.

7 "I _____ you at the school cafeteria _____ day."

8 _____, she was one of the cafeteria _____ at school.

9 "Amazing! She looks so _____ outside the school," I _____.

10 "I _____ write a graphic novel _____ her."

11 _____ I got home, I _____ to write a new graphic novel, *Lunch Lady Begins*.

12 In it, Lunch Lady is a _____.

13 She _____ a super scooter _____ can fly.

14 She _____ people from _____ around the world.

15 She _____ makes 100 cookies _____ second and gives them away to _____ children.

1	내 이름은 호진이고, 만화 소설 쓰는 것을 좋아한다.
2	지난주에 나는 학교에서 집으로 걸어가던 중에 스쿠터에 탄 여자를 보았다.
3	그녀는 정말 멋져 보였고 그녀의 스쿠터는 매우 독특했다.
4	"호진아, 너 집에 가는 중이니?" 그녀가 갑자기 나에게 말했다.
5	"네, 그런데 저를 아시나요?" 나는 물었다.
6	"물론이지."라고 그녀가 대답했다.
7	"난 매일 학교 식당에서 너를 본단다."
8	놀랍게도, 그녀는 학교 식당 직원 중 한 명이었다.
9	"놀라워! 그녀는 학교 밖에서는 아주 달라 보여."라고 나는 생각했다.
10	"그녀에 대한 만화 소설을 써야겠다."
11	집에 도착한 후, 나는 〈런치 레이디 탄생하다〉라는 새로운 만화 소설을 쓰기 시작했다.
12	그 소설에서 런치 레이디는 슈퍼히어로이다.
13	그녀는 날 수 있는 슈퍼 스쿠터를 탄다.
14	그녀는 전 세계의 위험에 빠진 사람들을 구한다.
15	그녀는 또한 1초에 100개의 쿠키를 만들어 배고픈 아이들에게 나누어 준다.

16 A few days _____, I showed my _____ novel to my friends.

17 "Awesome! I love this _____. She's so _____," said all my friends.

18 "Guess _____? I modeled her _____ Ms. Lee, one of our cafeteria _____," I told them.

19 I _____ my book _____ Ms. Lee.

20 She _____ it, too.

21 She _____ told me about her coworkers _____ had special _____.

22 Ms. Park, _____ cafeteria worker, won a _____ contest.

23 Mr. Kim, the _____ at our school, was _____ an adventurous park _____.

24 "I'd _____ to write superhero _____ about them. Do you _____ they'll like that?" I _____ Ms. Lee.

25 "Of _____ they will," she said _____.

26 "Let's _____ and say _____ to our new _____ friends."

---

16 며칠 후에 나는 나의 만화 소설을 친구들에게 보여 주었다.

17 "멋져! 나는 이 슈퍼히어로가 너무 좋아. 그녀는 아주 멋져."라고 내 모든 친구들이 말했다.

18 "있잖아, 나는 그녀를 우리 식당 직원 중 한 명인 이 여사를 모델로 했어."라고 나는 친구들에게 말했다.

19 나는 이 여사에게 내 책을 보여 주었다.

20 그녀도 그것을 아주 좋아했다.

21 그녀는 또한 나에게 특별한 재능을 가진 그녀의 동료들에 대해 말해 주었다.

22 또 다른 식당 직원인 박 여사는 댄스 경연대회에서 우승했다.

23 우리 학교의 관리인인 김 선생님은 한때 모험적인 공원 관리원이었다.

24 "저는 그들에 대한 슈퍼히어로 이야기를 쓰고 싶어요. 그분들이 그걸 좋아할 것 같아요?" 나는 이 여사한테 물어보았다.

25 "물론 그럴 거야."라고 그녀가 기분 좋게 말했다.

26 "가서 우리의 새 슈퍼히어로 친구들에게 인사하자."

● 우리말을 참고하여 본문을 영작하시오.

1 내 이름은 호진이고, 만화 소설 쓰는 것을 좋아한다.

➡ _____

2 지난주에 학교에서 집으로 걸어가던 중에 스쿠터에 탄 여자를 보았다.

➡ _____

3 그녀는 정말 멋져 보였고 그녀의 스쿠터는 매우 독특했다.

➡ _____

4 "호진아, 너 집에 가는 중이니?" 그녀가 갑자기 나에게 말했다.

➡ _____

5 "네, 그런데 저를 아시나요?" 나는 물었다.

➡ _____

6 "물론이지," 그녀가 대답했다.

➡ _____

7 "난 매일 학교 식당에서 너를 본단다."

➡ _____

8 놀랍게도, 그녀는 학교 식당 직원 중 한 명이었다.

➡ _____

9 "놀라워! 그녀는 학교 밖에서는 아주 달라 보여."라고 나는 생각했다.

➡ _____

10 "그녀에 대한 만화 소설을 써야겠다."

➡ _____

11 집에 도착한 후, 나는 〈런치 레이디 탄생하다〉라는 새로운 만화 소설을 쓰기 시작했다.

➡ _____

12 그 소설에서 런치 레이디는 슈퍼히어로이다.

➡ _____

13 그녀는 날 수 있는 슈퍼 스쿠터를 탄다.

➡ _____

14 그녀는 전 세계의 위험에 빠진 사람들을 구한다.

➡ _____

15 그녀는 또한 1초에 100개의 쿠키를 만들어 배고픈 아이들에게 나누어 준다.

➡ _____

16 며칠 후에 나는 나의 만화 소설을 친구들에게 보여 주었다.

➡ _____

17 "멋져! 나는 이 슈퍼히어로가 너무 좋아. 그녀는 아주 멋져."라고 내 모든 친구들이 말했다.

➡ _____

18 "있잖아, 나는 그녀를 우리 식당 직원 중 한 명인 이 여사를 모델로 했어."라고 나는 친구들에게 말했다.

➡ _____

19 나는 이 여사에게 내 책을 보여 주었다.

➡ _____

20 그녀도 그것을 아주 좋아했다.

➡ _____

21 그녀는 또한 나에게 특별한 재능을 가진 그녀의 동료들에 대해 말해 주었다.

➡ _____

22 또 다른 식당 직원인 박 여사는 댄스 경연대회에서 우승했다.

➡ _____

23 우리 학교의 관리인인 김 선생님은 한때 모험적인 공원 관리원이었다.

➡ _____

24 "저는 그들에 대한 슈퍼히어로 이야기를 쓰고 싶어요. 그분들이 그걸 좋아할 것 같아요?"
나는 이 여사한테 물어보았다.

➡ _____

25 "물론 그럴 거야."라고 그녀가 기분 좋게 말했다.

➡ _____

26 "가서 우리의 새 슈퍼히어로 친구들에게 인사하자."

➡ _____

[01~05] 다음 글을 읽고, 물음에 답하시오.

My name is Hojin, and I like to make graphic novels. (①) ___ⓐ___ I was walking home from school last week, I saw a woman on a scooter. (②)

"Are you going home, Hojin?" she said to me ⓑsudden. (③)

"Yes, but do I know you?" I asked. (④)

"Of course," she answered. "ⓒI see you at the school cafeteria every day." (⑤)

Surprisingly, she was one of the cafeteria workers at school.

01 위 글의 ①~⑤ 중 다음 주어진 문장이 들어갈 알맞은 곳은?

> She looked really cool, and her scooter was very unique.

①   ②   ③   ④   ⑤

 위 글의 빈칸 ⓐ에 알맞은 것은?

① If   ② After
③ While   ④ Before
⑤ Though

서답형

03 위 글의 밑줄 친 ⓑ를 알맞은 형으로 고치시오.

➡ _____

서답형

04 위 글의 밑줄 친 ⓒ를 우리말로 옮기시오.

➡ _____

05 위 글의 내용으로 보아 대답할 수 없는 질문은?

① What does Hojin like to do?
② When did Hojin see a woman on a scooter?
③ Where does Hojin lives?
④ Does the woman know Hojin?
⑤ What does the woman do?

[06~10] 다음 글을 읽고, 물음에 답하시오.

Surprisingly, the woman was one of the cafeteria workers at school.

"Amazing! She looks so ___ⓐ___ outside the school," I thought. "I should write a graphic novel about her."

___ⓑ___ I got home, I began to write a new graphic novel, *Lunch Lady Begins*. In it Lunch Lady is a superhero. She rides a super scooter that can fly. She saves people from ___ⓒ___ around the world. She also makes 100 cookies ⓓper second and gives them away to hungry children.   * I=Hojin

위 글의 빈칸 ⓐ에 알맞은 것은?

① same   ② happy
③ busy   ④ different
⑤ pleased

07 위 글의 빈칸 ⓑ에 알맞은 것은?

① Because   ② If
③ Before   ④ While
⑤ After

서답형

08 위 글의 빈칸 ⓒ에 다음 정의에 해당하는 단어를 주어진 글자로 시작하여 쓰시오.

> the possibility of something happening that will injure, harm, or kill someone

➡ d_____

중요

09 위 글의 밑줄 친 ⓓ와 바꿔 쓸 수 있는 것은?

① a   ② an
③ the   ④ that
⑤ some

10 위 글의 내용과 일치하지 않는 것은?

① The woman worked at the school cafeteria.
② Hojin didn't see the woman before.
③ Hojin wanted to write a graphic novel about her.
④ Lunch Lady rides a super scooter that can fly.
⑤ Lunch Lady saves people from danger around the world.

[11~14] 다음 글을 읽고, 물음에 답하시오.

A few days ⓐlate, I showed my graphic novel ___ⓑ___ my friends.

"Awesome! I love this superhero. She's so cool," said all my friends.

"___ⓒ___ what? I modeled her on Ms. Lee, one of our cafeteria workers," I told them.

* I=Hojin

11 위 글의 밑줄 친 ⓐ를 알맞은 형으로 바꿔 쓰시오.

➡ _____

12 위 글의 빈칸 ⓑ에 알맞은 것은?

① at   ② of
③ to   ④ for
⑤ with

13 위 글의 빈칸 ⓒ에 알맞은 것은?

① Say   ② Tell
③ Think   ④ Guess
⑤ Believe

서답형

14 Whom did Hojin model her on? Answer in English.

➡ _____
  _____

[15~19] 다음 글을 읽고, 물음에 답하시오.

I showed my book to Ms. Lee. She loved it, too. She also told me about her coworkers ⓐwho had special talents. Ms. Park, ___ⓑ___ cafeteria worker, won a dancing contest. Mr. Kim, the janitor at our school, was once an ⓒadventure park ranger.

"I'd like to write superhero stories about them. Do you think they'll like ⓓthat?" I asked Ms. Lee.

"Of course they will," she said cheerfully. "Let's go and say hello to our new superhero friends."

* I=Hojin

⭐중요
15 위 글의 밑줄 친 ⓐ 대신 쓸 수 있는 것은?

① whom   ② whose
③ that   ④ what
⑤ which

16 위 글의 빈칸 ⓑ에 알맞은 것은?

① any   ② some
③ other   ④ another
⑤ the other

서답형
17 위 글의 밑줄 친 ⓒ를 알맞은 형으로 고치시오.

➡ _____

서답형
18 위 글의 밑줄 친 ⓓ가 가리키는 것을 우리말로 쓰시오.

➡ _____

19 위 글의 내용으로 보아 대답할 수 없는 질문은?

① What did Hojin show to Ms. Lee?
② Whom did Ms. Lee tell Hojin about?
③ What does Mr. Kim do for a living?
④ When did Ms. Park win a dancing contest?
⑤ Why do Ms. Lee and Hojin go to their superhero friends?

[20~23] 다음 글을 읽고, 물음에 답하시오.

My aunt is my ___ⓐ___. She is smart, strong, and adventurous. In her 30s, she traveled to 70 different countries. ___ⓑ___ she was traveling, she made friends from all over the world. I want to be someone ⓒwho is not afraid of trying new things just ⓓlike her.

서답형
20 위 글의 빈칸 ⓐ에 다음 정의에 해당하는 말을 주어진 철자로 시작하여 쓰시오.

someone you admire and try to imitate

➡ r_____ m_____

21 위 글의 빈칸 ⓑ에 알맞은 것은?

① As   ② If
③ After   ④ Since
⑤ While

서답형
22 위 글의 밑줄 친 ⓒ 대신 쓸 수 있는 것을 쓰시오.

➡ _____

23 위 글의 밑줄 친 ⓓ와 용법이 같은 것은?

① Do you like their new house?
② I've never seen a pretty cat like his cat.
③ I didn't like to watch TV.
④ At weekends I like to sleep late.
⑤ We'd like you to come and visit us.

[24~27] 다음 글을 읽고, 물음에 답하시오.

Julia Child was a person ___ⓐ___ found her real ___ⓑ___ in her 30s. At age 36, she moved to Paris with her husband. She ___ⓒ___ a famous cooking school there. While she was studying, she decided ⓓto write a cookbook. That book became a big hit.

24 위 글의 빈칸 ⓐ에 알맞은 것은? (2개)

① who　　　　② whose
③ that　　　　④ what
⑤ which

25 위 글의 빈칸 ⓑ에 다음 정의에 해당하는 단어를 주어진 글자로 시작하여 쓰시오.

> the natural ability to do something well

➡ t_____

26 위 글의 빈칸 ⓒ에 알맞은 것은?

① went　　　　② visited
③ stayed　　　④ attended
⑤ studied

27 위 글의 밑줄 친 ⓓ와 같은 용법으로 쓰인 것은?

① I need a baseball cap to wear.
② We hoped to find the hidden treasure.
③ Were you glad to hear the news?
④ I went to a shopping mall to buy gloves.
⑤ Is there anything to eat in the fridge?

[28~31] 다음 글을 읽고, 물음에 답하시오.

My name is Hojin, and I like ①making graphic novels. ②While I was walking home from school last week, I saw a woman ___ⓑ___ a scooter. She looked really ③coolly, and her scooter was very unique.
"Are you going home, Hojin?" she said ④to me suddenly.
"Yes, ___ⓒ___ do I know you?" I asked.
"Of course," she answered. "I see you ⑤at the school cafeteria every day."

28 위 글의 밑줄 친 ①~⑤ 중 어법상 어색한 것은?

①　　②　　③　　④　　⑤

29 위 글의 빈칸 ⓑ에 알맞은 것은?

① by　　　　② on
③ in　　　　④ at
⑤ over

서답형

30 위 글의 빈칸 ⓒ에 알맞은 접속사를 쓰시오.

➡ _____

31 위 글의 내용으로 보아 알 수 없는 것은?

① 호진이는 만화 소설 쓰기를 좋아한다.
② 호진이는 지난주에 스쿠터를 탄 여인을 보았다.
③ 그 여인의 스쿠터는 아주 독특했다.
④ 그 여인은 호진이를 알아보았다.
⑤ 그 여인은 학교 식당에서 근무하고 있다.

[01~06] 다음 글을 읽고, 물음에 답하시오.

ⓐSurprising, she was one of the cafeteria workers at school.

"Amazing! She looks so ___ⓑ___ outside the school," I thought. "I should write a graphic novel about her."

After I got home, I began to write a new graphic novel, *Lunch Lady Begins*. In it Lunch Lady is a superhero. She rides a super scooter ⓒthat can fly. She saves people ___ⓓ___ danger around the world. She also makes 100 cookies per second and gives ⓔ them away to hungry children.

01 위 글의 밑줄 친 ⓐ를 알맞은 형으로 고치시오.

➡ _____

02 위 글의 빈칸 ⓑ에 same의 반의어를 쓰시오.

➡ _____

03 위 글의 밑줄 친 ⓒ 대신 쓸 수 있는 관계대명사를 쓰시오.

➡ _____

04 위 글의 빈칸 ⓓ에 알맞은 전치사를 쓰시오.

➡ _____

05 위 글의 밑줄 친 ⓔ가 가리키는 것을 영어로 쓰시오.

➡ _____

06 How many cookies does Lunch Lady make per second? Answer in Korean.

➡ _____

[07~09] 다음 글을 읽고, 물음에 답하시오.

A few days later, I showed my graphic novel ___ⓐ___ my friends.

"Awesome! I love this ___ⓑ___. She's so cool," said all my friends.

"Guess what? ⓒI modeled her on Ms. Lee, one of our cafeteria workers," I told them.

07 위 글의 빈칸 ⓐ에 알맞은 전치사를 쓰시오.

➡ _____

08 위 글의 빈칸 ⓑ에 다음 정의에 해당하는 단어를 주어진 글자로 시작하여 쓰시오.

a character in a cartoon or film who has special powers and fights against evil

➡ s_____

09 위 글의 밑줄 친 ⓒ를 우리말로 옮기시오.

➡ _____

[10~15] 다음 글을 읽고, 물음에 답하시오.

ⓐI showed Ms. Lee my book. She loved it, too. She also told me about her coworkers ⓑwho had special talents. ⓒMs. Park, other cafeteria worker, won a dancing contest. Mr. Kim, the janitor at our school, was once an adventurous park ranger.

"I'd like to write superhero stories about ⓓthem. Do you think they'll like that?" I asked Ms. Lee.

"Of course they will," she said ⓔcheerful. "Let's go and say hello to our new superhero friends."

10 위 글의 밑줄 친 ⓐ와 같은 뜻이 되도록 빈칸에 알맞은 말을 쓰시오.

I showed my book _____ Ms. Lee.

11 위 글의 밑줄 친 ⓑ 대신 쓸 수 있는 관계대명사를 쓰시오.

➡ _____

12 위 글의 밑줄 친 ⓒ에서 어법상 어색한 것을 고치시오.

_____ ➡ _____

13 위 글의 밑줄 친 ⓓ가 가리키는 것을 우리말로 구체적으로 쓰시오.

➡ _____

14 위 글의 밑줄 친 ⓔ를 알맞은 형으로 고치시오.

➡ _____

15 Was Ms. Park good at dancing? Answer in English.

➡ _____

[16~19] 다음 글을 읽고, 물음에 답하시오.

My aunt is my role model. She is smart, strong, and ⓐadventure. In her 30s, she traveled to 70 different countries. ⓑWhile she was traveling, she made a friend from all over the world. I want to be someone ⓒ_____ is not afraid ⓓ_____ trying new things just like her.

16 위 글의 밑줄 친 ⓐ를 알맞은 형으로 고치시오.

➡ _____

17 위 글의 밑줄 친 ⓑ에서 어법상 어색한 것을 고치시오.

_____ ➡ _____

18 위 글의 빈칸 ⓒ에 알맞은 관계대명사를 쓰시오.

➡ _____

19 위 글의 빈칸 ⓓ에 알맞은 전치사를 쓰시오.

➡ _____

해석

Listen & Speak 1-B

A: I'm good at jumping rope.
　　be good at+동명사: ~을 잘하다

B: Suji is good at jumping rope. I'm good at playing the guitar.

C: Suji is good at jumping rope. Hansu is good at playing the guitar. I'm
　　　　　　　　　　　　　　　　　　　　　　　　　　　　　　　　　　현재진행형
baking cookies.

구문해설　• be good at: ~을 잘하다　• jump rope: 줄넘기를 하다　• bake: 굽다　• cookie: 쿠키

A: 저는 줄넘기를 잘해요.

B: 수지는 줄넘기를 잘해요. 저는 기타를 잘 칩니다.

C: 수지는 줄넘기를 잘해요. 한수는 기타를 잘 칩니다. 저는 쿠키를 굽고 있어요.

Language Arts

Two boys are studying in a library. There is a fire. The boys can't get out.
　　　　　　　현재진행형　　　　　　　　　~이 있다
Lunch Lady flies on her scooter and saves them.
　　　　　　　　　　　　　　　　　　　= the boys

구문해설　• fire: 불, 화재　• get out: 나가다　• save: 구하다

두 소년이 도서관에서 공부하고 있다. 불이 났다. 그 소년들은 나갈 수 없다. Lunch Lady는 스쿠터를 타고 날아와서 그들을 구한다.

Write

My aunt is my role model. She is smart, strong, and adventurous. In her 30s,
　　　　　　　　　　　　　　　　　　　　　　　　　　　　　　　　in one's 30s: 30대에
she traveled to 70 different countries. While she was traveling, she made
　　　　　　　　　　　　　　　　　　　　접 ~하는 동안　　　　　　　　친구를 사귀다
friends from all over the world. I want to be someone who is not afraid of
전 세계에서　　　　　　　　　　　　　　　　　　주격 관계대명사(=that)　~을 두려워하다
trying new things just like her.
　　　　　　　　　　　　전 ~처럼

구문해설　• role model: 롤 모델　• adventurous: 모험심이 강한　• travel: 여행하다　• different: 다른
　　　• try: 시도하다

나의 이모는 내 롤 모델이다. 그녀는 똑똑하고, 강하고, 모험심이 강하다. 30대 때, 그녀는 70개국을 여행했다. 여행을 하는 동안, 그녀는 전 세계의 친구들을 사귀었다. 나는 그녀처럼 새로운 것을 시도하는 것을 두려워하지 않는 사람이 되고 싶다.

Culture Project - Share

Julia Child was a person who found her real talent in her 30s. At age 36, she
　　　　　　　　　　　주격 관계대명사 who(=that)　　　　　　　　　　36살에
moved to Paris with her husband. She attends a famous cooking school there.
　　　　　　　　~와 함께　　　　　　　　　　　　　　　　　　　　　　= in Paris
While she was studying, she decided to write a cookbook. That book became
접 ~하는 동안　　　　　　　decide to부정사: ~하기로 결정하다
a big hit.

구문해설　• person: 사람　• real: 진정한　• talent: 재능　• move: 이사하다　• husband: 남편
　　　• attend: ~에 다니다　• famous: 유명한　• cookbook: 요리책　• hit: 히트

Julia Child는 30대에 그녀의 진정한 재능을 발견한 사람이었다. 36살 때, 그녀는 남편과 함께 파리로 이사를 했다. 그녀는 그곳에서 유명한 요리 학교에 다닌다. 그녀는 공부하는 동안 요리책을 쓰기로 결심했다. 그 책은 큰 인기를 끌었다.

영역별 핵심문제

Words & Expressions

01 다음 중 짝지어진 단어의 관계가 나머지와 <u>다른</u> 것은?

① write – writer
② listen – listener
③ paint – painter
④ cook – cooker
⑤ speak – speaker

02 다음 빈칸에 들어갈 말로 적절하지 <u>않은</u> 것은?

- He is going to _____ a wedding.
- It is _____ with occasional showers.
- She felt _____ on her wedding day.
- Aluminum cans are very easy to _____.

① cloudy
② attend
③ repair
④ recycle
⑤ nervous

03 다음 짝지어진 두 단어의 관계가 같도록 빈칸에 주어진 글자로 시작하여 쓰시오.

cheap : expensive = right : w_____

04 다음 빈칸에 들어갈 말이 바르게 짝지어진 것은?

- Are you afraid _____ spiders?
- Exercise is good _____ the health.

① in – on
② on – off
③ of – for
④ for – after
⑤ from – for

05 다음 영영풀이에 해당하는 단어는?

to be present at a meeting or event

① join
② observe
③ share
④ visit
⑤ attend

06 다음 문장의 빈칸에 알맞은 것은?

Let me _____ a look at the map.

① take
② make
③ let
④ get
⑤ bring

07 다음 우리말에 맞게 빈칸에 알맞은 말을 쓰시오.

이 집은 우리가 살 수 있을 만큼 크지가 않다.
➡ This house isn't big _____ for us to live in.

Conversation

08 다음 대화의 빈칸에 알맞은 것은?

A: Can you jump high?
B: Yes, I can. I am _____ at jumping.

① poor
② good
③ well
④ bad
⑤ pretty

[09~14] 다음 대화를 읽고, 물음에 답하시오.

> Yuri: What are you doing, Jaden?
> Jaden: I'm drawing cartoons.
> Yuri: Really? Can I take a look at them?
> Jaden: ⓐNo, not yet.
> Yuri: _____ⓑ_____ not? You can show me a few, can't you?
> Jaden: Well, I guess so.
> Yuri: (*pause*) Ha, ha, ha! Awesome! I like your cartoons. You're really good _____ⓒ_____ drawing.
> Jaden: Do you think so? I want to be a cartoonist, _____ⓓ_____ I don't think my drawing skills are good enough.
> Yuri: Your cartoons are really funny, and you have unique characters. ⓔI'm sure you'll be a great cartoonist.
> Jaden: Thank you, Yuri. You just made my day.

09 위 대화의 밑줄 친 ⓐ를 생략되지 않은 문장으로 바꾸시오.

➡ _____

10 위 대화의 빈칸 ⓑ에 알맞은 것은?

① Why ② How
③ What ④ Who
⑤ Where

11 위 대화의 빈칸 ⓒ에 알맞은 것은?

① to ② in
③ at ④ for
⑤ with

12 위 대화의 빈칸 ⓓ에 알맞은 것은?

① so ② or
③ and ④ but
⑤ for

13 위 대화의 밑줄 친 ⓔ와 같은 뜻이 되도록 다음 문장의 빈칸에 알맞은 말을 쓰시오.

> _____ is _____ that you'll be a great cartoonist.

14 위 대화의 내용으로 보아 대답할 수 없는 질문은?

① What is Jaden doing?
② Why does Yuri want to look at Jaden's cartoons?
③ Does Jaden draw well?
④ Does Yuri like Jaden's cartoons?
⑤ What does Jaden hope to be?

15 다음 대화의 밑줄 친 부분의 의도로 알맞은 것은?

> A: Are you good at cooking?
> B: Yes, I know how to make cookies and sandwiches.

① 열거하기 ② 선호 표현하기
③ 의견 표현하기 ④ 능력 표현하기
⑤ 걱정 표현하기

16 다음 우리말에 맞도록 빈칸에 알맞은 말을 쓰시오.

> 너는 내가 그 영화를 좋아할 것이라고 확신하니?
> ➡ Are you _____ that I'll like that movie?

[17~18] 다음 문장의 빈칸에 알맞은 것을 고르시오.

17

Susan is the girl _____ comes from New Zealand.

① who   ② what
③ whom   ④ which
⑤ whose

18

Please be quiet _____ I'm talking to your teacher.

① and   ② so
③ unless   ④ while
⑤ after

19 다음 빈칸에 공통으로 알맞은 것은?

- Look at the bird _____ is standing with one leg.
- Mike, _____ food do you like better, pizza or hamburgers?

① who   ② which
③ that   ④ where
⑤ what

20 다음 우리말과 뜻이 같도록 괄호 안의 어구들을 바르게 배열하시오.

그는 저녁 식사를 마친 후, 양치질을 했다.
(his teeth, his dinner, he, he, after, finished, brushed).

➡ _____

21 다음 중 어법상 어색한 것은?

① He is the only man that can solve the problems.
② Korea is a country which exports cars all over the world.
③ I have a dog which has long ears.
④ There is a man at the door who wants to see you.
⑤ The men who is in front of the house are my friends.

22 다음 중 밑줄 친 부분의 쓰임이 나머지와 다른 것은?

① He went there before they arrived.
② I got up before the alarm clock rang.
③ I have to finish this work before seven o'clock.
④ They helped her before she asked for help.
⑤ Before you go out, make sure to turn off the light.

23 다음 중 밑줄 친 that의 쓰임이 나머지 넷과 다른 하나는?

① The park that is near my house is good.
② I think that golf is more interesting than tennis.
③ I know a man that works in a famous restaurant.
④ I live in an apartment that has no heating system.
⑤ We'll go to a restaurant that has a children's menu.

24 다음 문장의 빈칸에 알맞지 <u>않은</u> 것은?

> Everybody stopped to see _____ that were playing together.

① the boy   ② the tigers
③ the children   ④ a cat and a dog
⑤ a man and a monkey

25 다음 중 어법상 어색한 것은?

① Ann and I always play tennis after school is over.
② While I was sleeping, he made breakfast for me.
③ If you don't hurry, you will be late for the movie.
④ You can use my car while I'm studying.
⑤ Jenny arrived at the station after the train leaves.

26 다음 두 문장을 한 문장으로 바꿔 쓰시오.

> • What is the name of the tallest boy?
> • He just came in.

➡ _____

_____

27 다음 문장에서 어법상 옳지 <u>않은</u> 부분을 바르게 고쳐 쓰시오.

> Clean up that mess before your father will see it.

_____ ➡ _____

[28~31] 다음 글을 읽고, 물음에 답하시오.

> _____ⓐ_____ I got home, I began to write a new graphic novel, *Lunch Lady Begins*. In ⓑit Lunch Lady is a superhero. She rides a super scooter that can fly. ⓒ그녀는 전 세계에서 사람들을 위험으로부터 구한다. She also makes 100 cookies per second and gives them _____ⓓ_____ to hungry children.

28 위 글의 빈칸 ⓐ에 알맞은 것은?

① If   ② After
③ While   ④ Since
⑤ Before

29 위 글의 밑줄 친 ⓑ가 가리키는 것을 영어로 쓰시오.

➡ _____

30 위 글의 밑줄 친 ⓒ의 우리말을 괄호 안에 주어진 단어를 이용하여 영어로 옮기시오.

> (save, from, danger, around)

➡ _____

31 위 글의 빈칸 ⓓ에 알맞은 것은?

① up   ② on
③ from   ④ off
⑤ away

[32~37] 다음 글을 읽고, 물음에 답하시오.

A few days ___ⓐ___, I showed my graphic novel to my friends.

"Awesome! I love this superhero. She's so cool," said all my friends.

"Guess ___ⓑ___? I modeled her on Ms. Lee, one of our cafeteria ©work," I told them.

I showed my book to Ms. Lee. She loved it, too. She also told me about her coworkers ⓓthat had special talents. Ms. Park, another cafeteria worker, won a dancing contest. Mr. Kim, the janitor at our school, was once an adventurous park ___ⓔ___.

"I'd like to write superhero stories about them. Do you think they'll like that?" I asked Ms. Lee.

"Of course they will," she said cheerfully. "Let's go and say hello ___ⓕ___ our new superhero friends."

32 위 글의 빈칸 ⓐ에 알맞은 것은?

① late   ② early
③ earlier   ④ later
⑤ latter

33 위 글의 빈칸 ⓑ에 알맞은 것은?

① this   ② that
③ what   ④ who
⑤ which

34 위 글의 밑줄 친 ©를 알맞은 어형으로 바꿔 쓰시오.

➡ _____

35 위 글의 밑줄 친 ⓓ 대신 쓸 수 있는 관계대명사를 쓰시오.

➡ _____

36 위 글의 빈칸 ⓔ에 다음 정의에 해당하는 단어를 쓰시오.

a person whose job is to look after a forest or large park

➡ _____

37 위 글의 빈칸 ⓕ에 알맞은 전치사를 쓰시오.

➡ _____

[38~39] 다음 글을 읽고, 물음에 답하시오.

Two boys are studying in a library. ⓐThere is a fire. The boys can't get ___ⓑ___. Lunch Lady flies on her scooter and saves them.

38 위 글의 밑줄 친 ⓐ와 같은 뜻이 되도록 다음 문장의 빈칸에 알맞은 말을 쓰시오.

A fire breaks _____.

39 위 글의 빈칸 ⓑ에 알맞은 것은?

① in   ② of
③ into   ④ out
⑤ from

단원별 예상문제

01 다음 중 짝지어진 단어의 관계가 <u>다른</u> 것은?

① right : wrong
② long : short
③ different : same
④ funny : interesting
⑤ dangerous : safe

02 다음 빈칸에 공통으로 알맞은 것은?

• I made this doll out _____ an old dress.
• The bus stops right in front _____ our house.

① in
② of
③ from
④ with
⑤ onto

03 다음 짝지어진 두 단어의 관계가 같도록 빈칸에 알맞은 말을 쓰시오.

cloud : cloudy = rain : _____

04 다음 중 영영풀이가 <u>잘못된</u> 것은?

① awesome: very impressive and often frightening
② superhero: a character in a cartoon or film who has special powers and fights against evil
③ role model: someone you admire and try to imitate
④ adventurous: willing to take risks and to try new methods
⑤ poem: a long written story about imaginary people and events

05 다음 우리말에 맞게 빈칸에 알맞은 말을 쓰시오.

나는 그가 그의 우산을 선뜻 내놓을 것이라고는 기대하지 않았다.
➡ I didn't expect that he would give _____ his umbrella.

06 다음 대화의 밑줄 친 부분의 의도로 알맞은 것은?

A: What am I doing?
B: I think you're watering the flowers.
A: <u>Are you sure?</u>
B: Yes. I'm sure that you're watering the flowers.

① 설득하기
② 제안하기
③ 의견 묻기
④ 확신 여부 묻기
⑤ 충고 청하기

07 다음 중 짝지어진 대화가 <u>어색한</u> 것은?

① A: Is he good at solving puzzles?
　 B: Yes, he is.
② A: Are you certain that she'll win the race?
　 B: Sure.
③ A: Will you teach me how to play baduk?
　 B: Let me see. OK, I will.
④ A: When did he win first prize?
　 B: He won it last year.
⑤ A: Are you sure that you locked the door?
　 B: Yes, I'm sure. I'll go and check.

Yuri: What are you doing, Jaden?

Jaden: I'm drawing cartoons.

Yuri: Really? Can I ⓐtake a look at them?

Jaden: No, not yet.

Yuri: ⓑWhy not? You can show me a few, can't you?

Jaden: Well, I guess so.

Yuri: (*pause*) Ha, ha, ha! Awesome! I like your cartoons. You're really good at drawing.

Jaden: Do you think ⓒso? I want to be a cartoonist, but I don't think my drawing skills are good enough.

Yuri: Your cartoons are really funny, and you have unique characters. I'm sure you'll be a great cartoonist.

Jaden: Thank you, Yuri. ⓓYou just made my day.

08 위 대화의 밑줄 친 ⓐ 대신 쓸 수 있는 것은?

① do
② get
③ make
④ have
⑤ join

09 위 대화의 밑줄 친 ⓑ를 생략하지 않은 문장으로 바꿔 쓰시오.

➡ _____

10 위 대화의 밑줄 친 ⓒ가 가리키는 것을 영어로 쓰시오.

➡ _____

11 위 대화의 밑줄 친 ⓓ를 우리말로 옮기시오.

➡ _____

12 다음 두 문장을 한 문장으로 연결할 때 빈칸에 알맞은 것은?

> There is a girl. She is sitting on the bench.
> ➡ There is a girl _____ is sitting on the bench.

① who
② what
③ whom
④ which
⑤ whose

13 다음 문장의 빈칸에 알맞은 것은?

> _____ they are sleeping, somebody knocked on the door.

① Before
② After
③ While
④ If
⑤ Unless

14 다음 문장에서 어법상 어색한 것을 찾아 바르게 고치시오.

> A man who is dressed like Santa Claus gave presents to children.

_____ ➡ _____

15 다음 두 문장의 의미가 일치하도록 빈칸에 알맞은 말을 쓰시오

> He gave me this book after he read it.
> = He read this book _____ he gave it to me.

16 다음 빈칸에 알맞은 말이 순서대로 짝지어진 것은?

출제율 90%

> • I like pizza _____ has lots of cheese.
> • The people _____ work in the office are very friendly.

① who – whom   ② which – who
③ who – which   ④ whom – which
⑤ which – whom

[17~18] 다음 밑줄 친 부분의 쓰임이 다른 하나를 고르시오.

17 출제율 95%

① Please tell me <u>which</u> is your notebook?
② Can you see the bird <u>which</u> is flying over there?
③ Look at the castle <u>which</u> stands on the hill.
④ I will give him the vase <u>which</u> is very expensive.
⑤ This is the dictionary <u>which</u> gives me the meaning of words.

18 출제율 95%

① <u>While</u> you were out, your sister cleaned your room.
② Some are tall <u>while</u> others are short.
③ He turned on the music <u>while</u> he worked.
④ Work hard <u>while</u> you are young.
⑤ Frank finished the work <u>while</u> I was sleeping.

19 다음 밑줄 친 부분 중 어법상 어색한 것은?

출제율 100%

① I need a chair <u>which</u> is made of wood.
② The closet <u>that</u> they are carrying looks heavy.
③ Do you know the woman <u>who</u> is playing curling?
④ Jenny is the famous singer <u>who</u> appeared on TV last night.
⑤ Jane likes a man <u>whom</u> is tall and humorous.

[20~22] 다음 글을 읽고, 물음에 답하시오.

> (①) My aunt is my role model. (②) In her 30s, she traveled to 70 different countries. (③) While she was traveling, she ____ⓐ____ friends from all over the world. (④) ⓑI want to be someone who is not afraid of try new things just like her. (⑤)

20 위 글의 ①~⑤ 중 다음 주어진 문장이 들어갈 알맞은 곳은?

출제율 95%

> She is smart, strong, and adventurous.

①   ②   ③   ④   ⑤

21 위 글의 빈칸 ⓐ에 알맞은 것은?

출제율 100%

① did   ② got
③ made   ④ took
⑤ became

22 위 글의 밑줄 친 ⓑ에서 어법상 어색한 것을 고치시오.

출제율 95%

_____ ➡ _____

[23~27] 다음 글을 읽고, 물음에 답하시오.

My name is Hojin, and I like to make graphic novels. ⓐWhile I am walking home from school last week, I saw a woman on a scooter. ⓑShe looked really cool, and her scooter was very unique.

"Are you going home, Hojin?" she said to me ____ⓒ____.

"Yes, but do I know you?" I asked.

"Of course," she answered. "I see you at the school cafeteria every day."

Surprisingly, she was one of the cafeteria workers at school.

"ⓓAmaze! She looks so different outside the school," I thought. "I should write a graphic novel about her."

📝 출제율 100%

23 위 글의 밑줄 친 ⓐ에서 어법상 어색한 것을 고치시오.

_____ ➡ _____

📝 출제율 90%

24 위 글의 밑줄 친 ⓑ와 같은 문형으로 쓰인 것은?

① The candy tastes sweet.
② The song made me sad.
③ There are some apples in the basket.
④ She made us some cookies.
⑤ My father planted some trees.

📝 출제율 95%

25 위 글의 빈칸 ⓒ에 다음 정의에 해당하는 단어를 주어진 글자로 시작하여 쓰시오.

quickly and unexpectedly

➡ s_____

📝 출제율 90%

26 위 글의 밑줄 친 ⓓ를 알맞은 어형으로 고치시오.

➡ _____

📝 출제율 95%

27 위 글의 내용과 일치하지 <u>않는</u> 것은?

① Hojin likes to make graphic novels.
② Hojin saw a woman on a scooter last week.
③ Hojin recognized the woman immediately.
④ The woman sees Hojin at the school cafeteria every day.
⑤ Hojin wanted to write a graphic novel about the woman.

[28~29] 다음 글을 읽고, 물음에 답하시오.

Julia Child was a person who found her real talent in her 30s. ____ⓐ____ age 36, she moved to Paris with her husband. She attended a famous cooking school there. While she was studying, she decided to write a cookbook. That book ____ⓑ____ a big hit.

📝 출제율 90%

28 위 글의 빈칸 ⓐ에 알맞은 것은?

① In   ② On
③ For   ④ At
⑤ From

📝 출제율 90%

29 위 글의 빈칸 ⓑ에 알맞은 것은?

① did   ② got
③ came   ④ took
⑤ became

[01~03] 다음 대화를 읽고, 물음에 답하시오.

> B: ⓐIs something wrong?
> G: I have to give a speech in English. I'm so ⓑnerve.
> B: Don't worry. Practice your speech in front of your family. ⓒI'm sure you'll do a good job.
> G: Thank you. I'll try.

중요

01 위 대화의 밑줄 친 부분과 바꿔 쓸 수 있는 표현을 두 가지 쓰시오.

➡ _____

_____

_____

02 위 대화의 밑줄 친 ⓑ를 알맞은 형으로 고치시오.

➡ _____

03 위 대화의 밑줄 친 ⓒ를 우리말로 옮기시오.

➡ _____

중요

04 다음 대화의 순서를 바르게 배열하시오.

> (A) I'm sure your mom will love it.
> (B) Tomorrow is my mom's birthday. What should I do for her?
> (C) Why don't you bake a cake for her? You're good at baking.
> (D) That's a good idea. I hope my mom will like my cake.

➡ _____

05 다음 두 문장을 관계대명사를 써서 한 문장으로 나타내시오.

(1) Dad cooks me a fried egg. It is my favorite.

➡ _____

(2) I have an uncle. He is a math teacher.

➡ _____

(3) She has a bird. It speaks English.

➡ _____

06 다음 〈조건〉에 맞게 괄호 안의 단어를 이용하여 우리말을 영어로 옮기시오.

> ┤ 조건 ├
> 1. 주어진 단어를 모두 이용할 것.
> 2. 필요시 관사를 붙이거나 단어를 추가하고 동사의 어형 변화를 할 것.
> 3. 종속절이 주절의 뒤에 위치할 것.
> 4. 대·소문자 및 구두점에 유의할 것.

(1) Kathy는 목욕한 뒤에 잠자리에 들었다.
    (go, bed, take, bath)

➡ _____

(2) Smith 씨는 네가 외출한 동안 너를 보러 오셨다.
    (come, see, be out)

➡ _____

(3) 너는 어두워지기 전에 돌아와야 한다.
    (should, back, get dark)

➡ _____

07 다음 문장에서 어법상 어색한 것을 찾아 바르게 고치시오.

(1) The animals that is in cages are not happy.

_____ ➡ _____

(2) Where is the letter who came from Cathy this morning?

_____ ➡ _____

(3) The boy and the dog who fell into the river were saved.

_____ ➡ _____

[08~10] 다음 글을 읽고, 물음에 답하시오.

My aunt is my role model. She is smart, ___ⓐ___, and adventurous. In her 30s, she traveled to 70 ___ⓑ___ countries. While she was traveling, she made friends from all over the world. ⓒI want to be someone who is not afraid of trying new things just like her.

08 위 글의 빈칸 ⓐ에 weak의 반의어를 쓰시오.

➡ _____

09 위 글의 빈칸 ⓑ에 다음 정의에 해당하는 단어를 주어진 글자로 시작하여 쓰시오.

not like each other in one or more ways

➡ d_____

10 위 글의 밑줄 친 ⓒ를 우리말로 옮기시오.

➡ _____
_____

[11~14] 다음 글을 읽고, 물음에 답하시오.

Julia Child was a person ___ⓐ___ found her real talent in her 30s. At ___ⓑ___ 36, she moved to Paris with her husband. ⓒShe attended at a famous cooking school there. While she was studying, she decided ⓓ (to write, writing) a cookbook. That book became a big hit.

11 위 글의 빈칸 ⓐ에 알맞은 관계대명사를 쓰시오.

➡ _____

12 위 글의 빈칸 ⓑ에 다음 정의에 해당하는 단어를 쓰시오.

the number of years that you have lived

➡ _____

13 위 글의 밑줄 친 ⓒ를 어법상 어색한 것을 고쳐 다시 쓰시오.

➡ _____

14 위 글의 괄호 ⓓ에서 알맞은 것을 고르시오.

➡ _____

01 다음 주어진 단어를 활용하여 예시와 같이 쓰시오.

Teacher	teach, students, school	ex) A teacher is someone who teaches students at a school.
Waiter	serve, food, restaurant	(1)
Zookeeper	look after, animals, zoo	(2)
Dessert	sweet food, serve, after a meal	(3)

(1) _____

(2) _____

(3) _____

02 다음 〈보기〉처럼 두 문장을 괄호 안에 주어진 접속사를 사용하여 하나의 문장으로 바꿔 쓰시오.

> ┤ 보기 ├
>
> Kirk was in Paris. / He fell in love with a girl. (while)
> ➡ While Kirk was in Paris, he fell in love with a girl. / Kirk fell in love with a girl while he was in Paris.

(1) I leave this town. / I'm going to visit my friend. (before)

➡ _____
_____

(2) I bought the PS4. / I saw the advertisement on TV. (after)

➡ _____
_____

(3) The rain will stop. / You go out. (before)

➡ _____

(4) Please hold my bag. / I put on my coat. (while)

➡ _____

(5) We eat something. / We're going to see a movie. (after)

➡ _____
_____

(6) I came home. My sister was watching TV. (when)

➡ _____

(7) You go out. / You have to finish this. (before)

➡ _____

단원별 모의고사

01 다음 영영풀이에 해당하는 단어로 알맞은 것은?

> to choose to do something, usually after you have thought carefully about the other possibilities

① decide　　② advise
③ share　　④ select
⑤ mention

02 다음 중 우리말 뜻이 <u>잘못된</u> 것은?

① fall asleep: 잠들다
② do a good job: 잘하다
③ in front of: ~ 앞에(서)
④ be good for: ~을 잘하다
⑤ be afraid of: ~을 두려워하다

03 다음 빈칸에 알맞은 말이 바르게 짝지어진 것은?

> • My uncle cleans his car _____ a week.
> • They're on sale today, only 99 cents _____ pound.

① one – per　　② one – a
③ way – per　　④ once – per
⑤ once – the

04 다음 짝지어진 두 단어의 관계가 같도록 빈칸에 알맞은 말을 쓰시오.

> art : artist = cartoon : _____

05 다음 빈칸에 공통으로 들어갈 말을 쓰시오.

> • Let me take a look _____ the map.
> • Jack is good _____ singing and dancing.

➡ _____

[06~07] 다음 담화문을 읽고, 물음에 답하시오.

> W: ⓐEverybody are good at something. Some people are good at drawing. ⓑ _____ people are good at singing. What are you good at?

06 위 담화문의 밑줄 친 ⓐ에서 어법상 <u>어색한</u> 것을 고쳐 다시 쓰시오.

➡ _____

07 위 담화문의 빈칸 ⓑ에 알맞은 것은?

① Another　　② Other
③ Others　　④ The other
⑤ The others

[08~11] 다음 대화를 읽고, 물음에 답하시오.

> B: Hi, Cindy. ⓐIs something wrong?
> G: I have to give a speech in front of the whole school. I'm so ⓑ _____ .
> B: Don't worry. ⓒYou're a very good speaker. I'm ⓓ _____ you'll do a good job.
> G: Thanks, Minho. I feel much better now.

08 위 대화의 밑줄 친 ⓐ와 같은 뜻이 되도록 빈칸에 알맞은 말을 쓰시오.

➡ What's the _____ with you?

09 위 대화의 흐름상 빈칸 ⓑ에 알맞은 것은?

① tired   ② busy
③ nervous   ④ free
⑤ excited

10 위 대화의 밑줄 친 ⓒ와 같은 뜻이 되도록 빈칸에 알맞은 말을 쓰시오.

➡ You _____ very _____ .

11 위 대화의 빈칸 ⓓ에 알맞은 것은? (2개)

① well   ② right
③ sure   ④ good
⑤ certain

12 다음 빈칸에 알맞은 말이 순서대로 바르게 짝지어진 것은?

- Jenny is the famous singer _____ appeared on TV last night.
- I bought a chair _____ was made of wood.

① who – which   ② whom – that
③ which – who   ④ which – which
⑤ whose – that

13 다음 문장에서 틀린 것을 고치시오.

I have three books that tells us about China.

_____ ➡ _____

14 다음 문장의 빈칸에 문맥상 알맞은 것은?

While you are jogging, _____ .

① you get up late
② they may get a toothache
③ you won't get cold
④ watch out for dogs
⑤ he may be tired yesterday

15 다음 중 밑줄 친 부분의 쓰임이 나머지와 다른 것은?

① I want to know who she is.
② This is the boy who came from Africa.
③ The man who is in the room is my cousin.
④ Do you know the man who is wearing a blue jumper?
⑤ The teacher likes the students who ask many questions.

16 다음 문장의 빈칸에 공통으로 알맞은 것을 쓰시오.

- I've never seen such a horrible movie _____ .
- He raised his hand _____ the teacher called his name.

17 다음 두 문장을 한 문장으로 연결할 때 빈칸에 알맞은 것은?

> There is a boy. He is riding a bike.
> ➡There is a boy _____ is riding a bike.

① how ② who
③ whom ④ which
⑤ whose

18 다음 중 어법상 알맞지 <u>않은</u> 문장은?

① There's a house which has two chimneys.
② Can you see a boy who is running along the river?
③ I visited a town that is famous as a hot spring resort.
④ Mark is the cook who was on TV last night.
⑤ The man who is sitting on the box have a problem.

19 다음 두 문장의 뜻이 같도록 빈칸에 알맞은 말을 쓰시오.

> After the sun rises, she gets up.
> = _____ she gets up, the sun rises.

[20~21] 다음 글을 읽고, 물음에 답하시오.

I'm good ⓐ making spaghetti and doing push-ups. I'm also good ⓑ telling funny jokes. I play badminton, and ⓒI have long beautiful hairs. Who am I?

20 위 글의 빈칸 ⓐ와 ⓑ에 공통으로 알맞은 것은?

① to ② on
③ at ④ for
⑤ with

21 위 글의 밑줄 친 ⓒ에서 어법상 어색한 것을 고치시오.

_____ ➡ _____

[22~24] 다음 글을 읽고, 물음에 답하시오.

(①) After I got home, I began to write a new graphic novel, *Lunch Lady Begins*. (②) She rides a super scooter that can fly. (③) She saves people from danger around the world. (④) She also makes 100 cookies per ⓐ _____ and gives them away to hungry children. (⑤)

22 위 글의 ①~⑤ 중 다음 주어진 문장이 들어갈 알맞은 곳은?

> In it, Lunch Lady is a superhero.

① ② ③ ④ ⑤

23 위 글의 빈칸 ⓐ에 다음 정의에 해당하는 단어를 쓰시오.

> one of the sixty parts that a minute is divided into

➡ _____

24 위 글의 내용으로 보아 대답할 수 <u>없는</u> 질문은?

① When did the writer begin to write a new graphic novel?

② What does Lunch Lady ride?

③ Why is Lunch Lady a superhero?

④ How does Lunch Lady save people from danger?

⑤ To whom does Lunch Lady give away cookies?

[25~27] 다음 글을 읽고, 물음에 답하시오.

ⓐI showed my book to Ms. Lee. She loved it, ①too. She also told me ②about her coworkers who had special talents. Ms. Park, ③other cafeteria worker, won a dancing contest. Mr. Kim, the janitor ④at our school, was ⑤once an adventurous park ranger.

25 위 글의 밑줄 친 ①~⑤ 중 어법상 어색한 것은?

①   ②   ③   ④   ⑤

26 위 글의 밑줄 친 ⓐ와 문형이 같은 것은?

① Jane sent me a birthday card.

② The man is strong.

③ There are many books in the library.

④ The news made her glad.

⑤ My grandfather planted some trees last year.

27 What does Mr. Kim do for a living? Answer in English.

➡ _____

[28~30] 다음 글을 읽고, 물음에 답하시오.

My name is Hojin, and I like to make graphic novels. ____ⓐ____ I was walking home from school last week, I saw a woman on a scooter. ⓑShe looked really cool, and her scooter was very unique.

"Are you going home, Hojin?" she said to me suddenly.

"Yes, but do I know you?" I asked.

"Of course," she answered. "I see you at the school cafeteria every day."

28 위 글의 빈칸 ⓐ에 알맞은 것은?

① If   ② After

③ Before   ④ Since

⑤ While

29 위 글의 밑줄 친 ⓑ를 우리말로 옮기시오.

➡ _____

30 위 글의 내용과 일치하지 <u>않는</u> 것은?

① 호진이는 만화 소설 쓰기를 좋아한다.

② 호진이는 지난주에 한 여인을 만났다.

③ 그 여인의 스쿠터는 아주 독특했다.

④ 그 여인은 호진이를 알고 있었다.

⑤ 호진이는 그 여인을 학교 식당에서 매일 보았다.

Where Do People Live?

 의사소통 기능

- 의향 묻고 답하기

  A: What kind of house do you want to live in?

  B: I want to live in a cave house.

- 위치 묻고 답하기

  A: Where can I find men's hats?

  B: You can find them on the first floor.

언어 형식

- 현재완료

  People **have built** wooden houses for a long time.

- each

  Each house **is** big enough for a whole village.

Words & Expressions

Key Words

- □ **airplane-shaped** 형 비행기 모양의
- □ **avoid** [əvɔ́id] 동 방지하다, 막다, 피하다
- □ **become** [bikʌ́m] 동 ~이 되다
- □ **build** [bild] 동 짓다, 건설[건축]하다
- □ **cafeteria** [kæfətíəriə] 명 카페테리아, 구내식당
- □ **cave** [keiv] 명 동굴
- □ **century** [séntʃəri] 명 100년, 세기
- □ **collector** [kəléktər] 명 수집가, 징수원
- □ **cone** [koun] 명 원뿔, 원뿔형 물체
- □ **cover** [kʌ́vər] 동 씌우다, 가리다, 덮다
- □ **decide** [disáid] 동 결정하다, 결심하다
- □ **design** [dizáin] 명 디자인, 설계 동 디자인하다
- □ **dining room** 식당
- □ **else** [els] 부 또[그 밖에] 다른, 다른
- □ **enemy** [énəmi] 명 적
- □ **enough** [inʌ́f] 부 ~에 필요한 정도로, ~할 만큼 (충분히)
- □ **entrance** [éntrəns] 명 입구, 문
- □ **fifth** [fifθ] 형 다섯 번째의, 제5의
- □ **fine dust** 미세먼지
- □ **floor** [flɔːr] 명 마루, 바닥, (건물의) 층
- □ **forest** [fɔ́ːrist] 명 숲, 삼림
- □ **fresh** [freʃ] 형 신선한
- □ **gate** [geit] 명 문, 정문
- □ **goat** [gout] 명 염소
- □ **grass** [græs] 명 풀, 잔디
- □ **guesthouse** [gésthaus] 명 게스트하우스
- □ **guide** [gaid] 명 안내[가이드], 관광 안내 책자
- □ **harmony** [háːrməni] 명 조화, 화합
- □ **information** [ìnfərméiʃən] 명 정보
- □ **jeans** [dʒiːnz] 명 바지, 면[청]바지
- □ **kind** [kaind] 명 종류
- □ **lovely** [lʌ́vli] 형 사랑스러운, 아름다운
- □ **low** [lou] 형 낮은
- □ **mall** [mɔːl] 명 쇼핑몰, 쇼핑 센터
- □ **meal** [miːl] 명 식사, 끼니
- □ **nature** [néitʃər] 명 자연
- □ **ocean** [óuʃən] 명 대양, 바다
- □ **part** [paːrt] 명 부분
- □ **pay** [pei] 동 지불하다, 내다
- □ **piano-shaped** 형 피아노 모양의
- □ **plant** [plænt] 명 식물, 초목
- □ **practice** [præktis] 동 연습하다
- □ **protect** [prətékt] 동 보호하다, 지키다
- □ **restroom** [réstruːm] 명 화장실, 세면실
- □ **round** [raund] 형 둥근, 동그란 전 ~을 돌아
- □ **shaped** [ʃeipt] 형 ~의 모양[형태]의
- □ **since** [sins] 전 ~부터[이후]
- □ **sometimes** [sʌ́mtàimz] 부 때때로, 가끔
- □ **southern** [sʌ́ðərn] 형 남쪽[남부]에 위치한
- □ **stone** [stoun] 명 돌
- □ **storage** [stɔ́ːridʒ] 명 저장, 보관
- □ **story** [stɔ́ːri] 명 (건물의) 층
- □ **tax** [tæks] 명 세금
- □ **thousand** [θáuzənd] 명 1,000, 천 형 수천의
- □ **tour** [tuər] 명 여행, 관광
- □ **unique** [juːníːk] 형 유일무이한, 독특한
- □ **view** [vjuː] 명 경관, 전망
- □ **village** [víidʒ] 명 마을, 마을 사람들
- □ **welcome** [wélkəm] 동 맞이하다, 환영하다 형 환영받는
- □ **wind** [wind] 명 바람
- □ **without** [wiðáut] 전 ~ 없이, ~을 사용하지 않고
- □ **wooden** [wúdn] 형 나무로 된, 목재의

Key Expressions

- □ **be afraid of** ~을 두려워하다
- □ **be good at** ~을 잘하다
- □ **Excuse me.** (모르는 사람의 관심을 끌려고 할 때) 실례합니다.
- □ **give it a try** 시도하다, 한번 해 보다
- □ **in harmony with** ~와 조화를 이루어
- □ **kind of** 약간, 어느 정도
- □ **look at** ~을 보다
- □ **look for** ~을 찾다
- □ **next to** ~ 옆에
- □ **out of** ~의 안에서 밖으로, ~의 밖으로
- □ **pile up** 쌓아 올리다
- □ **take down** (구조물을 해체하여) 치우다
- □ **upside down** 거꾸로, 뒤집혀
- □ **watch out for** ~을 조심하다

Word Power

※ 기수와 서수

- one → first
- two → second
- three → third
- four → fourth
- five → fifth
- six → sixth
- seven → seventh

- eight → eighth
- nine → ninth
- ten → tenth
- eleven → eleventh
- twelve → twelfth
- nineteen → nineteenth
- twenty → twentieth

- thirty → thirtieth
- forty → fortieth
- eighty → eightieth
- ninety → ninetieth
- hundred → hundredth
- thousand → thousandth
- million → millionth

English Dictionary

- **avoid** 방지하다, 막다, 피하다
  → to take action in order to prevent something unpleasant from happening
  불쾌한 일이 일어나지 않도록 조치를 취하다

- **cave** 동굴
  → a large hole in the side of a cliff or hill, or one that is under the ground
  절벽이나 언덕의 측면에 있는 큰 구멍 또는 땅 밑에 있는 큰 구멍

- **cafeteria** 카페테리아, 구내식당
  → a restaurant where you choose your food from a counter and take it to your table after paying for it
  당신이 카운터에서 음식을 선택하고 그것에 대해 지불한 후에 테이블로 가져가는 레스토랑

- **century** 100년, 세기
  → a period of a hundred years that is used when stating a date
  날짜를 말할 때 사용되는 100년의 기간

- **collector** 징수원
  → someone whose job is to collect taxes or debts etc.
  세금이나 부채 등을 징수하는 사람

- **enemy** 적
  → someone who hates you or wants to harm you
  당신을 싫어하거나 해치고 싶어 하는 사람

- **forest** 숲, 삼림
  → a large area where trees grow close together
  나무들이 서로 가까이 자라는 넓은 지역

- **guesthouse** 게스트하우스
  → a private home or boarding house offering accommodation to travellers
  여행자에게 숙박을 제공하는 개인 주택 또는 기숙사

- **information** 정보
  → facts about someone or something
  어떤 사람 또는 어떤 것에 관한 사실들

- **plant** 식물, 초목, 나무
  → a living thing that grows in the earth and has a stem, leaves, and roots, especially one that is smaller than a tree or bush
  땅에서 자라고 줄기, 잎, 뿌리를 가진 생물, 특히 나무나 덤불보다 작은 생물

- **protect**: 보호하다, 지키다
  → to prevent someone or something from being harmed or damaged
  누군가 또는 무언가가 다치거나 손상되지 않도록 막다

- **restroom** 화장실, 세면실
  → a room with a toilet for customers to use
  손님이 사용하기 위한 변기가 있는 방

- **tax** 세금
  → an amount of money that you have to pay to the government so that you can use public services
  공공 서비스를 이용하기 위해 당신이 정부에 지불해야 하는 금액

- **thousand** 1,000, 천
  → the number 1,000
  1,000이라는 수

- **wind** 바람
  → a current of air that is moving across the earth's surface
  지구 표면을 가로질러 움직이는 공기의 흐름

- **wooden** 나무로 된, 목재의
  → made of wood
  나무로 만들어진

01 다음 중 나머지 넷을 대표할 수 있는 단어는?

① goat　　　　② animal
③ bear　　　　④ rabbit
⑤ giraffe

02 다음 빈칸에 알맞은 말이 바르게 짝지어진 것은?

• I think the dog is kind _____ strange.
• Henry was looking _____ his shoes.

① of – at　　　　② of – for
③ at – in　　　　④ at – with
⑤ to – over

03 다음 영영풀이에 해당하는 단어로 알맞은 것은?

the way into a place, for example a door or gate

① hall　　　　② yard
③ lobby　　　　④ entrance
⑤ bridge

서답형

04 다음 짝지어진 단어의 관계가 같도록 빈칸에 알맞은 말을 쓰시오.

cheap : expensive = low : _____

05 다음 우리말에 맞게 빈칸에 알맞은 것은?

천천히 물병을 거꾸로 뒤집어라.
➡ Slowly turn the jar upside _____.

① up　　　　② on
③ down　　　　④ from
⑤ along

서답형

06 다음 영영풀이에 해당하는 단어를 쓰시오.

casual trousers that are usually made of strong blue cotton cloth called denim

➡ _____

서답형

07 다음 우리말에 맞게 빈칸에 알맞은 말을 쓰시오.

마른 풀에 불이 붙었다.
➡ The dry _____ caught fire.

08 다음 빈칸에 공통으로 알맞은 것은?

• He took some coins out _____ his pocket.
• We had a lot _____ fun at the party.

① in　　　　② of
③ up　　　　④ about
⑤ at

01 다음 짝지어진 두 단어의 관계가 같도록 빈칸에 알맞은 말을 쓰시오.

(1) one : first = two : _____

(2) four : fourth = five : _____

(3) nine : _____ = seven : seventh

02 다음 우리말에 맞게 빈칸에 알맞은 말을 쓰시오.

(1) 전통 가옥들은 자연과 조화를 이루고 있다.
➡ Traditional houses are _____ _____ _____ nature.

(2) 우리는 서로 바로 옆에 앉았다.
➡ We sat _____ _____ each other.

(3) 너의 앨범을 봐도 될까?
➡ May I _____ _____ your album?

03 다음 빈칸에 들어갈 알맞은 말을 〈보기〉에서 골라 쓰시오.

┌─ 보기 ─┐
build   entrance   avoid   protect

(1) I left early to _____ the rush hour.

(2) He wanted to _____ his own house.

(3) Parents have the right to _____ their children.

(4) I'll meet you at the main _____ .

04 다음 괄호 안의 단어를 문맥에 맞게 고쳐 쓰시오.

(1) Kathy looked particularly _____ that night. (love)

(2) The river falls into the _____ sea. (south)

(3) I found a _____ box in the room. (wood)

05 다음 빈칸에 알맞은 말을 〈보기〉에서 골라 쓰시오.

┌─ 보기 ─┐
take down   look for   pile up   good at

(1) Nancy is _____ dancing.

(2) We have to _____ a tent.

(3) You had better _____ your dog at the park.

(4) Work is starting to _____ .

06 다음 영영풀이에 해당하는 단어를 주어진 철자로 시작하여 쓰시오.

(1) c_____ : someone whose job is to collect taxes or debts etc.

(2) e_____ : someone who hates you or wants to harm you

Conversation

① 의향 묻고 답하기

> **A** What kind of house do you want to live in? 너는 어떤 종류의 집에서 살고 싶니?
> **B** I want to live in a cave house. 나는 동굴 집에서 살고 싶어.

■ want to ~는 '~하고 싶다'의 뜻으로 상대방의 의향을 묻거나 대답할 때 쓰는 표현이다.

- A: What kind of movie do you want to see? 너는 어떤 종류의 영화를 보고 싶니?
  B: I want to see a horror movie. 나는 공포 영화를 보고 싶어.

- A: What do you want to read? 너는 무엇을 읽고 싶니?
  B: I want to read this book. 나는 이 책을 읽고 싶어.

■ what 대신 where, when 등의 의문사를 사용해 상대방이 원하는 것을 물을 수 있다.

- A: Where do you want to go? 너는 어디에 가고 싶니?
  B: I want to go to the zoo. 나는 동물원에 가고 싶어.

- A: When do you want to go to the movies? 너는 언제 영화 보러 가고 싶니?
  B: I want to go to the movies tomorrow. 나는 내일 영화 보러 가고 싶어.

■ Do you want to ~?는 '너는 ~하고 싶니?'의 뜻으로 상대방이 특정한 일을 하고 싶은지 물을 때 쓰인다.

- A: Do you want to buy this hat? 너는 이 모자를 사고 싶니?
  B: Sure, I do. 물론, 사고 싶어.

■ 무엇이 되고 싶은지 장래 희망을 물을 때는 What do you want to be in the future? / What would you like[do you want] to be when you grow up? 등의 표현을 사용한다. 이에 대한 응답으로 되고 싶은 것에 대해 말할 때는 I want to be ~ / I would like to be ~ 등의 표현을 사용한다.

- A: What do you want to be in the future? 너는 미래에 무엇이 되고 싶니?
  B: I want to be an animal doctor. 나는 수의사가 되고 싶어.

핵심 Check

1. 다음 우리말과 일치하도록 빈칸에 알맞은 말을 쓰시오.

   (1) A: What _____ of house do you _____ to live in? (너는 어떤 종류의 집에서 살고 싶니?)

   　　B: I want _____ _____ in a tree house. (나는 나무 위의 집에서 살고 싶어.)

   (2) A: _____ do you want to _____ in the future? (너는 미래에 무엇이 되고 싶니?)

   　　B: I _____ _____ be a computer programmer. (나는 컴퓨터 프로그래머가 되고 싶어.)

2 위치 묻고 답하기

    A Where can I find men's hats? 남성용 모자는 어디에 있어요?

    B You can find them on the first floor. 1층에서 찾을 수 있어요.

■ Where can I find ~?는 '~은 어디에 있습니까?'라는 뜻으로 위치를 묻는 표현이다.

    • A: Where can I find the nurse's office? 양호실은 어디에 있니?
      B: It's between teachers' office and the art room. 교무실과 미술실 사이에 있어.

■ Where can I find ~? 대신 Where is ~?를 써서 위치를 물을 수 있다.

    • A: Where is the Eiffel Tower? 에펠탑은 어디에 있니?
      B: It's in Paris. 파리에 있어.

장소를 묻는 여러 가지 표현

    • Where can I find ~?

    • Where is ~?

    • Can you tell me where ~ is[are]?

    • Do you know where ~ is[are]?

■ 장소를 말할 때는 「It's in+장소.(그것은 ~에 있다.)」의 표현을 이용할 수 있다.

    • A: Where is Chinatown? 차이나타운은 어디에 있니?
      B: It's in Incheon. 인천에 있어.

핵심 Check

2. 다음 우리말과 일치하도록 빈칸에 알맞은 말을 쓰시오.

(1) A: _____ can I _____ the restroom? (화장실은 어디 있습니까?)

    B: It's _____ to the elevator. (엘리베이터 옆에 있어요.)

(2) A: _____ is the bus stop? (버스 정류장은 어디에 있니?)

    B: It's _____ the bank. (은행 뒤에 있어.)

(3) A: _____ is the Haeundae Beach? (해운대는 어디에 있니?)

    B: It's _____ Busan. (부산에 있어.)

(4) A: Can you _____ me _____ the bus stop is? (버스 정류장은 어디에 있는지 알려주시겠어요?)

    B: It's in _____ of the bank. (은행 앞에 있습니다.)

Listen & Speak 1 A-1

B: Hey, ❶look at this house in the picture. ❷It looks like a big shoe!

G: Oh, it's very unique, ❸but I don't want to live in a shoe.

B: ❹What kind of house do you want to live in?

G: Well, I want to live in an airplane-shaped house.

B: 어이, 이 사진 속의 집을 봐. 그것은 큰 신발처럼 보여!

G: 오, 아주 독특하긴 하지만, 난 신발 속에서 살고 싶지 않아.

B: 넌 어떤 종류의 집에서 살고 싶니?

G: 음, 나는 비행기 모양의 집에서 살고 싶어.

❶ 동사원형으로 시작하는 명령문이다.
❷ look like: ~처럼 보이다
❸ want to: ~하기를 원하다
❹ What kind of ~?: 어떤 종류의 ~?

Check(√) True or False

(1) The house in the picture looks like a big shoe.　　T ☐ F ☐

(2) The girl doesn't want to live in an airplane-shaped house.　　T ☐ F ☐

Listen & Speak 1 A-2

M: ❶Excuse me, is there a restaurant in this mall?

W: Yes. What kind of food would you like?

M: ❷I'd like Chinese food.

W: There is a great restaurant on the fifth floor.

M: Thank you.

M: 실례합니다. 이 쇼핑몰에 식당이 있나요?

W: 네. 어떤 음식을 드시겠어요?

M: 중국 음식을 먹고 싶어요.

W: 5층에 멋진 식당이 있어요.

M: 감사합니다.

❶ Excuse me: 죄송합니다(모르는 사람에게 말을 걸 때 쓰는 관용적인 표현)
❷ I'd like = I want

Check(√) True or False

(3) There is a Korean restaurant in this mall.　　T ☐ F ☐

(4) The man likes Chinese food.　　T ☐ F ☐

Progress Check 2

W: Excuse me, where can I find women's shoes?

M: ❶You can find them on the second floor. ❷They're next to the elevator.

W: Thank you.

M: ❸You're welcome.

W: 실례합니다, 여자 신발은 어디에 있어요?

M: 2층에서 찾을 수 있어요. 엘리베이터 옆에 있어요.

W: 감사합니다.

M: 천만에요.

❶ them = women's shoes / on the second floor: 2층에
❷ next to: ~ 옆에
❸ You're welcome.: 감사에 대한 응답으로 Don't mention it., Not at all. 등도 같은 뜻으로 쓰인다.

Check(√) True or False

(5) The woman wants to buy women's shoes.　　T ☐ F ☐

(6) The woman can find women's shoes on the first floor.　　T ☐ F ☐

Listen & Speak 2 A-2

W: ❶Can I help you?

M: ❷I'm looking for watches. ❸Where can I find them?

W: ❹They're on the third floor, next to the restroom.

M: Thank you.

❶ Can I help you?: 도와드릴까요?(=May I help you? / What can I do for you?

❷ look for: ～을 찾다

❸ them = watches

❹ on the third floor: 3층에

 Communicate: A. Listen and Answer

Woman: ❶Welcome to Jeonju Hanok Guesthouse. ❷May I help you?

Man: Yes, ❸I'd like a room for two nights.

Woman: Well, what kind of room would you like?

Man: ❹Do you have a room with a garden view? You have a lovely garden.

Woman: Yes, we do. ❺Every room in our house has a garden view, but there are no beds in the rooms.

Man: ❻Do I have to sleep on the floor?

Woman: Yes, you do.

Man: O.K. ❼I'll give it a try. Where can I have breakfast?

Woman: You can have breakfast in the dining room, next to the kitchen.

Man: ❽I see.

Woman: O.K. You're in the Nabi room. ❾Here's your key.

Man: Thank you.

❶ Welcome to ～: ～에 오신 것을 환영합니다

❷ May I help you?: 도와 드릴까요?(= Can I help you?/ What can I do for you?)

❸ I'd like = I would like = I want

❹ a room with a garden view: 정원이 보이는 방

❺ 주어에 every가 있을 때는 단수동사로 받는다.

❻ Do I have to sleep ～? = Must I sleep ～?

❼ I'll give it a try.: 한번 시도해 볼게요.

❽ I see.: 알겠습니다.

❾ Here's ～ = Here is ～: 여기에 ～이 있다

 Work Together - Act

A: What kind of house do you want to build?

B: ❶I want to build a two-story house that looks like a boat.

A: ❷Where is the kitchen?

B: ❸It's on the second floor.

❶ that은 주격 관계대명사로 which로 바꿔 쓸 수 있다.

❷ Where is ～?: ～은 어디에 있니?

❸ It's = It is(이때의 is는 '있다'의 뜻임)

 Progress Check 1

B: Hey, ❶look at this unique house in the picture. It's upside down.

G: ❷Oh, it looks interesting, but I think it's kind of strange.

B: What kind of house do you want to live in?

G: ❸I like music, so I want to live in a piano-shaped house.

❶ in the picture: 사진에 있는(house를 수식하는 형용사구)

❷ kind of: 좀, 약간

❸ so: 그래서

 Progress Check 3

W: Excuse me, where can I find men's hats?

M: ❶You can find them on the second floor. ❷They're next to the elevator.

W: Thank you.

M: You're welcome.

❶ them = men's hats / on the second floor: 2층에

❷ They=Men's hats

● 다음 우리말과 일치하도록 빈칸에 알맞은 말을 쓰시오.

Listen & Speak 1 A. Listen and Check

1. **B:** Hey, _____ at this house _____ the picture. It looks _____ a big shoe!

   G: Oh, it's very _____, but I don't _____ _____ live in a shoe.

   B: What _____ of house do you want to _____ in?

   G: Well, I want _____ live in an airplane-shaped _____.

2. **M:** _____ me, is _____ a restaurant in this _____?

   W: Yes. What _____ of food _____ you like?

   M: I'd _____ Chinese food.

   W: _____ is a great restaurant _____ the fifth floor.

   M: _____ you.

Listen & Speak 2 A. Listen and Write

1. **W:** _____ me, where can I _____ women's shoes?

   M: You _____ find them on the _____ floor. They're _____ to the elevator.

   W: Thank _____.

   M: You're _____.

2. **W:** Can I _____ you?

   M: I'm looking _____ watches. Where _____ I find them?

   W: They're _____ the third floor, _____ to the restroom.

   M: Thank you.

Communicate A. Listen and Answer

Woman: _____ to Jeonju Hanok Guesthouse. _____ I help you?

Man: Yes, I'd _____ a room _____ two nights.

Woman: Well, what _____ of room would you _____?

Man: Do you have a room _____ a garden _____? You have a lovely _____.

Woman: Yes, we _____. Every _____ in our house has a garden _____, but there are _____ beds in the rooms.

Man: Do I _____ to sleep on the _____?

1. B: 어이, 이 사진 속의 집을 봐. 그것은 큰 신발처럼 보여!
   G: 오, 아주 독특하긴 하지만, 난 신발 속에서 살고 싶지 않아.
   B: 넌 어떤 종류의 집에서 살고 싶니?
   G: 음, 나는 비행기 모양의 집에서 살고 싶어.

2. M: 실례합니다, 이 쇼핑몰에 식당이 있나요?
   W: 네. 어떤 음식을 드시겠어요?
   M: 중국 음식을 먹고 싶어요.
   W: 5층에 멋진 식당이 있어요.
   M: 감사합니다.

1. W: 실례합니다, 여자 신발은 어디에 있어요?
   M: 2층에서 찾을 수 있어요. 엘리베이터 옆에 있어요.
   W: 감사합니다.
   M: 천만에요.

2. W: 뭘 도와드릴까요?
   M: 시계를 찾고 있어요. 어디에서 찾을 수 있습니까?
   W: 3층에, 화장실 옆에 있어요.
   M: 감사합니다.

W: 전주 한옥 게스트하우스에 오신 걸 환영합니다. 무엇을 도와드릴까요?
M: 네, 이틀 밤 묵을 방을 원해요.
W: 음, 어떤 방을 원하세요?
M: 정원이 보이는 방이 있어요? 정원이 아름답군요.
W: 네, 그렇습니다. 우리 집 모든 방에서는 정원이 보입니다. 하지만 방에는 침대가 없어요.
M: 바닥에서 자야 합니까?

Woman: Yes, you _____.

Man: O.K. I'll _____ it a _____. _____ can I _____ breakfast?

Woman: You _____ have breakfast in the _____ room, next _____ the kitchen.

Man: I _____.

Woman: O.K. You're _____ the Nabi room. _____ your key.

Man: _____ you.

Progress Check

1. **B:** Hey, look _____ this unique house _____ the picture. It's upside _____.

   G: Oh, it _____ interesting, _____ I think it's _____ of strange.

   B: What _____ of house do you _____ to live in?

   G: I like music, _____ I want to _____ in a piano-shaped house.

2. **W:** _____ me, where can I _____ women's jeans?

   M: You can _____ them on the _____ floor. They're _____ to the elevator.

   W: _____ you.

   M: You're _____.

3. **M:** Excuse me, _____ can I find men's _____?

   W: You _____ find them on the second _____. They're next _____ the elevator.

   M: Thank _____.

   W: You're _____.

Work -Act

A: _____ kind of house do you want to _____?

B: I want _____ build a two-story house _____ looks _____ a boat.

A: _____ is the kitchen?

B: It's on the _____ floor.

해석

W: 네, 그렇습니다.
M: 알았습니다. 한번 시도해 볼게요. 아침 식사는 어디서 해요?
W: 아침 식사는 부엌 옆에 있는 식당에서 할 수 있어요.
M: 알겠습니다.
W: 좋아요, 나비 방에 들어가세요. 여기 당신의 열쇠가 있습니다.
M: 고맙습니다.

1. B: 이봐, 사진 속의 이 독특한 집을 봐. 집이 거꾸로 있어.
   G: 아, 재미있어 보이지만, 좀 이상한 것 같아.
   B: 넌 어떤 집에서 살고 싶니?
   G: 나는 음악을 좋아해서 피아노 모양의 집에서 살고 싶어.
2. W: 실례합니다. 여자 청바지는 어디에 있나요?
   M: 2층에서 찾을 수 있어요. 엘리베이터 옆에 있어요.
   W: 감사합니다.
   M: 천만에요.
3. M: 실례합니다. 남성용 모자는 어디에 있나요?
   W: 2층에서 찾을 수 있어요. 엘리베이터 옆에 있어요.
   M: 감사합니다.
   W: 천만에요.

A: 넌 어떤 집을 짓고 싶어?
B: 보트처럼 생긴 2층짜리 집을 짓고 싶어.
A: 부엌이 어디 있어?
B: 2층에 있어.

Conversation 시험대비 기본평가

01 다음 대화의 빈칸에 알맞은 말을 쓰시오.

> **A:** What kind of house do you _____ to live in?
> **B:** I _____ to live in a cave house.

cave 동굴

02 다음 대화의 밑줄 친 부분과 바꿔 쓸 수 있는 것은? (2개)

> **A:** Excuse me. I'm looking for shoes. <u>Where can I find them?</u>
> **B:** They're on the first floor.
> **A:** Thank you very much.

Excuse me.: 죄송합니다.
look for: ~을 찾다

① Where are they?   ② How may I help you?
③ Where can I buy them?   ④ Where do I need to go?
⑤ What do you want to have?

03 다음 대화의 밑줄 친 부분의 의도로 알맞은 것은?

> **A:** <u>What kind of house do you want to live in?</u>
> **B:** I want to live in a piano-shaped house.

① 의향 묻기   ② 주의하기
③ 요청하기   ④ 제안하기
⑤ 계획 묻기

04 다음 대화의 빈칸에 알맞은 것은?

> **A:** Excuse me. Where can I find women's clothes?
> **B:** _____
> **A:** Oh, I see. Thanks.

① You're welcome.   ② You can't miss it.
③ It's on the first floor.   ④ They're on the second floor.
⑤ I'm looking for them, too.

01 다음 대화를 의미가 통하도록 알맞게 배열한 것은?

> (A) What kind of house do you want to live in?
> (B) Hey, look at this house in the picture. It looks like a big shoe!
> (C) Oh, it's very unique, but I don't want to live in a shoe.
> (D) Well, I want to live in an airplane-shaped house.

① (A) – (D) – (B) – (C)
② (B) – (C) – (A) – (D)
③ (C) – (D) – (B) – (A)
④ (D) – (B) – (C) – (A)
⑤ (D) – (C) – (B) – (A)

02 다음 의도하는 바가 나머지 넷과 다른 하나는?

① Where can I find it?
② How can I go there?
③ How do I get there?
④ How may I help you?
⑤ Can you tell me where it is?

서답형
[03~04] 다음 대화의 빈칸에 알맞은 말을 쓰시오.

03
> A: _____ can I find men's clothes?
> B: They're on the second floor.
> A: Oh, I see. Thanks.

04
> A: Do you want to go on a picnic on Sunday?
> B: Sure. I _____.

05 다음 대화의 밑줄 친 부분의 의도로 알맞은 것은?

> A: Excuse me. <u>Do you know where I can find ball pens?</u>
> B: Yes. They are on shelf A in aisle 1.

① 요청하기
② 의도 묻기
③ 위치 묻기
④ 능력 여부 묻기
⑤ 관심 사항 묻기

06 다음 중 짝지어진 대화가 어색한 것은?

① A: Where can I find women's clothes?
   B: They're on the first floor.
② A: How can I get to the bookstore?
   B: Go straight two blocks and turn left.
③ A: Where can I find socks?
   B: They are on shelf C in aisle 1.
④ A: Where is the Statue of Liberty?
   B: It's in New York.
⑤ A: Do you know where I can find the library?
   B: Yes, that's right.

[07~11] 다음 대화를 읽고, 물음에 답하시오.

> Woman: Welcome to Jeonju Hanok Guesthouse. ⓐMay I help you?
>
> Man: Yes, I'd like a room for two nights.
>
> Woman: Well, what kind of room would you like?
>
> Man: Do you have a room ⓑwith a garden view? You have a lovely garden.
>
> Woman: Yes, we do. Every room in our house has a garden view, but there are no beds in the rooms.
>
> Man: Do I have to sleep on the floor?
>
> Woman: Yes, you do.
>
> Man: O.K. I'll _____ⓒ_____ it a try. Where can I have breakfast?
>
> Woman: You can have breakfast in the dining room, next to the kitchen.
>
> Man: ⓓI see.
>
> Woman: O.K. You're in the Nabi room. Here's your key.
>
> Man: Thank you.

서답형

07 위 대화의 밑줄 친 ⓐ와 같은 뜻이 되도록 바꿔 쓸 때 빈칸에 알맞은 말을 쓰시오.

> _____ _____ I do for you?

08 위 대화의 밑줄 친 ⓑ와 같은 의미로 쓰인 것은?

① I often play with my classmates.
② Lucy is the girl with long hair.
③ Don't write with a pencil.
④ Do you agree with him?
⑤ Ben was pleased with the present.

서답형

09 위 대화의 빈칸 ⓒ에 알맞은 말을 쓰시오.

➡ _____

서답형

10 위 대화의 밑줄 친 ⓓ를 우리말로 옮기시오.

➡ _____

11 위 대화의 내용과 일치하지 <u>않는</u> 것은?

① 남자는 이틀 밤을 묵기를 원한다.
② 남자는 정원을 볼 수 있는 방을 원한다.
③ 남자는 침대에서 자는 것에 익숙하다.
④ 남자는 침대가 있는 방을 원한다.
⑤ 남자는 식당에서 아침식사를 할 것이다.

[12~13] 다음 대화를 읽고, 물음에 답하시오.

> B: Hey, look _____ⓐ_____ this house in the picture. It looks like a big shoe!
>
> G: Oh, it's very unique, _____ⓑ_____ I don't want to live in a shoe.
>
> B: What kind of house do you want to live in?
>
> G: Well, I want to live in an airplane-shaped house.

서답형

12 위 대화의 빈칸 ⓐ에 알맞은 전치사를 쓰시오.

➡ _____

중요

13 위 대화의 빈칸 ⓑ에 알맞은 것은?

① but　　　　② so
③ or　　　　④ for
⑤ and

Conversation 서술형 시험대비

01 다음 대화의 밑줄 친 우리말에 맞도록 주어진 단어를 이용하여 완성하시오.

> A: Where can I find computers?
> B: 그것들은 4층에 있다. (floor)
> A: Oh, I see. Thanks.

➡ _____

02 다음 대화의 괄호 안의 단어들을 바르게 배열하시오.

> A: (to / of / do / you / have / kind / what / pet / want)
> B: I want to have a rabbit.

➡ _____

[03~04] 다음 대화를 의미가 통하도록 알맞게 배열하시오.

03
> (A) You're welcome.
> (B) Thank you.
> (C) Excuse me, where can I find women's shoes?
> (D) You can find them on the second floor. They're next to the elevator.

➡ _____

04
> (A) Where is the kitchen?
> (B) What kind of house do you want to build?
> (C) It's on the second floor.
> (D) I want to build a two-story house that looks like a boat.

➡ _____

[05~08] 다음 대화를 읽고, 물음에 답하시오.

> M: ___ⓐ___ me, is there a restaurant in this mall?
> W: Yes. What ___ⓑ___ of food would you like?
> M: I'd like Chinese food.
> W: There is a great restaurant on the ⓒfive floor.
> M: Thank you.
> W: ⓓYou're welcome.

05 위 대화의 빈칸 ⓐ에 알맞은 것은?

① Guess   ② Forgive
③ Believe   ④ Pardon
⑤ Excuse

06 위 대화의 빈칸 ⓑ에 알맞은 말을 쓰시오.

➡ _____

07 위 대화의 밑줄 친 ⓒ를 알맞은 어형으로 고치시오.

➡ _____

08 위 대화의 밑줄 친 ⓓ와 같은 뜻이 되도록 다음 문장의 빈칸에 알맞은 말을 쓰시오.

> Don't _____ it.

교과서 Grammar

① 현재완료

> • People **have built** wooden houses for a long time. 사람들은 오랫동안 나무로 집을 지었다.
>
> • **Have** you ever **seen** a goat on the roof of a house?
> 당신은 집 지붕 위에 있는 염소를 본 적이 있나요?

■ **현재완료의 형태**
'have[has]+과거분사'의 형태를 취한다.

• It **has been** such a long time. 정말 오랜만이다.
• I **have had** many different jobs. 나는 많은 다양한 직업을 가져왔다.

cf. yesterday, two days ago, last Sunday 등과 같이 특정한 과거 시점을 나타내는 표현이 오면 현재완료시제로 쓰지 않고 과거시제로 써야 한다.

• I **read** the book yesterday.　　(○) 나는 어제 그 책을 읽었다.
　I have read the book yesterday. (✕)

■ **현재완료의 용법**
현재완료는 경험, 계속, 완료, 결과의 용법이 있다.

분류	용법	예문
경험	• 과거부터 현재까지의 경험 • before, ever, never, often 등과 쓰임	I **have** never **been** to Rome. 나는 로마에 가 본 적이 없다.
계속	• 과거의 일이 지금까지 계속됨 • 'since+특정 시점', 'for+기간' 등과 쓰임	I **have known** him since I was a little child. 나는 어릴 때부터 그를 알아 왔다.
완료	• 과거에 시작된 일이 이제 막 완료됨 • just, already, yet 등과 쓰임	He **has** just **finished** his homework. 그는 방금 숙제를 끝냈다.
결과	• 과거의 일이 현재의 결과를 가져옴 • '~해서 (지금) …하다'의 의미임	They **have gone** to Madrid. 그들은 마드리드에 가고 없다.

■ **현재완료의 부정문**
have[has]와 과거분사 사이에 not을 넣는다.

• He **has not written** the letter yet. 그는 아직 그 편지를 쓰지 않았다.

■ **현재완료의 의문문**
'Have[Has]+주어+과거분사 ~?'의 형태를 취한다.

• **Have** you ever **seen** a lion? 너는 사자를 본 적이 있니?

핵심 Check

1. 다음 괄호 안에서 알맞은 것을 고르시오.

　(1) Ann has just (did / done) her homework.

　(2) They (have / has) not (ate / eaten) the pizza.

　(3) He (lived, has lived) in this town since he was seven.

　(4) I have known her (for / since) three years.

② each

- **Each** house **is** big enough for a whole village. 각 집은 마을 전체가 살 만큼 크다.
- **Each** person **has** different strengths. 각 사람은 각기 다른 강점을 가지고 있다.
- **Each** of the girls **has** her own desk. 소녀들 각각은 그녀 자신의 책상을 가지고 있다.

■ each가 형용사로 쓰일 때는 '각각의'라는 의미로, 전체를 구성하는 하나하나의 개별적인 것을 가리킨다. 「each+단수 명사+단수 동사」의 형태로 쓴다.

- **Each** artist **has** his own character. 예술가는 각자 자신의 특성을 지니고 있다.

■ each가 대명사로 쓰일 때는 '각각, 각자'라는 의미로, 단수로 취급한다. 「each of+복수 명사+단수 동사」의 형태로 '~의 각각'이라는 의미를 나타낼 수 있다.

- **Each** of them **has** different interests. 그들은 각자 다른 흥미를 갖고 있다.

■ each가 부사로 쓰일 때는 '각각, 하나에'의 의미로 사용된다.

- I gave them two dollars **each**. 나는 그들에게 각각 2달러씩 주었다.

■ each other는 '서로'의 뜻으로 관용적으로 쓰인다.

- You should help **each other**. 너희들은 서로 도와야 한다.

■ every는 '모든'의 뜻으로 형용사로만 쓰인다. each와 마찬가지로 뒤에 오는 명사는 단수형이 된다.

- **Every** student **knows** him. 모든 학생이 그를 알고 있다.

■ both는 '둘 다'의 뜻으로 형용사와 대명사로 쓰인다. both가 형용사로 쓰일 때는 뒤에 복수 명사가 오고 복수 동사로 받는다.

- **Both** teams **have** to get two points. [형용사] 두 팀 다 2점을 얻어야 한다.
- **Both** of them **are** kind. [대명사] 그들은 둘 다 친절하다.

핵심 Check

2. 다음 괄호 안에서 알맞은 것을 고르시오.

(1) Each of the boys (have / has) a bike.

(2) Each student (is / are) carrying a lunch box.

(3) All of us help (each / every) other.

(4) I always get up early every (day / days).

(5) Both of us (is / are) Korean tourists.

Grammar 시험대비 기본평가

01 다음 괄호 안에서 알맞은 것을 고르시오.

> reach 도착하다

(1) Jane (was / has been) busy since last week.

(2) How often have you (gone / been) to the United States?

(3) He (has finished / finished) reading two hours ago.

(4) He (has just finished / just finishes) his homework.

(5) We (arrived / have arrived) here yesterday.

(6) When (have you reached / did you reach) here?

02 다음 괄호 안에서 알맞은 것을 고르시오.

> do one's best 최선을 다하다
> own 자신의
> side 쪽, 편

(1) Each of the girls (do / does) her best.

(2) Each student (have / has) his own desk.

(3) There are some trees on each (side / sides) of the street.

(4) Each of the (student / students) is doing his homework.

(5) Every (boy / boys) was kind to me.

(6) Both her parents (is / are) teachers.

03 다음 괄호 안에 주어진 단어를 어법상 알맞은 형태로 바꾸어 문장을 완성하시오.

> sick 아픈
> newspaper 신문

(1) He (be) sick in bed since last Friday.

➡ _____

(2) How long (you know) Miss Smith?

➡ _____

(3) (you ever read) Christmas Carol?

➡ _____

(4) My father (not read) the newspaper yet.

➡ _____

01 다음 두 문장을 한 문장으로 만들 때 빈칸에 알맞은 것은?

I moved here two years ago. I still live here.

➡ I _____ here for two years.

① live
② lived
③ will live
④ am living
⑤ have lived

[02~03] 다음 문장의 빈칸에 알맞은 것을 고르시오.

02 Each of the girls _____ willing to join the game.

① am
② are
③ was
④ were
⑤ being

03 Ted is hungry, because he _____ nothing since this morning.

① eat
② eats
③ ate
④ has eaten
⑤ had eaten

서답형
[04~05] 다음 빈칸에 공통으로 알맞은 말을 쓰시오

04
• _____ room is furnished with a table and chairs.
• _____ of my friends bought me a present for my birthday.

05
• Sorry to _____ kept you waiting. I _____ been to the station.
• We _____ known each other since our childhood.

06 다음 중 밑줄 친 부분의 쓰임이 나머지 넷과 <u>다른</u> 것은?

① They got two cookies <u>each</u>.
② He had a bottle in <u>each</u> hand.
③ <u>Each</u> ticket costs 20 dollars.
④ <u>Each</u> boy has his own cell phone.
⑤ Bake the bread for five minutes on <u>each</u> side.

07 다음 문장의 빈칸에 알맞지 <u>않은</u> 것은?

They have been to England _____.

① once
② twice
③ before
④ never
⑤ many times

08 다음 문장의 빈칸에 알맞은 것은?

The two girls smiled at _____.

① another
② other
③ the other
④ each other
⑤ one the other

09 중요 다음 괄호 안에 주어진 단어를 어법상 바르게 쓴 것은?

> I know some good restaurants here because I (live) in this town for five years.

① live ② lived
③ is living ④ have lived
⑤ had lived

10 중요 다음 각 문장의 빈칸에 들어갈 수 <u>없는</u> 것은? (대 · 소문자 무시)

> • I enjoyed _____ minute of the party.
> • _____ the brothers are dead.
> • _____ the eggs in the box were broken.
> • She cut the cake into pieces and gave one to _____ of them.

① each ② both
③ all ④ some
⑤ every

서답형

11 다음 빈칸에 알맞은 말을 쓰시오.

> My mother has gone shopping. She is _____ here.

12 다음 문장의 빈칸에 알맞은 것은?

> The teacher gave two books to _____ boy.

① all ② each
③ other ④ each of
⑤ all of

서답형

13 다음 두 문장의 의미가 같도록 빈칸에 알맞은 말을 쓰시오.

> We have been married for ten years.
> = Ten years have passed _____ we got married.

14 중요 다음 빈칸에 알맞은 말이 바르게 짝지어진 것은?

> This year's School Sports Day was held on the school playing field. ⓐ class showed its best teamwork, and ⓑ the students had great fun.

① All − all ② All − each
③ Each − every ④ Each − all
⑤ Each of − each

15 다음 대화의 빈칸에 알맞은 것은?

> A: Have you ever heard the news?
> B: No, I _____ the news.

① heard ② have not heard
③ was not heard ④ did not heard
⑤ had not heard

서답형

16 다음 우리말을 영어로 옮길 때 빈칸에 알맞은 말을 쓰시오.

> 이 반의 각 학생은 영어를 매우 잘한다.
> ➡ _____ _____ in this class _____ English vey well.

17 다음 중 밑줄 친 부분의 쓰임이 나머지 넷과 다른 것은?

① <u>Each</u> man has his own taste.
② <u>Each</u> of them loves the other.
③ <u>Each</u> country has its own custom.
④ The elevator stopped at <u>each</u> floor.
⑤ The poem has 12 lines with 20 letters in <u>each</u> line.

[18~19] 다음 중 어법상 어색한 것을 고르시오.

18 ① I have had a fever since last Friday.
② Two years have passed since I came here.
③ We have known each other for many years.
④ He has been seventy years old when he died.
⑤ It has been a long time since I saw you.

19

① He gave money to each of his sons.
② Each of us has his or her opinion.
③ Each of these plans have their merits and demerits.
④ The teacher shook hands with each of his pupils.
⑤ Each of his friends is going camping this summer.

20 다음 대화의 빈칸에 알맞은 말을 쓰시오.

> **A:** How long has she been absent from school?
> **B:** She _____ _____ _____ from school since this Wednesday.

21 다음 빈칸에 공통으로 알맞은 말을 쓰시오.

> • Have you done your homework _____?
> • She hasn't come home _____.

22 다음 중 밑줄 친 부분의 쓰임이 바르지 <u>않은</u> 것은?

① <u>All the rooms are</u> full today.
② <u>Every student</u> passed the test.
③ <u>Each of us have</u> a responsibility for our own health.
④ <u>Each year</u> thousands of people fall ill with flu.
⑤ We've known <u>each other</u> for ten years.

23 다음 중 밑줄 친 부분의 쓰임이 나머지 넷과 <u>다른</u> 하나는?

① I <u>have seen</u> the movie before.
② My uncle <u>has never lived</u> in China before.
③ How many times <u>have</u> they <u>been</u> to England?
④ Mr. Smith <u>has gone</u> to Berlin on business.
⑤ Paul and Marie <u>have been</u> to America once.

01 다음 우리말을 참조하여 문장을 완성하시오.

(1) 그들은 이미 콘서트를 시작했다.
➡ They _____ already _____ the
concert.

(2) 그는 아직 런던에서 돌아오지 않았다.
➡ He _____ _____ _____ from
London yet.

(3) 죄송하지만, 그녀는 회의에 가고 없습니다.
➡ I'm sorry, but she _____ _____
_____ a meeting.

02 다음 빈칸에 알맞은 말을 〈보기〉에서 골라 쓰시오.

┌─── 보기 ───┐
both   all   each   every
└──────────┘

(1) They sell oranges 5 cents _____.
(2) _____ of my parents look happy.
(3) _____ the chairs are broken.
(4) Please tell me about the meaning of
_____ of the words.
(5) Not _____ student passed the exam.

03 다음 문장에서 어법상 어색한 것을 찾아 바르게 고쳐 쓰시오.

(1) She has gone to Bangladesh last Friday.
_____ ➡ _____
(2) My father hasn't left Seoul already.
_____ ➡ _____

04 다음 빈칸에 공통으로 알맞은 말을 쓰시오.

┌──────────────────────────┐
│ • _____ student has to answer the
│   question.
│ • They have known _____ other for a
│   long time.
└──────────────────────────┘

05 다음 문장에서 어법상 어색한 것을 찾아 바르게 고쳐 쓰시오.

(1) I didn't see him since then.
_____ ➡ _____
(2) The weather is good for ten days.
_____ ➡ _____

06 다음 주어진 단어를 바르게 배열하여 문장을 완성하시오.

(1) (Italy / many / he / to / been / times /
has)
➡ _____
(2) (very / days / I / busy / these / been /
have)
➡ _____
(3) (have / Paris / before / I / visited /
never)
➡ _____

07 다음 〈보기〉에서 알맞은 말을 골라 빈칸에 쓰시오.

┌─ 보기 ─────────────────────────┐
all each both every some any
└────────────────────────────────┘

(1) Kirk lost _____ his money.

(2) Jenny enjoyed _____ minute of the party.

(3) They don't eat _____ meat.

(4) Tim cut the apple into pieces and gave one to _____ of us.

(5) Linda borrowed _____ money from him.

(6) Frank pulled the rope with _____ hands.

08 다음 문장에서 어법상 어색한 부분을 바르게 고쳐 문장을 다시 쓰시오.

(1) I have gone to London four years ago.

➡ _____

(2) When have you seen a white lion?

➡ _____

(3) I have often played with her when I was a child.

➡ _____

(4) He has been ill in bed last month.

➡ _____

09 다음 문장에서 어법상 어색한 부분을 고쳐 문장을 다시 쓰시오.

(1) Each of us have to finish our project.

➡ _____

(2) There were four book on the table. Each book was in a different color.

➡ _____
_____

(3) Every drivers should be careful.

➡ _____

10 다음 주어진 단어를 이용하여 우리말을 영어로 옮기시오.

(1) 그는 1970년 이래로 뉴욕에서 살았다.
(live, since)

➡ _____

(2) 너는 이 이야기를 벌써 다 읽었니?
(finish, this, story, yet)

➡ _____

(3) 나는 그 영화를 한 번 본 적이 있다.
(see, once)

➡ _____

11 다음 우리말과 일치하도록 문장을 완성하시오.

┌────────────────────────────────┐
각각의 학생은 자신의 최선을 다해야 한다.
➡ _____ student _____ to do his or her best.
└────────────────────────────────┘

Roofs Around the World

Grass Roofs

Have you ever seen a goat on the roof of a house? In Norway, we
현재완료 의문문   집의 지붕 위에 있는 –goat를 수식하는 형용사구

can see animals on roofs. Norway has large forests. In harmony with
          지붕들 위에 있는   ~와 조화롭게

nature, people have built wooden houses for a long time. To build
         계속적 용법의 현재완료   오랫동안   목적을 나타내는 부사적 용법의 to부정사

strong and warm houses, they cover their roofs with grass. The grass

roofs protect them from the long cold winters and strong winds.
          = people

Sometimes, trees or plants grow out of the grass roofs, and some
빈도부사   ~에서   (복수 명사와 함께 쓰여) 몇몇의

animals enjoy their meals there.
                      = on the grass roofs

Cone-shaped Roofs

A roof is an essential part of a house, but long ago some people built

roofs only to take them down easily. Centuries ago in southern Italy,
      오직, 단지 –to take ~를 수식   목적을 나타내는 부사적 용법의 to부정사   수세기 전에   south의 형용사형

people who had a house without a roof paid lower taxes.
         관계대명사 주격   house를 수식하는 형용사구

---

goat 염소
animal 동물, 짐승
forest 숲, 삼림
harmony 조화
nature 자연
build 짓다, 건설하다
wooden 나무의, 목재의
cover A with B B로 A를 덮다
protect A from B B로부터 A를 보호하다
sometimes 때때로
plant 식물, 초목
grow 자라다, 성장하다
grass 풀, 잔디
meal 음식
cone-shaped 원뿔 모양의
essential 필수적인, 본질적인
part 부분
take down 철거하다
easily 쉽게
century 세기, 100년
southern 남부의, 남쪽의
pay 지불하다
low 낮은
tax 세금

 확인문제

- 다음 문장이 본문의 내용과 일치하면 T, 일치하지 않으면 F를 쓰시오.

1 In Norway, you can see a goat on the roof of a house. ☐

2 People have built stone houses in Norway for a long time. ☐

3 Some animals sometimes enjoy their meals on the grass roofs. ☐

4 A roof is an essential part of a house. ☐

5 In southern Italy, people who had a house with a roof paid lower taxes centuries ago. ☐

To avoid high taxes on their houses, some people built cone-shaped
목적을 나타내는 부사적 용법의 to부정사   build의 과거형 build—built—built
roofs by piling up stones. When tax collectors came to the town,
     by+동명사   때를 나타내는 접속사
people took their roofs down quickly. After the tax collectors left, they
        '타동사+목적어(명사)+부사'의 이어동사   접 ~한 후에
piled up the stones again.

Big Round Roofs

From the sky in a part of southern China, you can see round roofs
                  sky를 수식하는 형용사구   일반 사람을 나타내는 you
that look like big doughnuts. They are the roofs of the big round houses
= which ~처럼 보이다   = The round roofs   = the big round houses
of the Hakka people. They have lived in houses like these for about a
                              계속적 용법의 현재완료   ~와 같은
thousand years to protect themselves from enemies. The houses have
                          재귀 용법의 재귀대명사
only one gate without any windows on the first floor. Each house is big
          without any windows on the first floor.
                        1층에는 창문이 하나도 없이
enough for a whole village. It usually has four stories. It has kitchens
사+enough+for: ~을 위해 충분히 …한   빈도부사: 일반동사 앞에 위치
on the first floor, storage rooms on the second floor, and living rooms
        one의 서수   two의 서수
and bedrooms on the third and fourth floors.
                  three의 서수   four+-th

avoid 피하다	
cone-shaped 원뿔 모양의	
pile up 쌓다	
stone 돌	
collector 징수원, 수집가	
take down 철거하다	
quickly 빨리	
round 둥근	
sky 하늘	
doughnut 도넛	
about 약	
thousand 천, 1,000	
enemy 적	
gate 문, 대문	
without ~이 없는	
each 각각의; 각각	
enough 충분히	
whole 전체의	
village 마을, 마을 사람들	
story 층	
kitchen 부엌	
storage 저장	
living room 거실	

 확인문제

● 다음 문장이 본문의 내용과 일치하면 T, 일치하지 <u>않으면</u> F를 쓰시오.

1 In southern Italy, some people built cone-shaped roofs. ☐

2 When tax collectors came to the town, people built roofs by piling up stones. ☐

3 People can see round roofs that look like big doughnuts in a part of southern China. ☐

4 The Hakka people have lived in the big round houses for about a hundred years. ☐

5 The houses have only one gate without any windows on the first floor. ☐

● 우리말을 참고하여 빈칸에 알맞은 말을 쓰시오.

1 _____ you ever _____ a goat on the _____ of a house?

2 In Norway, we can _____ animals _____ roofs.

3 Norway has large _____.

4 In _____ with nature, people have _____ wooden houses _____ a long time.

5 To _____ strong and warm houses, they _____ their roofs _____ grass.

6 The grass roofs _____ them _____ the long cold winters and _____ winds.

7 Sometimes, trees or plants _____ out of the grass roofs, and _____ animals enjoy their _____ there.

8 A roof is an essential _____ of a house, but long _____ some people built roofs _____ to take them down easily.

9 _____ ago in southern Italy, people _____ had a house without a roof _____ lower taxes.

10 To _____ high taxes on their houses, _____ people built cone-shaped roofs by _____ up stones.

1	여러분은 집의 지붕 위에 있는 염소를 본 적이 있는가?
2	노르웨이에서, 우리는 지붕 위에 있는 동물들을 볼 수 있다.
3	노르웨이는 큰 숲을 가지고 있다.
4	자연과 조화를 이루면서, 사람들은 오랫동안 나무로 집을 지었다.
5	강하고 따뜻한 집을 만들기 위해, 그들은 지붕을 잔디로 덮는다.
6	잔디 지붕은 길고 추운 겨울과 강한 바람으로부터 그들을 보호한다.
7	때때로, 나무나 식물들이 잔디 지붕에서 자라며, 어떤 동물들은 거기서 식사를 즐긴다.
8	지붕은 집의 필수적인 부분이지만, 오래 전에 어떤 사람들은 오직 지붕을 쉽게 철거하기 위해 지었다.
9	수세기 전 남부 이탈리아에서는 지붕 없는 집을 가진 사람들이 더 적은 세금을 냈다.
10	그들의 집에 부과되는 높은 세금을 피하기 위해, 어떤 사람들은 돌을 쌓아 올려 원뿔 모양의 지붕을 만들었다.

11 _____ tax collectors came to the _____ , people _____ their roofs _____ quickly.

12 _____ the tax collectors left, they _____ up the _____ again.

13 From the _____ in a part of _____ China, you can see _____ roofs that look _____ big doughnuts.

14 They are the _____ of the big round houses of the Hakka _____ .

15 They _____ lived in houses like these for _____ a thousand years to protect _____ from enemies.

16 The houses have _____ one gate _____ any windows on the first floor.

17 Each house _____ big enough for a _____ village.

18 It _____ has four stories.

19 It has kitchens on the _____ floor, storage rooms on the _____ floor, and _____ rooms and bedrooms on the third and _____ floors.

11 세금 징수원들이 마을에 오면, 사람들은 재빨리 지붕을 철거했다.

12 세금 징수원들이 떠난 후 그들은 다시 돌을 쌓아 올렸다.

13 중국 남부의 일부 지역의 하늘에서 보면, 여러분은 큰 도넛처럼 생긴 둥근 지붕들을 볼 수 있다.

14 그것들은 하카족의 크고 둥근 집들의 지붕이다.

15 그들은 적으로부터 스스로를 보호하기 위해 약 천 년 동안 이런 집에서 살아왔다.

16 그 집들에는 1층에 창문이 하나도 없고 문이 하나만 있다.

17 각각의 집은 전체 마을이 들어갈 만큼 크다.

18 그 집은 보통 4개의 층을 가지고 있다.

19 1층에는 주방, 2층에는 창고, 3층과 4층에는 거실과 침실이 있다.

● 우리말을 참고하여 본문을 영작하시오.

1 여러분은 집의 지붕 위에 있는 염소를 본 적이 있는가?

➡ _____

2 노르웨이에서, 우리는 지붕 위에 있는 동물들을 볼 수 있다.

➡ _____

3 노르웨이는 큰 숲을 가지고 있다.

➡ _____

4 자연과 조화를 이루면서, 사람들은 오랫동안 나무로 집을 지었다.

➡ _____

5 강하고 따뜻한 집을 만들기 위해, 그들은 지붕을 잔디로 덮는다.

➡ _____

6 잔디 지붕은 길고 추운 겨울과 강한 바람으로부터 그들을 보호한다.

➡ _____

7 때때로, 나무나 식물들이 잔디 지붕에서 자라며, 어떤 동물들은 거기서 식사를 즐긴다.

➡ _____

8 지붕은 집의 필수적인 부분이지만, 오래 전에 어떤 사람들은 오직 지붕을 쉽게 철거하기 위해 지었다.

➡ _____

9 수세기 전 남부 이탈리아에서는 지붕 없는 집을 가진 사람들이 더 적은 세금을 냈다.

➡ _____

10 그들의 집에 부과되는 높은 세금을 피하기 위해, 어떤 사람들은 돌을 쌓아 올려 원뿔 모양의 지붕을 만들었다.

➡ _____

11 세금 징수원들이 마을에 오면, 사람들은 재빨리 지붕을 철거했다.

➡ _____

12 세금 징수원들이 떠난 후 그들은 다시 돌을 쌓아 올렸다.

➡ _____

13 중국 남부의 일부 지역의 하늘에서 보면, 여러분은 큰 도넛처럼 생긴 둥근 지붕들을 볼 수 있다.

➡ _____

14 그것들은 하카족의 크고 둥근 집들의 지붕이다.

➡ _____

15 그들은 적으로부터 스스로를 보호하기 위해 약 천 년 동안 이런 집에서 살아왔다.

➡ _____

16 그 집들에는 1층에 창문이 하나도 없고 문이 하나만 있다.

➡ _____

17 각각의 집은 전체 마을이 들어갈 만큼 크다.

➡ _____

18 그 집은 보통 4개의 층을 가지고 있다.

➡ _____

19 1층에는 주방, 2층에는 창고, 3층과 4층에는 거실과 침실이 있다.

➡ _____
_____

[01~05] 다음 글을 읽고, 물음에 답하시오.

(①) Have you ever seen a goat on the roof of a house? (②) Norway has large forests. (③) In harmony ____ⓐ____ nature, people have built ⓑwood houses for a long time. (④) ⓒTo build strong and warm houses, they cover their roofs ____ⓓ____ grass. (⑤)

01 위 글의 ①~⑤ 중 다음 주어진 문장이 들어갈 알맞은 곳은?

In Norway, we can see animals on roofs.

①   ②   ③   ④   ⑤

02 위 글의 빈칸 ⓐ와 ⓓ에 공통으로 알맞은 것은?

① of   ② to
③ with   ④ from
⑤ along

서답형

03 위 글의 밑줄 친 ⓑ를 알맞은 형으로 고치시오.

➡ _____

04 위 글의 밑줄 친 ⓒ와 같은 용법으로 쓰인 것은?

① I have a baseball cap to wear.
② Love is to trust each other.
③ To live without air is impossible.
④ I went to a shopping mall to buy clothes.
⑤ I have some homework to do today.

05 위 글의 내용으로 보아 알 수 없는 것은?

① 노르웨이의 집들의 지붕 위에는 염소가 올라간다.
② 노르웨이는 큰 숲들이 있다.
③ 노르웨이 사람들은 오랫동안 나무로 된 집을 지어 왔다.
④ 노르웨이 사람들은 강하고 따뜻한 집을 짓기를 원한다.
⑤ 노르웨이 사람들은 지붕을 잔디로 덮는다.

[06~07] 다음 글을 읽고, 물음에 답하시오.

The grass roofs protect them ____ⓐ____ the long cold winters and strong winds. Sometimes, trees or plants grow out of the grass roofs, and some animals enjoy their meals ⓑthere.

06 위 글의 빈칸 ⓐ에 알맞은 것은?

① of   ② to
③ over   ④ from
⑤ with

서답형

07 위 글의 밑줄 친 ⓑ가 구체적으로 가리키는 것을 우리말로 쓰시오.

➡ _____

[08~12] 다음 글을 읽고, 물음에 답하시오.

A roof is an essential part of a house, _____ⓐ_____ long ago some people built roofs only to take them _____ⓑ_____ easily. Centuries ago in ⓒsouth Italy, people ⓓwho had a house without a roof ⓔpay lower taxes.

08 위 글의 빈칸 ⓐ에 알맞은 것은?

① and　　　　② or
③ so　　　　④ for
⑤ but

09 위 글의 빈칸 ⓑ에 알맞은 것은?

① up　　　　② on
③ off　　　　④ down
⑤ with

서답형
10 위 글의 밑줄 친 ⓒ를 알맞은 형으로 고쳐 쓰시오.

➡ _____

11 위 글의 밑줄 친 ⓓ 대신 쓸 수 있는 것은?

① why　　　　② that
③ what　　　　④ which
⑤ whose

서답형
12 위 글의 밑줄 친 ⓔ를 알맞은 형으로 고쳐 쓰시오.

➡ _____

[13~17] 다음 글을 읽고, 물음에 답하시오.

To _____ⓐ_____ high taxes on their houses, some people built cone-shaped roofs by ⓑpile up stones. _____ⓒ_____ tax collectors came to the town, people took their roofs down quickly. _____ⓓ_____ the tax collectors left, they piled up the stones again.

13 위 글의 빈칸 ⓐ에 알맞은 것은?

① avoid　　　　② pay
③ give　　　　④ lend
⑤ follow

서답형
14 위 글의 밑줄 친 ⓑ를 알맞은 형으로 고치시오.

➡ _____

15 위 글의 빈칸 ⓒ에 알맞은 것은?

① If　　　　② Since
③ While　　　　④ When
⑤ Though

16 위 글의 빈칸 ⓓ에 알맞은 것은?

① During　　　　② Though
③ After　　　　④ While
⑤ Before

서답형
17 위 글의 내용과 일치하도록 다음 문장의 빈칸에 알맞은 말을 쓰시오.

세금을 많이 내지 않기 위해 어떤 사람들은 _____. 그리고 세금 징수원이 마을에 왔을 때 _____.

[18~20] 다음 글을 읽고, 물음에 답하시오.

From the ⓐ_____ in a part of southern China, you can see round roofs ⓑthat look like big doughnuts. They are the roofs of the big round houses of the Hakka people. They ⓒhave lived in houses like these for about a thousand years to protect themselves from enemies.

서답형

18 위 글의 빈칸 ⓐ에 다음 정의에 해당하는 말을 주어진 글자로 시작하여 쓰시오.

> the space around the earth which you can see when you stand outside and look upwards

➡ _____

서답형

19 위 글의 밑줄 친 ⓑ와 바꿔 쓸 수 있는 관계대명사를 쓰시오.

➡ _____

중요

20 위 글의 밑줄 친 ⓒ와 같은 용법으로 쓰인 것은?

① I have known her for ten years.
② I have seen a bear in the mountain.
③ Nancy has already had lunch.
④ He has been to Rome three times.
⑤ The man has lost his money, so he couldn't buy the hat.

[21~24] 다음 글을 읽고, 물음에 답하시오.

The houses have only one gate without _____ⓐ windows on the first floor. ⓑEach house are big enough for a whole village. It usually has four stories. It has ⓒ_____ on the first floor, storage rooms on the second floor, and living rooms and bedrooms on the third and fourth floors.

중요

21 위 글의 빈칸 ⓐ에 알맞은 것은?

① no   ② any
③ some   ④ few
⑤ little

서답형

22 위 글의 밑줄 친 ⓑ에서 어법상 어색한 것을 고치시오.

_____ ➡ _____

서답형

23 위 글의 빈칸 ⓒ에 다음 정의에 해당하는 단어를 쓰시오. 필요하면 어형 변화를 하시오.

> a room that is used for cooking and for household jobs such as washing dishes

➡ _____

24 위 글의 내용으로 보아 대답할 수 없는 질문은?

① How many gates do the house have?
② How many windows are there on the first floor of the house?
③ How many stories does the house usually have?
④ What is on the second floor?
⑤ How many bedrooms are there on the fourth floor?

[25~29] 다음 글을 읽고, 물음에 답하시오.

　　Have you ever ⓐ<u>see</u> a goat on the roof of a house? (①) In Norway, we can see animals on roofs. (②) Norway has large forests. (③) In harmony with nature, people ⓑ<u>have built</u> wooden houses for a long time. (④) To build strong and warm houses, they cover their roofs ___ⓒ___ grass. (⑤) Sometimes, trees or plants grow out of the grass roofs, and some animals enjoy their meals there.

25 위 글의 ①~⑤ 중 다음 주어진 문장이 들어갈 알맞은 곳은?

> The grass roofs protect them from the long cold winters and strong winds.

① ② ③ ④ ⑤

서답형
26 위 글의 밑줄 친 ⓐ를 알맞은 어형으로 고치시오.

➡ _____

27 위 글의 밑줄 친 ⓑ와 용법이 같은 것은? (2개)

① I <u>have been</u> in this country since last month.
② Yumi <u>has seen</u> this movies many times.
③ Mike <u>has</u> just <u>cleaned</u> his room.
④ Lisa <u>has had</u> this cat for ten years.
⑤ She <u>has gone</u> to Europe for her summer holidays.

서답형
28 위 글의 빈칸 ⓒ에 알맞은 전치사를 쓰시오.

➡ _____

29 위 글의 내용으로 보아 알 수 <u>없는</u> 것은?

① In Norway, we can see a goat on the roof of a house.
② There are large forests in Norway.
③ People have built wooden houses for a long time in Norway.
④ People in Norway want to build strong and warm houses.
⑤ Some animals live on the roofs of houses.

[30~32] 다음 글을 읽고, 물음에 답하시오.

　　A roof is an essential part of a house, but ①<u>long ago</u> some people built roofs only ②<u>to take them down</u> ③<u>easily</u>. ④<u>Centuries before</u> in ⓐ<u>south Italy</u>, ⓑ<u>people who had a house without a roof</u> paid ⑤<u>lower</u> taxes.

30 위 글의 밑줄 친 ①~⑤ 중 어법상 <u>어색한</u> 것은?

① ② ③ ④ ⑤

서답형
31 위 글의 밑줄 친 ⓐ를 알맞은 어형으로 고치시오.

➡ _____

32 위 글의 밑줄 친 ⓑ와 같은 뜻이 되도록 바꿔 쓸 때 빈칸에 알맞은 말이 바르게 짝지어진 것은? (2개)

> people who had a house _____ has _____ roof

① that / no　　② that / any
③ that / some　④ which / no
⑤ which / some

[01~05] 다음 글을 읽고, 물음에 답하시오.

ⓐ(To avoid, Avoiding) high taxes on their houses, some people built cone-shaped roofs ⓑ_____ piling up stones. ⓒWhen tax collectors came to the town, people took their roofs ⓓ_____ quickly. ⓔAfter the tax collectors left, they piled up the stones again.

01 위 글의 괄호 ⓐ에서 알맞은 것을 고르시오.

➡ _____

02 위 글의 빈칸 ⓑ에 알맞은 말을 쓰시오.

➡ _____

03 위 글의 밑줄 친 ⓒ 대신 쓸 수 있는 접속사를 쓰시오.

➡ _____

04 위 글의 빈칸 ⓓ에 알맞은 부사를 쓰시오.

➡ _____

05 위 글의 밑줄 친 ⓔ를 우리말로 옮기시오.

➡ _____

[06~09] 다음 글을 읽고, 물음에 답하시오.

From the sky in a part of southern China, you can see round roofs ⓐthat look like big ⓑ_____ . They are the roofs of the big round houses of the Hakka people. They ⓒ(lived, have lived) in houses like these for about a thousand years to protect ⓓthem from enemies.

06 위 글의 밑줄 친 ⓐ 대신 쓸 수 있는 관계대명사를 쓰시오.

➡ _____

07 위 글의 빈칸 ⓑ에 다음 정의에 해당하는 단어를 쓰시오. (필요하면 어형을 바꾸시오.)

a bread-like cake made from sweet dough that has been cooked in hot fat

➡ _____

08 위 글의 괄호 ⓒ에서 알맞은 것을 고르시오.

➡ _____

09 위 글의 밑줄 친 ⓓ를 알맞은 어형으로 고치시오.

➡ _____

[10~14] 다음 글을 읽고, 물음에 답하시오.

The houses have only one gate ⓐwithout any windows on the first floor. Each house is big enough ___ⓑ___ a whole village. ⓒIt usually has four stories. It has kitchens on the first floor, storage rooms on the second floor, and living rooms and bedrooms on the ⓓthree and fourth floors.

10 위 글의 밑줄 친 ⓐ를 우리말로 옮기시오.

➡ _____

11 위 글의 빈칸 ⓑ에 알맞은 전치사를 쓰시오.

➡ _____

12 위 글의 밑줄 친 ⓒ가 가리키는 것을 영어로 쓰시오.

➡ _____

13 위 글의 밑줄 친 ⓓ를 알맞은 어형으로 고치시오.

➡ _____

14 Where are storage rooms? Answer in English.

➡ _____

[15~19] 다음 글을 읽고, 물음에 답하시오.

Sejong National Library is ___ⓐ___ Sejong, Korea. ⓑIt is a four-stories building that looks like an open book. It has about 400 thousand books on the first and second floors and a large cafeteria on the top floor. It opened in 2013. ⓒ(Since, For) then, many people have visited this unique building.

15 위 글의 빈칸 ⓐ에 알맞은 전치사를 쓰시오.

➡ _____

16 위 글의 밑줄 친 ⓑ에서 어법상 어색한 것을 고치시오.

_____ ➡ _____

17 위 글의 괄호 ⓒ에서 알맞은 것을 고르시오.

➡ _____

18 How many books are there in Sejong National Library? Answer in English.

➡ _____

19 When did Sejong National Library open? Answer in English.

➡ _____

해석

Link

I can't open windows because of the fine dust these days. How about making a
　　　　　　　　　　～ 때문에　　　　　　　　　　　　　　　　～하는 것이 어때?
small garden on the roof?

나는 요즘 미세먼지 때문에 창문을 열 수가 없어요. 지붕에 작은 정원을 만드는 것은 어떨까요?

구문해설 • fine dust: 미세 먼지　• these days: 요즘

Fine dust has been a big problem in the spring. We designed a roof that has a
　　　　　 현재완료　　　　　　　　　　　　　　　　　　　　　　관계대명사 주격
small garden with trees and many other plants. This garden will give us fresh
　　　　　　　～이 있는　　　　many other+복수명사
air.

봄에는 미세먼지가 큰 문제가 되어 왔다. 우리는 나무와 다른 많은 식물들이 있는 작은 정원을 가진 지붕을 설계했다. 이 정원은 우리에게 신선한 공기를 줄 것이다.

구문해설 • problem: 문제　• design: 설계하다　• plant: 식물

Write

Sejong National Library is in Sejong, Korea. It is a four-story building that
　　　　　　　　　　　　　　　　　　= Sejong National Library　　　　　주격 관계대명사
looks like an open book. It has about 400 thousand books on the first and
～처럼 보이다
second floors and a large cafeteria on the top floor. It opened in 2013. Since
　　　　　　　　　　　　　　　　　　　　　　　　　　　　　　　in + 연도
then, many people have visited this unique building.
　　　　　　　계속 용법의 현재완료

국립 세종 도서관은 한국의 세종시에 있다. 그것은 펴놓은 책처럼 보이는 4층 건물이다. 1층과 2층에는 약 40만 권의 책이 있고, 맨 위층에는 큰 구내식당이 있다. 그것은 2013년에 문을 열었다. 그 이후로, 많은 사람들이 이 독특한 건물을 방문했다.

구문해설 • national: 국립의　• story: (건물의) 층　• open: 펼쳐 놓은　• floor: (건물의) 층
• unique: 독특한

Culture Project

In Granada, Spain, some people have lived in cave houses for a long time.
in + 도시　　　　　　　　　　　 현재완료의 계속 용법　　　　　　　　　　오랫동안
The weather in this place is very hot in the summer and cold in the winter. It's
　　　　　　　　　　　　　　　　　　　　　　　　　　　　날씨를 나타내는 비인칭 주어 it
not too cold or hot in cave houses.
　　 not A or B: A도 B도 아닌

스페인의 그라나다에서는, 몇몇 사람들이 오랫동안 동굴 집에서 살아왔다. 이곳의 날씨는 여름에는 매우 덥고 겨울에는 춥다. 동굴 집은 너무 춥거나 덥지도 않다.

구문해설 • cave: 동굴　• weather: 날씨　• hot: 더운　• cold: 추운

영역별 핵심문제

01 다음 중 짝지어진 단어의 관계가 나머지와 <u>다른</u> 것은? (2개)

① slow – slowly
② love – lovely
③ kind – kindly
④ friend – friendly
⑤ quick – quickly

02 다음 빈칸에 들어갈 말로 적절하지 <u>않은</u> 것은?

- I'd like a room with a _____.
- He was at the door to _____ us.
- He found the place _____ difficulty.
- What _____ did he say?

① else
② without
③ other
④ view
⑤ welcome

03 다음 짝지어진 두 단어의 관계가 같도록 빈칸에 알맞은 말을 쓰시오.

warm : cool = high : _____

04 다음 문장의 빈칸에 알맞은 것은?

Vegetables are good _____ the health.

① in
② on
③ to
④ for
⑤ with

05 다음 영영풀이에 해당하는 단어는?

a large area where trees grow close together

① zoo
② park
③ jungle
④ garden
⑤ forest

06 다음 문장의 빈칸에 공통으로 들어갈 말을 쓰시오.

- What _____ of movies do you like?
- That made me feel _____ of stupid.

07 다음 우리말에 맞게 빈칸에 알맞은 말을 쓰시오.

나는 보통 이런 종류의 기계를 다루지는 않지만, 한번 해 보기는 하겠다.
➡ I don't usually work with these kinds of machines but I'll _____ it _____ _____.

08 다음 대화의 빈칸에 알맞은 말을 쓰시오.

A: _____ can I find men's shirts?
B: They're on the second floor.
A: Oh, I see. Thanks.
B: No problem.

[09~15] 다음 대화를 읽고, 물음에 답하시오.

> Woman: Welcome ___ⓐ___ Jeonju Hanok Guesthouse. ___ⓑ___ I help you?
>
> Man: Yes, I'd like a room for two nights.
>
> Woman: Well, what kind of room would you like?
>
> Man: Do you have a room with a garden view? You have a ⓒ<u>love</u> garden.
>
> Woman: Yes, we do. ⓓ<u>Every room in our house have a garden view</u>, ___ⓔ___ there are no beds in the rooms.
>
> Man: Do I have to sleep on the floor?
>
> Woman: Yes, you do.
>
> Man: O.K. ⓕ<u>I'll give it a try.</u> Where can I have breakfast?
>
> Woman: You can have breakfast in the dining room, next to the kitchen.
>
> Man: I see.
>
> Woman: O.K. You're in the Nabi room. Here's your key.
>
> Man: Thank you.

09 위 대화의 빈칸 ⓐ에 알맞은 말을 쓰시오.

➡ _____

10 위 대화의 빈칸 ⓑ에 알맞은 것은? (2개)

① May
② Will
③ Must
④ Can
⑤ Should

11 위 대화의 밑줄 친 ⓒ를 알맞은 어형으로 고치시오.

➡ _____

12 위 대화의 밑줄 친 ⓓ에서 어법상 어색한 것을 고치시오.

_____ ➡ _____

13 위 대화의 빈칸 ⓔ에 알맞은 것은?

① so
② or
③ and
④ but
⑤ for

14 위 대화의 밑줄 친 ⓕ를 우리말로 옮기시오.

➡ _____

15 위 대화의 내용으로 보아 대답할 수 <u>없는</u> 질문은?

① Where is the man now?
② How many nights is the man going to stay?
③ What room does the man want?
④ Why are there no beds in the rooms?
⑤ Where can the man have breakfast?

16 다음 대화의 빈칸에 알맞은 것은?

> A: _____
>
> B: Yes. I'm looking for smart phones.
>
> A: They're near the escalator.

① May I help you?
② What should I do?
③ Where can I find them?
④ What are you looking for?
⑤ Where can I take an escalator?

17 다음 문장의 빈칸에 알맞은 것은?

> I _____ never seen such a beautiful mountain.

① be　　② did
③ have　④ was
⑤ must

18 다음 문장의 빈칸에 알맞은 말이 바르게 짝지어진 것은?

> • Each of the children _____ a toy car.
> • Some of these books _____ interesting, but others are not.

① has – is　② has – be
③ have – is　④ has – are
⑤ have – are

19 다음 괄호 안에 주어진 단어를 어법상 바르게 쓴 것은?

> Jack (want) this video game since last year.

① want　　② wants
③ wanted　④ has wanted
⑤ is wanting

20 다음 괄호 안에서 알맞은 말을 고르시오.

> A: How's Janet? Do you see her often?
> B: She's good. We call (each other / each others) regularly.

21 다음 중 어법상 어색한 것은?

① He has been sick in bed for a week.
② How long have you stayed in America?
③ I have climbed that mountain last week.
④ You have already walked 100 kilometers.
⑤ I have never been to America.

22 다음 중 빈칸에 들어갈 말이 다른 하나는? (대·소문자 무시)

① These cups were five dollars _____.
② _____ ticket costs 20 dollars.
③ When the children arrive, give _____ of them a balloon.
④ _____ student came forward to receive a medal.
⑤ Almost _____ window was broken.

23 다음 문장과 뜻이 가장 가까운 것은?

> Jack's father has gone to Rome.

① Jack's father is going to Rome.
② Jack's father went to Rome.
③ Jack's father went to Rome but he is here now.
④ Jack's father went to Rome and he isn't here now.
⑤ Jack's father went to Rome and he has just come back.

24 다음 〈보기〉의 밑줄 친 부분과 같은 용법으로 사용된 것은?

> ─ 보기 ─
> Nancy has read the novel three times.

① I have lived here since last year.
② Ted has seen a panda before.
③ My mother has finished washing the dishes already.
④ Jack has wanted to have a cat for a long time.
⑤ Mrs. Brown has lost her purse somewhere.

25 다음 중 어법상 어색한 것은?

① Each weekend, they work at home.
② Each member has to pay a membership fee.
③ Each the students received a special gift.
④ We each wanted the bedroom with the TV.
⑤ Each of the buildings is surrounded by tall trees.

26 다음 중 밑줄 친 부분의 쓰임이 올바르지 않은 것은?

① He has gone to Madrid ten years ago.
② Kate has lived in Seoul for five years.
③ Mike has been sick in hospital since last Monday.
④ She has never seen such a beautiful lake.
⑤ How often have you been to Paris?

27 다음 밑줄 친 부분을 어법상 바르게 고쳐 쓰시오.

> Each their opinions has both good points and bad points.

➡ _____

Reading

[28~32] 다음 글을 읽고, 물음에 답하시오.

ⓐHave you ever seen a goat on the roof of a house? In Norway, we can see animals on roofs. ⓑNorway has large forests. In harmony with nature, people have built wooden houses for a long time. To build strong and warm houses, they cover their roofs ⓒ grass. The grass roofs ⓓ them from the long cold winters and strong winds. Sometimes, trees or plants grow out of the grass roofs, and some animals enjoy their meals there.

28 위 글의 밑줄 친 ⓐ와 같은 용법으로 쓰인 것은?

① I have been in Japan since last month.
② Kirk has seen a panda before.
③ My father has already eaten breakfast.
④ He has wanted to be a painter for a long time.
⑤ She has lost her smartphone somewhere.

29 위 글의 밑줄 친 ⓑ와 같은 뜻이 되도록 다음 문장의 빈칸에 알맞은 말을 쓰시오.

> _____ _____ large forests in Norway.

30 위 글의 빈칸 ⓒ에 알맞은 것은?

① of   ② in
③ at   ④ with
⑤ from

31 위 글의 빈칸 ⓓ에 다음 정의에 해당하는 단어를 쓰시오.

> to prevent someone or something from being harmed or damaged

➡ _____

32 위 글의 내용으로 보아 알 수 없는 것은?

① 노르웨이에서는 집 지붕 위에 동물들이 올라가기도 한다.
② 노르웨이 사람들은 오랫동안 목조 가옥을 지어 왔다.
③ 노르웨이 사람들은 잔디로 지붕을 덮는다.
④ 노르웨이의 겨울은 길고 바람이 강하게 분다.
⑤ 노르웨이에서는 동물들이 보통 집 지붕 위에서 사료를 먹는다.

[33~36] 다음 글을 읽고, 물음에 답하시오.

> In Granada, Spain, some people have lived in cave houses ⓐ a long time. ⓑThe weather in this place is very hot in the summer and cold in the winter. It's not too cold ⓒ hot in cave houses.

33 위 글의 빈칸 ⓐ에 알맞은 것은?

① in ② to
③ with ④ for
⑤ since

34 위 글의 밑줄 친 ⓑ를 우리말로 옮기시오.

➡ _____

35 위 글의 빈칸 ⓒ에 알맞은 것은?

① or ② so
③ and ④ but
⑤ for

36 스페인의 그라나다에서 사람들이 동굴 집에서 사는 이유를 우리말로 간단히 쓰시오.

➡ _____

[37~38] 다음 글을 읽고, 물음에 답하시오.

> Sejong National Library is in Sejong, Korea. It is a four-story building that looks ⓐ an open book. It has ⓑabout 400 thousand books on the first and second floors and a large cafeteria on the top floor. It opened in 2013. Since then, many people have visited this unique building.

37 위 글의 빈칸 ⓐ에 알맞은 말을 쓰시오.

➡ _____

38 위 글의 밑줄 친 ⓑ와 같은 의미로 쓰인 것은?

① I know nothing about her.
② He studies about two hours a day.
③ Books were thrown about the room.
④ I want an easy book about wild birds.
⑤ The girls walked about in the park.

출제율 95%

01 다음 중 짝지어진 단어의 관계가 나머지 넷과 <u>다른</u> 것은?

① wrong : right ② high : low
③ enemy : friend ④ near : close
⑤ entrance : exit

출제율 95%

02 다음 빈칸에 공통으로 알맞은 것은?

- I was fond _____ sports when I was young.
- The prisoner hopes to get out _____ jail within a few months.

① in ② of
③ from ④ with
⑤ onto

출제율 90%

03 다음 짝지어진 두 단어의 관계가 같도록 빈칸에 알맞은 말을 쓰시오.

one : first = three : _____

출제율 100%

04 다음 중 영영풀이가 <u>잘못된</u> 것은?

① wooden: made of wood
② sometimes: on some occasions rather than all the time
③ restroom: a room with a toilet for customers to use
④ dress: casual trousers that are usually made of strong blue cotton cloth called denim
⑤ meal: an occasion when people sit down and eat, usually at a regular time

출제율 85%

05 다음 우리말에 맞게 빈칸에 알맞은 말을 쓰시오.

박쥐에게 거꾸로 매달리는 것은 지극히 정상입니다.
➡ To bats hanging _____ _____ is perfectly normal.

출제율 95%

06 다음 대화의 의도로 알맞은 것은?

A: Excuse me. Where can I find children's toys?
B: You can find them on the sixth floor.
A: Thank you very much.
B: You're welcome.

① 요청하기 ② 충고하기
③ 제안하기 ④ 위치 묻기
⑤ 상품 광고하기

출제율 90%

07 다음 대화의 빈칸에 알맞지 <u>않은</u> 것은?

A: What do you want to be in the future?
B: _____

① I haven't decided yet.
② I'm going to have tea.
③ Well, I'm not sure. How about you?
④ I want to be a reporter like my dad.
⑤ Well, I have several jobs in my mind.

08 다음 중 짝지어진 대화가 <u>어색한</u> 것은?

① A: What kind of food would you like?
   B: I'd like Chinese food.

② A: What kind of house do you want to live in?
   B: Well, I want to live in an airplane-shaped house.

③ A: Do you want to see the baseball game?
   B: Yes, I do.

④ A: What do you want to do on your birthday?
   B: Yes, I want to go to Fun Park.

⑤ A: I'm looking for the cheese. Where can I find it?
   B: It's in aisle B.

[09~11] 다음 대화를 읽고, 물음에 답하시오.

A: _____ @ _____ men's clothes.
B: You can find them at Men's Day.
A: Where is that?
B: ⓑ <u>그것은 2층에 있어요.</u>
A: Thank you.
B: ⓒ<u>No problem.</u>

09 위 대화의 빈칸 @에 알맞은 것은?

① I'm wondering   ② I'm checking
③ I'm looking for   ④ I'm waiting for
⑤ I'm looking around

10 위 대화의 밑줄 친 ⓑ를 영어로 바르게 옮긴 것은?

① There are two floors.
② It's on the two floor.
③ It's on the second floor.
④ It's over the second floor.
⑤ Here is the second floor.

11 위 대화의 밑줄 친 ⓒ 대신 쓸 수 <u>없는</u> 것은? (2개)

① You're welcome.
② You're right.
③ That's fine with me.
④ That's all right.
⑤ Don't mention it.

12 다음 문장의 빈칸에 알맞지 <u>않은</u> 것은?

> Frank has been to London _____.

① once   ② twice
③ never   ④ before
⑤ many times

13 다음 문장의 빈칸에 알맞은 말이 바르게 짝지어진 것은?

> • Each person _____ to finish the project by tomorrow.
> • I think all of the children _____ hungry now.

① has – be   ② has – is
③ have – is   ④ have – are
⑤ has – are

14 다음 밑줄 친 단어의 올바른 형태를 쓰시오.

> Jane <u>lived</u> in England since she was ten years old.

➡ _____

15 다음 두 문장의 의미가 일치하도록 빈칸에 알맞은 말을 쓰시오

> He gave me this book after he read it.
> = He read this book _____ he gave it to me.

16 다음 각 문장의 빈칸에 들어갈 수 없는 것은? (대·소문자 무시)

> • She has a flower in _____ hand.
> • _____ of us want to see the movie.
> • _____ of the milk was spilled.
> • _____ word in this dictionary is important

① all   ② both   ③ each
④ any   ⑤ every

17 다음 〈보기〉 문장과 뜻이 가장 가까운 것은?

> ┌─ 보기 ─┐
> Tom has lost his watch.

① Tom lost his watch.
② Tom lost his watch and he forgot it.
③ Tom lost his watch, but he found it.
④ Tom lost his watch, and he hasn't found it yet.
⑤ Tom lost his watch, so he is going to buy a new one.

18 다음 중 어법상 어색한 문장은?

① Each of the girls has her own bed.
② Every player has to do his best.
③ Both of them looks very tired.
④ You can have all the cake.
⑤ All the boys are playing baseball at the park.

19 다음 밑줄 친 부분의 쓰임이 나머지 넷과 다른 하나는?

① Lily <u>has seen</u> the movie before.
② My grandfather <u>has</u> never <u>visited</u> Seoul.
③ Mr. Lincoln <u>has gone</u> to Berlin on business.
④ How many times <u>have</u> they <u>been</u> to China?
⑤ They <u>have been</u> to Italy three times.

[20~24] 다음 글을 읽고, 물음에 답하시오.

> A roof is an essential part of a house, ⓐ_____ long ago some people built roofs only to take them down ⓑeasy. Centuries ago in southern Italy, people who had a house without a roof paid ⓒ_____ taxes. To avoid high taxes on their houses, some people built cone-shaped roofs ⓓ_____ piling up stones. When tax collectors came to the town, people took their roofs down quickly. After the tax collectors left, they piled up the stones again.

20 위 글의 빈칸 ⓐ에 알맞은 것은?

① but   ② or
③ so   ④ and
⑤ for

📝 출제율 100%

21 위 글의 밑줄 친 ⓑ를 알맞은 형으로 고치시오.

➡ _____

📝 출제율 95%

22 위 글의 빈칸 ⓒ에 알맞은 것은?

① much   ② less
③ lower   ④ more
⑤ higher

📝 출제율 95%

23 위 글의 빈칸 ⓓ에 알맞은 것은?

① to   ② by
③ in   ④ with
⑤ from

📝 출제율 90%

24 위 글의 내용과 일치하도록 다음 물음에 대하여 우리말로 간단히 쓰시오.

(1) 세금 징수원들이 마을에 왔을 때 사람들이 한 일
➡ _____

(2) 세금 징수원들이 마을에 떠났을 때 사람들이 한 일
➡ _____

[25~29] 다음 글을 읽고, 물음에 답하시오.

> ___ⓐ___ the sky in a part of southern China, you can see round roofs ___ⓑ___ look like big doughnuts. ⓒThey are the roofs of the big round houses of the Hakka people. They ___ⓓ___ in houses like these for about a thousand years to protect ⓔthem from enemies.

📝 출제율 90%

25 위 글의 빈칸 ⓐ에 알맞은 것은?

① In   ② On
③ From   ④ Over
⑤ Along

📝 출제율 100%

26 위 글의 빈칸 ⓑ에 알맞은 것은? (2개)

① who   ② what
③ whose   ④ that
⑤ which

📝 출제율 90%

27 위 글의 밑줄 친 ⓒ가 가리키는 것을 우리말로 쓰시오.

➡ _____

📝 출제율 90%

28 위 글의 빈칸 ⓓ에 알맞은 것은?

① live   ② lived
③ are living   ④ have lived
⑤ had lived

📝 출제율 90%

29 위 글의 밑줄 친 ⓔ를 알맞은 어형으로 고치시오.

➡ _____

단원별 예상문제 **101**

[01~03] 다음 대화를 읽고, 물음에 답하시오.

M: _____ⓐ_____ me, is there a restaurant in this mall?
W: Yes. ___ⓑ___ kind of food would you like?
M: I'd like Chinese food.
W: There is a great restaurant on the fifth floor.
M: Thank you.
W: ⓒYou're welcome.

01 위 대화의 빈칸 ⓑ에 알맞은 말을 쓰시오.

➡ _____

 02 위 대화의 빈칸 ⓐ에 알맞은 말을 쓰시오.

➡ _____

03 위 대화의 밑줄 친 ⓒ와 같은 뜻이 되도록 빈칸에 알맞은 말을 쓰시오.

No _____ .

 04 다음 대화의 순서를 바르게 배열하시오.

(A) Thank you.
(B) You're welcome.
(C) Excuse me, where can I find women's jeans?
(D) You can find them on the second floor. They're next to the elevator.

➡ _____

 05 다음 〈보기〉와 같이 현재완료 시제를 이용해 두 문장을 한 문장으로 쓰시오.

┤ 보기 ├
Jane moved to Tokyo ten years ago. She still lives there.
➡ Jane has lived in Tokyo for ten years.

(1) Peter moved to Peking in 2010. He still lives in Peking.

➡ _____

(2) Tom went to hospital a week ago. He is still in hospital.

➡ _____

(3) My mother went shopping. She is not here.

➡ _____

06 다음 〈조건〉에 맞게 괄호 안의 단어를 이용하여 우리말을 영어로 옮기시오.

┤ 조건 ├
1. 주어진 단어를 모두 이용할 것.
2. 필요시 관사를 붙이거나 단어를 추가하고 동사의 어형변화를 할 것.
3. 대·소문자 및 구두점에 유의할 것.

(1) 나는 런던에 머무는 동안 매일 아침을 먹었다.
(eat, each, during, stay, in)

➡ _____

(2) 문의 양쪽에 나무가 있다.
(there, on, both, side, gate)

➡ _____

(3) 그에게는 매일 매일이 똑같이 여겨진다.
(every, seem, same, to)

➡ _____

07 다음 문장에서 어법상 어색한 것을 찾아 바르게 고치시오.

(1) He has been to Spain last year.

_____ ➡ _____

(2) When have you seen Kathy's little brother?

_____ ➡ _____

(3) I have often played the piano when I was a child.

_____ ➡ _____

[08~11] 다음 글을 읽고, 물음에 답하시오.

The houses have only one ___ⓐ___ without any windows on the first floor. ⓑEach houses is big enough for a whole village. It usually has four stories. It has kitchens on the first floor, storage rooms on the second floor, and living rooms and bedrooms on the third and ⓒfour floors.

08 위 글의 빈칸 ⓐ에 다음 정의에 해당하는 단어를 쓰시오.

a structure like a door which is used at the entrance to a field, a garden, or the grounds of a building

➡ _____

09 위 글의 밑줄 친 ⓑ에서 어법상 어색한 것을 고치시오.

_____ ➡ _____

10 위 글의 밑줄 친 ⓒ를 알맞은 어형으로 고치시오.

➡ _____

11 Where are kitchens? Answer in English.

➡ _____

[12~15] 다음 글을 읽고, 물음에 답하시오.

Sejong National Library is ___ⓐ___ Sejong, Korea. It is a four-story building ___ⓑ___ looks like an open book. It has about 400 thousand books on the first and second floors and a large ___ⓒ___ on the top floor. It opened in 2013. ⓓSince then, many people visited this unique building.

12 위 글의 빈칸 ⓐ에 알맞은 전치사를 쓰시오.

➡ _____

13 위 글의 빈칸 ⓑ에 알맞은 관계대명사를 쓰시오.

➡ _____

14 위 글의 빈칸 ⓒ에 다음 정의에 해당하는 단어를 쓰시오.

a restaurant where you choose your food from a counter and take it to your table after paying for it

➡ _____

15 위 글의 밑줄 친 ⓓ에서 어법상 어색한 것을 고치시오.

_____ ➡ _____

01 다음 빈칸에 알맞은 말을 넣어 대화를 완성하시오.

> (1) **A:** What do you want to do this weekend?
>
> **B:** _____
>
> **A:** Let's go to the movies this Saturday.
>
> **B:** OK.

> (2) **A:** Do you want to play chess?
>
> **B:** _____
>
> **A:** Let's play chess after supper.
>
> **B:** All right.

02 다음 대화의 밑줄 친 표현과 바꾸어 쓸 수 있는 것을 2개 쓰시오.

> **A:** I'm looking for shoes. Where can I find them?
>
> **B:** They're on the first floor.

➡ _____

03 다음 (A), (B), (C)에 주어진 단어를 이용하여 4개의 문장을 만드시오.

(A)	(B)	(C)
each	friends of mine	has a TV
each of	the films	are very kind
every	student	has passed the exam
all	room	was very wonderful

(1) _____

(2) _____

(3) _____

(4) _____

단원별 모의고사

01 다음 중 우리말 뜻이 <u>잘못된</u> 것은?

① next to: ~ 옆에
② kind of: 약간, 어느 정도
③ in harmony with: ~와 조화를 이루어
④ take down: ~을 운반하다
⑤ give it a try: 시도하다, 한번 해보다

02 다음 영영풀이에 해당하는 단어로 알맞은 것은?

> a living thing that grows in the earth and has a stem, leaves, and roots

① garden　　② plant　　③ flower
④ grass　　⑤ animal

03 다음 빈칸에 알맞은 말이 바르게 짝지어진 것은?

> • Her office is on the second _____.
> • Ask somebody _____ to help you.

① hall – else　　② floor – other
③ hall – other　　④ floor – else
⑤ story – other

04 다음 짝지어진 두 단어의 관계가 같도록 빈칸에 알맞은 말을 쓰시오.

> paint : painter = collect : _____

05 다음 빈칸에 공통으로 들어갈 말을 쓰시오.

> • Let's pile _____ stones here.
> • We walked _____ to the sixth floor.

➡ _____

06 다음 대화를 의미가 통하도록 알맞게 배열한 것은?

> (A) What kind of house do you want to live in?
> (B) I like music, so I want to live in a piano-shaped house.
> (C) Oh, it looks interesting, but I think it's kind of strange.
> (D) Hey, look at this unique house in the picture. It's upside down.

① (A) – (D) – (B) – (C)
② (B) – (C) – (A) – (D)
③ (C) – (D) – (B) – (A)
④ (D) – (B) – (C) – (A)
⑤ (D) – (C) – (A) – (B)

07 다음 중 짝지어진 대화가 <u>어색한</u> 것은?

① A: I'm looking for a hat store.
　B: You can go to Lucy's Hats.
② A: How do I get to the bank?
　B: Go straight one block and turn right.
③ A: Is there a bookshop near here?
　B: Yes, there's one across from the post office.
④ A: How may I help you?
　B: I'm looking for women's clothes.
⑤ A: I'm looking for women's shoes.
　B: How do I get there?

08 다음 대화의 빈칸에 공통으로 알맞은 말을 쓰시오.

> A: Where can I _____ children's toys?
> B: You can _____ them on the sixth floor.

➡ _____

10 위 대화의 밑줄 친 ⓑ를 우리말로 옮기시오.

➡ _____

11 위 대화의 밑줄 친 ⓒ와 같은 뜻이 되도록 빈칸에 알맞은 말을 쓰시오.

➡ but the rooms _____ _____ beds.

[09~13] 다음 대화를 읽고, 물음에 답하시오.

Woman: Welcome to Jeonju Hanok Guesthouse. ⓐMay I help you?
Man: Yes, I'd like a room for two nights.
Woman: Well, what kind of room would you like?
Man: ⓑDo you have a room with a garden view? You have a lovely garden.
Woman: Yes, we do. Every room in our house has a garden view, ⓒbut there are no beds in the rooms.
Man: Do I have to sleep on the floor?
Woman: Yes, you do.
Man: O.K. I'll give it a try. Where can I have breakfast?
Woman: You can have breakfast in the dining room, next ___ⓓ___ the kitchen.
Man: I see.
Woman: O.K. You're in the Nabi room. Here's your key.
Man: Thank you.

12 위 대화의 빈칸 ⓓ에 알맞은 것은?

① to
② at
③ in
④ on
⑤ from

13 위 대화의 내용과 일치하지 않는 것은?

① The man is in Jeonju Hanok Guesthouse now.
② The man wants a room for two nights.
③ There is a lovely garden in the guesthouse.
④ The man often sleeps on the floor.
⑤ The man will have breakfast in the dining room.

09 위 대화의 밑줄 친 ⓐ 대신 쓸 수 없는 것은? (2개)

① Can I help you?
② Should I help you?
③ Why do I help you?
④ What can I do for you?
⑤ How may I help you?

14 다음 괄호 안에 주어진 단어를 어법상 바르게 쓴 것은?

> He left home at six and (not return) yet.

① doesn't return
② wasn't returned
③ didn't return
④ hasn't returned
⑤ hadn't returned

15 다음 문장의 빈칸에 알맞은 것은? (2개)

> The teacher gave a ball pen to _____ student.

① all   ② each
③ other   ④ each of
⑤ every

16 다음 문장 중 어법상 어색한 것은?

① I've gone to Paris five years ago.
② Jack has practiced the piano since last year.
③ Ann has been sick in bed for two weeks.
④ I have never seen such a wonderful movie.
⑤ Has your teacher ever been to Europe?

17 다음 문장 중 어법상 어색한 것은?

① All the boys were kind to Ann.
② Every boy likes baseball.
③ Each of them have a ticket for the concert.
④ There is a tree on each side of the gate.
⑤ They have known each other for twenty years.

18 다음 두 문장의 뜻이 같도록 빈칸에 알맞은 말을 쓰시오.

> I _____ _____ my car key.
> = I lost my car key. I don't have it now.

19 다음 우리말과 일치하도록 주어진 어구를 바르게 배열하여 문장을 완성하시오.

> 보트 안의 모든 사람은 팀으로 함께 일해야 한다.
> (the boat / together / has to / a team / in / work / everyone / as)

➡ _____

_____

20 다음 빈칸에 알맞은 것은?

> Frank _____ never seen such a cute cat.

① be   ② did
③ has   ④ was
⑤ must

[21~23] 다음 글을 읽고, 물음에 답하시오.

> Fine dust has been a big problem ⓐ the spring. We designed a roof that has a small garden ⓑwith trees and many other plants. ⓒ This garden will give us fresh air.

21 위 글의 빈칸 ⓐ에 알맞은 것은?

① to   ② at
③ in   ④ on
⑤ from

22 위 글의 밑줄 친 ⓑ와 같은 의미로 쓰인 것은?

① I'm pleased with your present.
② Who is the man with the beard?
③ Wash it with soap and water.
④ Bill went for a walk with his dog.
⑤ Frank was in bed with the flu.

23 위 글의 밑줄 친 ⓒ와 같은 뜻이 되도록 다음 문장의 빈칸에 알맞은 말을 쓰시오.

➡ This garden will give fresh air _____ us.

27 위 글의 빈칸 ⓒ에 알맞은 것은?

① high　　　　② low
③ little　　　　④ much
⑤ least

[24~27] 다음 글을 읽고, 물음에 답하시오.

(①) A roof is an essential part of a house, ⓐbut long ago some people have built roofs only to take them down easily. (②) Centuries ago in southern Italy, people who had a house ⓑ(with, without) a roof paid lower taxes. (③) To avoid ____ⓒ____ taxes on their houses, some people built cone-shaped roofs by piling up stones. (④) After the tax collectors left, they piled up the stones again. (⑤)

[28~30] 다음 글을 읽고, 물음에 답하시오.

Have you ever seen a goat on the roof of a house? In Norway, we can see animals on roofs. Norway has large forests. In harmony ____ⓐ____ nature, people ⓑ(build) wooden houses for a long time. To build strong and warm houses, they cover their roofs ____ⓒ____ grass. The grass roofs protect them from the long cold winters and strong winds. Sometimes, trees or plants grow out of the grass roofs, and some animals enjoy their meals ⓓthere.

24 위 글의 ①~⑤ 중 다음 주어진 문장이 들어갈 알맞은 곳은?

When tax collectors came to the town, people took their roofs down quickly.

①　　　②　　　③　　　④　　　⑤

28 위 글의 빈칸 ⓐ와 ⓒ에 공통으로 알맞은 것은?

① on　　　　② in
③ with　　　④ to
⑤ from

25 위 글의 밑줄 친 ⓐ에서 어법상 어색한 것을 고치시오.

_____ ➡ _____

29 위 글의 괄호 ⓑ의 단어를 알맞은 형태로 쓰시오.

➡ _____

26 위 글의 괄호 ⓑ에서 알맞은 것을 고르시오.

➡ _____

30 위 글의 밑줄 친 ⓓ가 가리키는 것을 전치사 on을 사용하여 쓰시오.

➡ _____

Lesson 3

My Travel, My Way

의사소통 기능

- 경험 묻고 답하기
  A: Have you ever eaten pancakes?
  B: Yes, I have.

- 날씨 묻고 답하기
  A: How's the weather in London in March?
  B: It's rainy and cool.

언어 형식

- to부정사의 형용사적 용법
  A B&B is a popular place **to stay** in England.

- 가주어 it
  It was just amazing **to see** the ring of huge stones.

Words & Expressions

Key Words

- **actually** [ǽktʃuəli] 부 실제로, 정말로
- **admire** [ædmáiər] 동 존경하다, 감탄하며 바라보다
- **amazing** [əméiziŋ] 형 놀라운
- **anything** [éniθiŋ] 대 무엇, 아무것, 무엇이든
- **appear** [əpíər] 동 나타나다, 출연하다
- **around** [əráund] 전 ~ 둘레에, ~ 주위에, ~을 돌아
- **avatar** [ǽvətɑːr] 명 화신, 아바타
- **become** [bikʌ́m] 동 ~(해)지다, ~이 되다
- **bungee jumping** 번지 점프
- **capture** [kǽptʃər] 동 잡다, 포착하다, 담아내다
- **chance** [tʃæns] 명 가능성, 기회
- **check** [tʃek] 동 살피다, 점검하다
- **cloudy** [kláudi] 형 흐린, 구름이 잔뜩 낀
- **college** [kálidʒ] 명 대학, 전문학교
- **create** [kriéit] 동 창조[창작/창출]하다
- **decide** [disáid] 동 결정하다, 결심하다
- **diary** [dáiəri] 명 수첩, 일기
- **different** [dífərənt] 명 다른
- **drawing** [drɔ́ːiŋ] 명 그림, 소묘, 데생
- **drive** [draiv] 동 (차량을) 몰다, 운전하다
- **during** [djúəriŋ] 전 ~ 동안[내내], (~하는) 중에
- **earth** [əːrθ] 명 지구, 땅
- **else** [els] 부 또 다른, 다른
- **enough** [inʌ́f] 형 필요한 만큼의, 충분한
- **expect** [ikspékt] 동 예상[기대]하다
- **ever** [évər] 부 언제든, 한번이라도
- **famous** [féiməs] 형 유명한
- **field trip** 견학 여행, 현장 학습
- **finally** [fáinəli] 부 마침내
- **food** [fuːd] 명 식량, 음식
- **forecast** [fɔ́rkæst] 명 예측, 예보

- **foreign** [fɔ́ːrən] 형 외국의
- **freezing** [fríːziŋ] 형 꽁꽁 얼게[너무나] 추운
- **graduate** [grǽdʒuət] 동 졸업하다
- **guess** [ges] 동 추측하다, 짐작하다
- **huge** [hjuːdʒ] 형 큰, 거대한
- **indoors** [indɔ́ːrz] 부 실내에, 집안에
- **invite** [inváit] 동 초대하다, 초청하다
- **island** [áilənd] 명 섬
- **journal** [dʒɔ́ːnl] 명 일기
- **market** [máːrkit] 명 시장
- **moment** [móumənt] 명 잠깐, 잠시, 순간
- **mostly** [móustli] 부 주로, 대개
- **mystery** [místəri] 명 수수께끼, 미스터리
- **object** [ábdʒikt] 명 물건, 물체
- **pack** [pæk] 동 (짐을) 싸다[꾸리다/챙기다]
- **perfect** [pə́ːrfikt] 형 완전한
- **plate** [pleit] 명 접시, 그릇
- **portrait** [pɔ́ːrtrit] 명 초상화
- **relax** [rilǽks] 동 휴식을 취하다
- **remain** [riméin] 동 남다, 남아 있다
- **scary** [skɛ́əri] 형 무서운, 겁나는
- **seafood** [síːfud] 명 해산물
- **simple** [símpl] 형 간단한, 단순한
- **touch** [tʌtʃ] 동 만지다, 건드리다
- **travel** [trǽvəl] 명 여행 동 여행하다
- **trip** [trip] 명 여행
- **turtle** [tə́ːtl] 명 거북, 바다거북
- **university** [jùːnəvə́ːrsəti] 명 대학교
- **vacation** [veikéiʃən] 명 방학, 휴가
- **weather** [wéðər] 명 날씨
- **windy** [wíndi] 형 바람이 많이 부는

Key Expressions

- **a few** 소수의, 약간의
- **a little** 좀, 약간; 약간의
- **a lot of** 많은
- **at last** 마침내
- **be full of** ~으로 가득 차다
- **get into** ~에 들어가다, ~에 타다

- **get to** ~에 도착하다
- **right now** 지금, 당장
- **set foot at[in]** ~에 발을 들여놓다
- **show up** 나타나다
- **stay[keep] indoors** 집안에 머물러 있다
- **such as** ~와 같은

Word Power

※ 날씨를 나타내는 단어

- □ **hot** (더운) → **cold** (추운)
- □ **warm** (따뜻한) → **cool** (서늘한)

- □ **fine** (맑은, 비가 안 오는)
- □ **mild** (온화한, 포근한)

※ 다음은 명사에 -y가 붙어 날씨를 나타내는 형용사가 되는 단어들이다. -y를 붙일 때 철자가 변하는 것이 있으므로 주의해야 한다.

- □ **sun** (해, 태양) → **sunny** (화창한)
- □ **rain** (비) → **rainy** (비가 오는)
- □ **snow** (눈) → **snowy** (눈이 오는)

- □ **cloud** (구름) → **cloudy** (구름이 낀, 흐린)
- □ **wind** (바람) → **windy** (바람이 부는)
- □ **fog** (안개) → **foggy** (안개가 낀)

English Dictionary

- □ **admire** 존경하다
  → to like and respect someone or something very much
  누군가 또는 무언가를 매우 좋아하고 존중하다

- □ **amazing** 놀라운
  → very surprising and making you feel pleasure, approval, or wonder
  매우 놀랍고 당신을 기쁨, 승인, 또는 놀라움을 느끼게 만드는

- □ **beach** 해변, 바닷가
  → an area of sand or stones beside the sea
  바다 옆에 모래나 돌이 있는 지역

- □ **chance** 가능성
  → the possibility that something will happen
  무슨 일이 일어날 가능성

- □ **create** 창조[창작/창출]하다
  → to cause something to happen or exist
  어떤 일이 발생하거나 존재하게 하다

- □ **decide** 결정하다, 결심하다
  → to choose to do something, usually after you have thought carefully about the other possibilities
  보통 당신이 다른 가능성에 대해 신중하게 고려한 후에, 무언가를 하기로 선택하다

- □ **drawing** 그림, 소묘, 데생
  → a picture made with a pencil or pen
  연필이나 펜으로 그린 그림

- □ **drive** (차량을) 몰다, 운전하다
  → to operate a car or other vehicle and control its movement and direction
  자동차나 다른 차량을 조작하여 그 움직임과 방향을 제어하다

- □ **food** 식량, 음식
  → what people and animals eat
  사람과 동물이 먹는 것

- □ **invite** 초대하다, 초청하다
  → to ask someone to come to something such as a party
  어떤 사람에게 파티와 같은 것에 와 달라고 청하다

- □ **island** 섬
  → a piece of land that is completely surrounded by water
  물에 완전히 둘러싸인 땅

- □ **market** 시장
  → a place where goods are bought and sold, usually outdoors
  보통 옥외에서 물건을 사고파는 장소

- □ **mystery** 수수께끼, 미스터리
  → something that is not understood or known about
  이해되거나 알려지지 않은 어떤 것

- □ **pack** (짐을) 싸다[꾸리다/챙기다]
  → to put clothes and other things into a bag, because you are leaving a place
  당신이 어떤 곳을 떠나기 때문에 옷이나 다른 것들을 가방에 넣다

- □ **relax** 휴식을 취하다
  → to spend time resting or doing something enjoyable especially after you have been doing work
  특히 일이 끝난 후 쉬거나 즐거운 일을 하면서 시간을 보내다

- □ **strange** 이상한, 낯선
  → unusual or unexpected, and making you feel slightly nervous or afraid
  이상하거나 예상치 못한, 그리고 당신을 약간 긴장시키거나 두려워하게 만드는

- □ **travel** 여행하다
  → to go from one place to another, often to a place that is far away
  한 장소에서 다른 곳, 종종 멀리 떨어진 곳으로 가다

01 다음 중 짝지어진 단어의 성격이 <u>다른</u> 하나는?

① wind – windy　　② health – healthy
③ snow – snowy　　④ fog – foggy
⑤ sun – sunny

02 다음 빈칸에 알맞은 말이 바르게 짝지어진 것은?

- Ann has a lot _____ friends here.
- I put on my seat belt as soon as I get _____ the car.

① into – at　　② of – into
③ on – in　　④ out – with
⑤ off – over

03 다음 영영풀이에 해당하는 단어로 알맞은 것은?

a place where goods are bought and sold, usually outdoors

① mart　　② area
③ field　　④ market
⑤ factory

서답형

04 다음 짝지어진 단어의 관계가 같도록 빈칸에 알맞은 말을 쓰시오.

advise : advice = decide : _____

05 다음 우리말에 맞게 빈칸에 알맞은 것은?

나는 그의 사진을 몇 장 가지고 있다.
➡ I have _____ pictures of him.

① few　　② little
③ a few　　④ a little
⑤ a lot

서답형

06 다음 영영풀이에 해당하는 단어를 주어진 철자로 시작하여 쓰시오.

the possibility that something will happen

➡ c_____

서답형

07 다음 우리말에 맞게 빈칸에 알맞은 말을 쓰시오.

내가 창문을 잠갔는지 가서 확인해 봐.
➡ Go and _____ that I've locked the windows.

08 다음 빈칸에 공통으로 알맞은 것은?

- The parking lot is full _____ snow.
- I can't think _____ her name at the moment.

① in　　② of
③ up　　④ about
⑤ at

01 다음 짝지어진 두 단어의 관계가 같도록 빈칸에 알맞은 말을 쓰시오.

(1) wind : windy = snow : _____

(2) hot : cold = warm : _____

(3) teach : teacher = create : _____

02 다음 우리말에 맞게 빈칸에 알맞은 말을 쓰시오.

(1) 마침내 여름방학이 왔다.

➡ Summer vacation has come _____
_____ .

(2) Jane은 중국어를 좀 한다.

➡ Jane speaks Chinese _____ .

(3) 더 이상 나는 집안에 머물지 않아도 될 것이다.

➡ I won't have to _____ _____ any more.

03 다음 빈칸에 들어갈 알맞은 말을 〈보기〉에서 골라 쓰시오.

┌─ 보기 ─┐
pack mostly different anything

(1) Would you like _____ else?

(2) The sauce is _____ cream.

(3) Did you _____ the camera?

(4) They are sold in many _____ colours.

04 다음 괄호 안의 단어를 문맥에 맞게 고쳐 쓰시오.

(1) It's not _____ raining now. (actual)

(2) That's _____, isn't it? (amaze)

(3) A _____ young woman is living next door. (mystery)

05 다음 빈칸에 알맞은 말을 〈보기〉에서 골라 쓰시오.

┌─ 보기 ─┐
get to   right now
is full of   catch a cold

(1) I'm coming down _____ .

(2) We will _____ London at eight.

(3) The room _____ children.

(4) If you _____, you will cough a lot.

06 다음 영영풀이에 해당하는 단어를 주어진 철자로 시작하여 쓰시오.

(1) a_____ : to like and respect someone or something very much

(2) d_____ : a picture made with a pencil or pen

(3) f_____ : what people and animals eat

Conversation

① 경험 묻고 답하기

> **A** Have you ever eaten pancakes? 넌 팬케이크를 먹어 본 적이 있니?
> **B** Yes, I have. 응, 있어.

■ **경험 묻기**
'~해 본 적이 있나요?'라고 과거부터 현재까지의 상대방의 경험을 물을 때는 「Have you (ever)+과거분사 ~?」 형태인 현재완료 의문문으로 물을 수 있다.

■ **경험에 대한 물음에 대답하기**
경험이 있으면 Yes, I have. / Yes, I have+과거분사. 등으로 한다.
경험이 없으면 No, I haven't. / No, I have never+과거분사 / Not yet. 등으로 한다.

• A: Have you ever seen a bear? 너는 곰을 본 적이 있니?
  B: Yes, I have. / No, I haven't. 응, 본 적이 있어. / 아니, 본 적이 없어.

cf. '~에 가본 적 있니?'라고 묻는 표현은 Have you ever gone to ~?가 아니라 Have you ever been to ~?임에 주의한다.

• have been to: ~에 가본 적이 있다(경험) / ~에 갔다왔다(완료)
• have gone to: ~ 에 가버렸다(결과)

■ 경험을 나타낼 때는 다음과 같은 부사(구)를 함께 쓰는 경우가 많다. ever(지금까지), never(~한 적 없는), before(이전에), once(한 번), twice(두 번), 「숫자+times(~번, ~차례)」, many times(여러 번), often(자주)

• She has made fried rice many times. 그녀는 볶음밥을 여러 번 만든 적이 있다.

핵심 Check

1. 다음 우리말과 일치하도록 빈칸에 알맞은 말을 쓰시오.

(1) **A:** _____ you ever _____ *Les Miserables*? (너 '레미제라블' 읽어 봤니?)

    B: Yes, I _____. (응, 있어.)

(2) **A:** _____ you _____ this food? (너는 이 음식을 먹어 봤니?)

    B: No, I _____. (아니, 나는 못 먹어 봤어.)

② 날씨 묻고 답하기

> **A** How's the weather in London in March? 3월에 런던 날씨는 어떠니?
>
> **B** It's rainy and cool. 비가 오고 시원해.

- **날씨 묻기**

  오늘 날씨가 어떤지 물을 때는 What's the weather like today?, 혹은 How's the weather today?라고 한다. 특정 지역의 날씨를 물을 때는 What's the weather like in+지역명? 혹은 How's the weather in+지역명?으로 나타낸다.

  ### 비슷한 표현

  - What's today's forecast? 오늘 일기 예보가 어떻습니까?

- **날씨 말하기**

  날씨에 대해 말할 때에는 비인칭 주어 it을 사용해 It's ~라고 한다. 날씨에 따라서 fine, sunny, warm, cool, hot, cold, cloudy, snowy, rainy 등의 표현을 사용한다.

  - A: What's the weather like today? 오늘 날씨는 어떠니?
    B: It's rainy / sunny / hot / cold / cloudy / snowy.

  cf. 현재진행형을 사용하여 '비가[눈이] 오는 중'이라고 말할 때는 「It's 동사원형+-ing.」라고 말한다. 또한 「It's+형용사.」 형태를 사용하여 말할 수도 있다.

  - A: What's the weather like outside? 바깥 날씨 어떠니?
    B: It's raining. / It's rainy. 비가 내리고 있어.

  cf. it은 날씨, 온도, 명암, 날짜 등을 말할 때 쓰는 주어로 인칭을 나타내는 주어가 아니기 때문에 비인칭 주어라고 한다.

핵심 Check

2. 다음 우리말과 일치하도록 빈칸에 알맞은 말을 쓰시오.

(1) A: _____ is the _____ in Cleveland? (클리브랜드의 날씨는 어때?)

   B: It's _____ and cold this time of year. (이맘때는 눈이 오고 추워.)

(2) A: _____ the weather _____ today? (오늘 날씨는 어떠니?)

   B: It's _____ and sunny. (덥고 화창해.)

(3) A: _____ the weather? (날씨가 어때?)

   B: It's _____ a lot. Let's stay at home. (비가 많이 와. 집에 있도록 하자.)

Listen & Speak 1 A-1

G: ❶Have you ever tried Indian food?

B: ❷Yes, I have, but I've only tried Indian curry.

G: ❸How was it?

B: ❹It was really hot, but I loved it.

G: 너 인도 음식을 먹어 본 적이 있니?

B: 응, 있어. 하지만 인도 카레만 먹어 봤어.

G: 어땠어?

B: 정말 매웠지만, 아주 좋았어.

❶ 경험을 나타내는 현재완료는 경험을 묻는 표현으로 사용된다.
❷ I have 다음에는 tried Indian food이 생략되었다.
❸ It은 Indian curry를 가리킨다.
❹ hot은 '뜨거운'이라는 뜻 외에 '매운'이라는 뜻이 있다.

Check(√) True or False

(1) The girl wants to eat Indian food.　　　　　　　　T ☐ F ☐

(2) The boy has only tried Indian curry.　　　　　　　T ☐ F ☐

Listen & Speak 1 A-2

G: ❶Bill, have you ever gone bungee jumping?

B: ❷No, I haven't. ❸How about you, Katie?

G: ❹When I visited New Zealand, I tried bungee jumping once.

B: ❺Wasn't it scary?

G: No, I liked it. I want to do it again.

G: Bill, 번지 점프하러 가 본 적 있니?

B: 아니, 없어. Katie, 넌 어때?

G: 뉴질랜드를 방문했을 때, 번지 점프를 한 번 해봤어.

B: 무섭지 않았어?

G: 아니, 좋았어. 또 하고 싶어.

❶ go bungee jumping: 번지 점프하러 가다
❷ I haven't = I haven't gone bungee jumping
❸ How about you?: 너는 어때?
❹ once: 한 번
❺ 부정의문문으로 Was it not scary?로 바꿔 쓸 수 있다.

Check(√) True or False

(3) Bill has ever gone bungee jumping.　　　　　　　T ☐ F ☐

(4) Katie did bungee jumping once.　　　　　　　　　T ☐ F ☐

Listen & Speak 2 A-1

B: ❶Mom, how's the weather today? Do I need an umbrella?

W: ❷It's quite cloudy outside. I'll check the weather forecast.

B: Thank you, Mom.

W: ❸Well, it's not going to rain today.

B: Good! Then, I don't need an umbrella today.

B: 엄마, 오늘 날씨 어때요? 우산이 필요한가요?

W: 바깥 날씨가 아주 흐려. 일기 예보를 확인해 볼게.

B: 고마워요, 엄마.

W: 음, 오늘은 비가 안 올 거야.

B: 좋아요! 그럼, 오늘은 우산이 필요 없어요.

❶ how's = how is
❷ It은 날씨를 나타내는 비인칭 주어로 우리말로 옮기지 않는다.
❸ be going to는 가까운 미래를 나타내는 어구이다.

Check(√) True or False

(5) It's quite cloudy outside now.　　　　　　　　　T ☐ F ☐

(6) The boy needs an umbrella today.　　　　　　　T ☐ F ☐

Listen and Speak 2 A-2

W: Good morning, and ❶welcome to the weather forecast. ❷It's sunny outside, but we're expecting some rain in the afternoon. ❸Don't leave home without your umbrella. That's the weather forecast for today. Have a nice day.

❶ welcome to ~: ~에 오신 걸 환영하다 / weather forecast: 일기 예보
❷ It: 날씨를 나타내는 비인칭 주어 / expect: 예상하다
❸ Don't + 동사원형 ~: ~하지 마라

Communicate: A. Listen and Answer

Suho: ❶Anna, have you been to Australia before?
Anna: ❷Yes, I have. Actually, I lived in Sydney for a year.
Suho: Great! ❸How's the weather there in April? I'm going to visit Sydney on vacation next week.
Anna: ❹April is a great time to visit Sydney. In April, it's autumn in Australia.
Suho: Good. ❺I'm planning to spend some time on the beach and relax in the sun.
Anna: ❻Well, it often rains in April, but you may have some sunny days.
Suho: I'll take my hat and pack an umbrella, too.
Anna: ❼That's a good idea. Have a great time.

❶ Have you been to ~?: ~에 가 본 적이 있니?
❷ have = have been to Australia
❸ How's the weather there in April? = What's the weather like there in April?
❹ to visit Sydney는 time을 수식하는 형용사적 용법의 to부정사이다.
❺ be planning to: ~할 계획이다
❻ often은 빈도부사로 일반동사 앞에 위치한다.
❼ That은 지시대명사로 앞 문장의 내용을 받는다.

Communicate B. Make Your Own Dialogue

A: ❶Have you been to any special places in Korea?
B: Yes, I have. ❷I went to Ulleungdo last summer with my family.
A: How was the weather there?
B: ❸It was mostly sunny, but the weather changed often.

❶ have been to: ~에 다녀오다
❷ last summer: 지난 여름에
❸ It은 날씨를 나타내는 비인칭 주어이다. mostly: 주로, 대개

Progress Check 1

G: ❶Have you ever ridden a horse?
B: Yes, I have. How about you?
G: ❷No, I haven't. ❸How was it?
B: It was fun, but it was a little scary, too.

❶ ride – rode – ridden
❷ I haven't=I haven't ridden a horse
❸ it은 인칭대명사로 말을 탄 것을 가리킨다.

Progress Check 2

B: Mom, how's the weather today?
W: ❶It's quite cloudy outside. ❷I'll check the weather forecast.
B: Thanks, Mom.
W: ❸Well, it's going to rain in the afternoon.

❶ quite: 아주 / cloudy: 흐린, 구름이 많은
❷ the weather forecast: 일기 예보
❸ be going to: ~할 것이다

Progress Check 3

M: ❶Good evening, and welcome to the weather forecast. ❷It's raining right now, but we're expecting a sunny day tomorrow. ❸Don't leave home tomorrow without your hat.

❶ welcome to ~: ~에 오신 것을 환영합니다
❷ 현재진행형 문장이다. right now: 지금, 당장
❸ leave home: 집을 떠나다 / without: ~이 없이, ~을 사용하지 않고

● 다음 우리말과 일치하도록 빈칸에 알맞은 말을 쓰시오.

📌 **Listen & Speak 1 A. Listen and Check**

1. **G:** _____ you ever _____ Indian food?

   B: Yes, I _____, but I've only _____ Indian curry.

   G: _____ was it?

   B: It was really hot, _____ I loved it.

2. **G:** Bill, have you _____ gone bungee _____?

   B: No, I _____. How _____ you, Katie?

   G: _____ I visited New Zealand, I _____ bungee jumping once.

   B: _____ it scary?

   G: No, I _____ it. I _____ to do it again.

📌 **Listen & Speak 2 A. Listen and Answer**

1. **B:** Mom, how's the _____ today? Do I _____ an umbrella?

   W: It's quite cloudy _____. I'll _____ the weather forecast.

   B: Thank you, Mom.

   W: Well, it's not _____ to rain today.

   B: Good! Then, I _____ need an umbrella today.

2. **W:** _____ morning, and _____ to the weather _____. It's _____ outside, _____ we're expecting some _____ in the afternoon. Don't leave _____ without your umbrella. That's the weather _____ for today. _____ a nice day.

해석

1. **G:** 너 인도 음식을 먹어 본 적이 있니?
   B: 응, 있어, 하지만 인도 카레만 먹어 봤어.
   G: 어땠어?
   B: 정말 매웠지만, 아주 좋았어.

2. **G:** Bill, 번지 점프하러 가 본 적 있니?
   B: 아니, 없어. Katie, 넌 어때?
   G: 뉴질랜드를 방문했을 때, 번지 점프를 한 번 해봤어.
   B: 무섭지 않았어?
   G: 아니, 좋았어. 또 하고 싶어.

1. **B:** 엄마, 오늘 날씨 어때요? 우산이 필요한가요?
   W: 바깥 날씨가 아주 흐려. 일기예보를 확인해 볼게.
   B: 고마워요, 엄마.
   W: 음, 오늘은 비가 안 올 거야.
   B: 좋아요! 그럼, 오늘은 우산이 필요 없어요.

2. **W:** 좋은 아침입니다, 일기예보에 오신 것을 환영합니다. 밖은 화창하지만 오후에는 약간의 비가 예상됩니다. 우산 없이 집을 나서지 마세요. 오늘의 일기예보입니다. 좋은 하루 되세요.

Communicate A~B

A. **Suho** Anna, have you _____ to Australia _____?

   Anna: Yes, I _____. Actually, I _____ in Sydney _____ a year.

   Suho: Great! How's the _____ there in April? I'm _____ to visit Sydney on _____ next week.

   Anna: April is a great _____ to _____ Sydney. In April, it's _____ in Australia.

   Suho: Good. I'm _____ to spend some time on the beach and _____ in the sun.

   Anna: Well, it _____ rains in April, but you _____ have some sunny days.

   Suho: I'll _____ my hat and _____ an umbrella, too.

   Anna: That's a good _____. Have a _____ time.

B. **A:** Have you _____ to any special _____ in Korea?

   B: Yes, I _____. I went to Ulleungdo _____ summer with my family.

   A: _____ was the _____ there?

   B: It was _____ sunny, but the weather _____ often.

Progress Check

1. **G:** Have you ever _____ a horse?

   B: Yes, I _____. How _____ you?

   G: No, I _____. How _____ it?

   B: It was _____, but it was a _____ scary, too.

2. **B:** Mom, how's the _____ today?

   W: It's _____ cloudy outside. I'll _____ the weather forecast.

   B: _____, Mom.

   W: Well, it's _____ to rain in the afternoon.

3. **M:** _____ evening, and _____ to the weather forecast. It's _____ right now, _____ we're expecting a _____ day tomorrow. Don't _____ home tomorrow _____ your hat.

해석

A. 수호: Anna, 너 전에 호주에 가본 적 있어?

   Anna: 응, 있어. 사실, 나는 시드니에서 1년 동안 살았어.

   수호: 멋지다! 그곳의 4월 날씨는 어때? 난 다음 주 방학 때 시드니에 갈 거야.

   Anna: 4월은 시드니를 방문하기에 좋은 시기야. 4월에, 호주는 가을이야.

   수호: 좋아. 나는 해변에서 시간을 좀 보내고 햇빛을 쐬며 휴식을 취할 계획이야.

   Anna: 음, 4월에는 종종 비가 오지만, 맑은 날도 좀 있을 거야.

   수호: 나도 모자를 가져가고 우산도 챙길 거야.

   Anna: 좋은 생각이야. 좋은 시간 보내.

B. A: 넌 한국의 어느 특별한 장소들을 가본 적이 있니?

   B: 응, 있어. 나는 작년 여름에 가족과 울릉도에 갔어.

   A: 거기 날씨는 어땠어?

   B: 대체로 맑았지만, 날씨가 자주 바뀌었어.

1. G: 너 말을 타본 적 있니?

   B: 응, 있어. 너는 어때?

   G: 아니, 난 없어. 말 타는 거 어땠어?

   B: 재미있었지만, 조금 무섭기도 했어.

2. B: 엄마, 오늘 날씨 어때요?

   W: 바깥 날씨가 꽤 흐려. 일기예보를 확인해 볼게.

   B: 고마워요, 엄마.

   W: 음, 오후에 비가 올 거야.

3. M: 안녕하세요, 일기예보에 오신 것을 환영합니다. 지금은 비가 오지만 내일은 화창한 날씨가 예상됩니다. 내일 모자를 쓰지 않고 집을 나서지 마세요.

Conversation 시험대비 기본평가

01 다음 두 문장의 의미가 같도록 빈칸에 알맞은 말을 쓰시오.

How's the weather today?
= _____ the weather _____ today?

02 다음 대화의 밑줄 친 우리말에 해당하는 것은?

A: Jina, I'm going to Vietnam with my family this winter.
B: Wow. That sounds like fun.
A: 너 전에 그곳에 가 본 적 있니?
B: No, I haven't.

① Did you be there before?
② Had you been there before?
③ Have you been there before?
④ Have you gone there before?
⑤ When did you get there before?

03 다음 대화의 빈칸에 알맞지 <u>않은</u> 것은?

A: What's the weather like outside?
B: _____

① It's snowing.　　　　② It's very cold.
③ It's really cloudy.　　④ It will be very hot.
⑤ It's raining outside.

04 다음 대화의 빈칸에 알맞은 것은?

A: Have you eaten this food?
B: No, _____.

① I don't　　　　② I didn't
③ I haven't　　　④ I hadn't
⑤ I loved it

중요

01 다음 대화의 빈칸에 알맞은 것은?

> A: What's the weather like outside?
> B: _____

① It's fall.
② It's windy.
③ It's too cold to drink.
④ I like rainy days.
⑤ I dislike cold weather.

서답형

02 다음 대화의 빈칸에 알맞은 말을 쓰시오.

> A: _____ you _____ tried gimchi, Ann?
> B: Yes, I _____. It was very tasty.

03 다음 대화를 의미가 통하도록 알맞게 배열한 것은?

> (A) Well, it's going to rain in the afternoon.
> (B) Thanks, Mom.
> (C) Mom, how's the weather today?
> (D) It's quite cloudy outside. I'll check the weather forecast.

① (A) – (D) – (B) – (C)
② (B) – (C) – (D) – (A)
③ (C) – (D) – (B) – (A)
④ (D) – (B) – (C) – (A)
⑤ (D) – (C) – (B) – (A)

04 다음 대화의 빈칸에 가장 알맞은 것은?

> A: Have you seen the movie, *Avatar*, Sue?
> B: No, I haven't. _____
> A: Yes, it's my favorite movie.

① Do you?
② Will you?
③ Had you?
④ Have you?
⑤ What do you want to see?

중요

05 다음 대화의 빈칸에 알맞은 것은?

> A: How's the weather today?
> B: _____
> A: Really? I should wear my sunglasses then. Thanks.

① It's sunny and hot.
② I don't like sunny days.
③ It's cloudy and windy.
④ It looks like rain soon.
⑤ We have good weather in the fall.

[06~09] 다음 대화를 읽고, 물음에 답하시오.

> G: Bill, _____ⓐ_____ you ever gone bungee jumping?
> B: No, I haven't. _____ⓑ_____ about you, Katie?
> G: ⓒWhen I visited New Zealand, I tried bungee jumping once.
> B: Wasn't ⓓit scary?
> G: No, I liked it. I want to do it again.

06 위 대화의 빈칸 ⓐ에 알맞은 것은?

① do
② did
③ were
④ had
⑤ have

07 위 대화의 빈칸 ⓑ에 알맞은 것은? (2개)

① Why   ② How

③ Who   ④ Which

⑤ What

서답형

08 위 대화의 밑줄 친 ⓒ를 우리말로 옮기시오.

➡ _____

서답형

09 위 대화의 밑줄 친 ⓓ가 가리키는 것을 영어로 쓰시오.

➡ _____

---

10 위 대화의 빈칸 ⓐ에 알맞은 것은?

① were   ② go

③ be   ④ been

⑤ gone

서답형

11 위 대화의 밑줄 친 ⓑ를 알맞은 어형으로 고치시오.

➡ _____

중요

12 위 대화의 밑줄 친 ⓒ와 같은 뜻이 되도록 다음 문장의 빈칸에 알맞은 말을 쓰시오.

_____ the weather _____ there in April?

서답형

13 위 대화의 빈칸 ⓓ에 다음 영영풀이에 해당하는 단어를 쓰시오.

to spend time resting or doing something enjoyable especially after you have been doing work

➡ _____

[10~14] 다음 대화를 읽고, 물음에 답하시오.

Suho: Anna, have you _____ⓐ_____ to Australia before?

Anna: Yes, I have. ⓑActual, I lived in Sydney for a year.

Suho: Great! ⓒHow's the weather there in April? I'm going to visit Sydney on vacation next week.

Anna: April is a great time to visit Sydney. In April, it's autumn in Australia.

Suho: Good. I'm planning to spend some time on the beach and _____ⓓ_____ in the sun.

Anna: Well, it often rains in April, but you may have some sunny days.

Suho: I'll take my hat and pack an umbrella, too.

Anna: That's a good idea. Have a great time.

14 위 대화를 읽고, 답할 수 없는 질문은?

① When did Ann go to Australia?

② Where did Ann live in Australia?

③ When will Suho visit Australia?

④ How is the weather in Sydney in April?

⑤ What will Suho take?

[01~02] 다음 대화의 빈칸에 알맞은 말을 쓰시오.

01

A: What's the weather _____ today?

B: _____ is warm and sunny.

02

A: _____ you ever slept in a tent?

B: No, I _____ .

03 다음 대화를 의미가 통하도록 알맞게 배열하시오.

(A) It was really hot, but I loved it.
(B) Have you ever tried Indian food?
(C) Yes, I have, but I've only tried Indian curry.
(D) How was it?

➡ _____

[04~06] 다음 대화를 읽고, 물음에 답하시오.

B: Mom, how's the ___ⓐ___ today? Do I need an umbrella?

W: It's quite ⓑcloud outside. I'll check the weather ___ⓒ___ .

B: Thank you, Mom.

W: Well, it's not going to rain today.

B: Good! Then, I don't need an umbrella today.

04 위 대화의 빈칸 ⓐ에 알맞은 말을 쓰시오.

➡ _____

05 위 대화의 밑줄 친 ⓑ를 알맞은 어형으로 고치시오.

➡ _____

06 위 대화의 빈칸 ⓒ에 다음 정의에 해당하는 단어를 쓰시오.

a statement of what is expected to happen in the future, especially in relation to a particular event or situation

➡ _____

[07~09] 다음 담화문을 읽고, 물음에 답하시오.

W: Good morning, and ___ⓐ___ to the weather forecast. It's ⓑsun outside, but we're expecting some rain in the afternoon. Don't leave home without your umbrella. That's the weather forecast for today. Have a nice day.

07 위 담화문의 빈칸 ⓐ에 알맞은 말을 쓰시오.

➡ _____

08 위 담화문의 밑줄 친 ⓑ를 알맞은 어형으로 고치시오.

➡ _____

09 What's the weather like in the afternoon? Answer in Korean.

➡ _____

Grammar

① to부정사의 형용사적 용법

> • A B&B is a popular place **to stay** in England. B&B는 영국에서 머무는 곳으로 인기가 있다.
>
> • They need something **to drink**. 그들은 마실 것이 필요하다.
>
> • I have a lot of homework **to do** tonight. 나는 오늘밤 해야 할 숙제가 많다.

■ to부정사의 형용사적 용법은 명사나 대명사 뒤에서 '~하는, ~할'의 뜻으로 쓰인다. 이 때 앞의 명사는 to부정사의 주어 또는 목적어 역할을 한다.

  • I have no money **to give** you. [목적어] 나는 너에게 줄 돈이 없다.
    = I have no money that I can give you.

  • He had no friends **to help** him. [주어] 그는 자기를 도와줄 친구가 하나도 없었다.
    = He had no friends who would help him.

■ to부정사의 수식을 받는 명사가 전치사의 목적어일 경우, to부정사 뒤에 전치사가 온다.

  • Ann has elderly parents **to look** after. Ann은 돌보아야 할 나이 드신 부모가 있다.
  • I want a small room **to live** in by myself. 나는 혼자 살 작은 방을 원한다.

■ -thing으로 끝나는 부정대명사는 「-thing+(형용사+)to부정사」의 어순을 따른다.

  • I want something cold **to drink**. 나는 차가운 마실 것을 원한다.
  • You feel that you have nothing **to wear**. 너는 입을 것이 아무것도 없다고 느낀다.

핵심 Check

1. 다음 괄호 안에서 알맞은 것을 고르시오.

  (1) It's time (go / to go) to school.

  (2) Jack has a lot of friends (helping / to help).

  (3) Give me a pen (to write / to write with).

  (4) Would you like something (to cold drink / cold to drink)?

② 가주어 it

- **It** was just amazing **to see** the ring of huge stones.
  거대한 돌들의 고리를 보는 것은 아주 놀라웠다.

- **It** is easy **to bake** cookies. 쿠키를 굽는 것은 쉽다.

- **It** will be nice **to become** a musician. 음악가가 되는 것은 멋질 거야.

■ 가주어 it

to부정사구가 문장 안에서 주어로 쓰일 경우, to부정사구를 문장의 뒤로 보내고 그 자리에 it을 쓴다. 이때의 it은 아무런 의미가 없는 주어로 '가주어'라고 하고, to부정사구를 '진주어'라고 한다.

- **To master** English in a month is impossible. 영어를 한 달 동안에 습득하는 것은 불가능하다.

  → **It** is impossible <u>**to master**</u> English in a month.
     가주어   진주어

cf. to부정사 이외에도 진주어로 명사절이 쓰일 때가 있다. 이때 명사절을 이끄는 접속사는 보통 that이 쓰인다.

- **It** is a bad habit **that** people read in bed. 침대에서 독서하는 것은 나쁜 버릇이다.

■ to부정사의 의미상의 주어

to부정사의 의미상의 주어가 문장의 주어와 일치하지 않는 경우, 일반적으로 「for+목적격」의 형태로 진주어 앞에 쓴다. kind, foolish, wise, honest, polite 등과 같이 사람의 성격을 나타내는 형용사가 보어로 쓰이면 의미상의 주어로 「of+목적격」의 형태를 쓴다.

- **It** is natural **for** your parents **to get** angry. 너희 부모님이 화를 내시는 것은 당연한 것이다.

- **It** is very kind **of** you **to help** me. 나를 도와주다니 넌 참 친절하다.

핵심 Check

2. 다음 괄호 안에서 알맞은 것을 고르시오.

(1) It is hard (understanding / to understand) his words.

(2) (It / That) is interesting to watch basketball games.

(3) It is good for your health (to exercise / exercise) every day.

(4) It is honest (for / of) you to say so.

(5) It is not easy (for / of) us to learn foreign languages.

01 다음 괄호 안에서 알맞은 것을 고르시오.

(1) There are many places (visit / to visit) in Jeju.

(2) Do you have anything (to do / doing) this evening?

(3) (It / That) is fun to travel to some countries in Asia.

(4) It is very kind (of / for) you to help me.

(5) It is hard (of / for) me to solve this problem.

> travel 여행하다
> solve 풀다

02 다음 밑줄 친 부분을 바르게 고쳐 쓰시오.

(1) It's difficult exercise every day.

➡ _____

(2) It is impossible finish this work in an hour.

➡ _____

(3) That is very important to learn a foreign language.

➡ _____

(4) It was brave for him to save the child.

➡ _____

(5) It was easy of me to answer all the questions.

➡ _____

> exercise 운동하다
> impossible 불가능한
> save 구하다

03 다음 우리말과 일치하도록 빈칸에 알맞은 말을 쓰시오.

(1) 우리는 일정을 바꿀 시간이 없다.

➡ We have no time _____ _____ the schedule.

(2) 그는 우리나라를 방문한 최초의 미국인이었다.

➡ He was the first American _____ _____ our country.

(3) 나는 기차에서 읽을 책을 가져가고 싶다.

➡ I want to bring a book _____ _____ on the train.

> schedule 일정
> country 나라

Grammar 시험대비 실력평가

[01~02] 다음 문장의 빈칸에 알맞은 것을 고르시오.

01

It is good for the health _____ early.

① get up
② got up
③ to get up
④ to getting up
⑤ to be getting up

02 중요

Do you have anything _____?

① read
② reads
③ reading
④ to read
⑤ to be reading

03 다음 중 밑줄 친 부분의 쓰임이 나머지 넷과 <u>다른</u> 것은?

① He is always the first to come.
② He has nothing to write with.
③ He went to England to study English.
④ There are a lot of things for him to do.
⑤ He was looking for an apartment to live in.

04 서답형 다음 두 문장의 뜻이 같도록 빈칸에 알맞은 말을 쓰시오.

I have a lot of letters _____ _____.
= I have a lot of letters that I should write.

05 서답형 다음 두 문장의 뜻이 같도록 빈칸에 알맞은 말을 쓰시오

To change the schedule is very difficult.

➡ _____ is very difficult _____ change the schedule.

06 다음 우리말과 같도록 할 때, 빈칸에 알맞은 말이 바르게 짝 지어진 것은?

자전거를 탈 때는 헬멧을 쓰는 것이 안전하다.
➡ _____ is safe _____ a helmet when you ride a bike.

① It − to wear
② This − wear
③ It − wears
④ It − wear
⑤ That − to wear

07 다음 중 밑줄 친 부분의 쓰임이 <보기>와 같은 것은?

┤ 보기 ├
I have lots of books to read by next month.

① Jina has no chair to sit on.
② My hobby is to listen to music.
③ She is glad to get a letter from Tony.
④ He wants to play baseball after school.
⑤ I went to the market to buy some eggs.

서답형

08 다음 우리말과 일치하도록 주어진 단어를 바르게 배열하여 문장을 완성하시오.

> 너 뭐 좀 먹을래?
>
> (anything / you / want / do / eat / to)

➡ _____

_____

중요

 다음 중 어법상 <u>어색한</u> 문장은?

① It's almost time to go to bed.
② It's time to get aboard a plane.
③ It is time to eat dinner.
④ It's time for the children to going to bed.
⑤ It's time for my dad to buy a new car.

중요

 다음 중 밑줄 친 *it*의 쓰임이 나머지 넷과 <u>다른</u> 하나는?

① <u>It</u>'s important to be kind to others.
② Is <u>it</u> fun to play computer games?
③ <u>It</u> is not surprising for him to say so.
④ It's hard to believe, but <u>it</u>'s a flower.
⑤ <u>It</u>'s not easy to understand other cultures.

서답형

11 다음 괄호 안에 주어진 말을 사용하여 우리말을 영작하시오.

> 그 기계를 고치는 것은 어렵다.
>
> (it / difficult / fix / machine)

➡ _____

중요

 다음 빈칸에 알맞은 말이 바르게 짝지어진 것은?

> • It is very kind _____ you to say so.
> • It is natural _____ a baby to cry.

① of – of   ② of – for
③ for – for   ④ for – of
⑤ for – with

13 다음 빈칸에 공통으로 알맞은 것은?

> • It was honest _____ you to tell the truth.
> • It is wise _____ her to make such a decision.

① of   ② for
③ with   ④ at
⑤ upon

서답형

14 다음 빈칸에 공통으로 알맞은 말을 쓰시오.

> • You don't have _____ worry about it.
> • I have no reason _____ be angry at you.

중요

15 다음 빈칸에 들어갈 동사의 형태로 적절한 것은?

> It's necessary _____ on time.

① to be   ② is
③ be   ④ are
⑤ will be

16 다음 문장의 빈칸에 to를 쓸 수 <u>없는</u> 것은?

① It is natural for your mom _____ get angry.

② She hopes _____ visit her uncle.

③ He is kind enough _____ help us.

④ It is easy _____ speak English.

⑤ She made me _____ wash the dishes.

17 다음 문장에서 어법상 어색한 부분을 바르게 고쳐 쓰시오.

> I need a chair to sit.

_____ ➡ _____

18 다음 중 밑줄 친 부분의 쓰임이 바르지 <u>않은</u> 것은?

① There is no bench <u>to sit on</u>.

② I have no money <u>to give</u> you.

③ Judy has a lot of friends <u>to talk</u>.

④ She doesn't have a house <u>to live in</u>.

⑤ Do you have a pen <u>to write with</u>?

19 다음 중 밑줄 친 부분의 쓰임이 나머지 넷과 <u>다른</u> 것은?

① <u>It</u> will soon be a new year.

② Is <u>it</u> easy to use this camera?

③ <u>It</u> is a lot of fun to ski in winter.

④ <u>It</u> isn't difficult to use the computer.

⑤ <u>It</u> is interesting to read English books.

20 다음 중 밑줄 친 to부정사의 쓰임이 <u>다른</u> 하나는?

① It is important <u>to try</u> your best.

② My dream is <u>to be</u> a singer.

③ I want a house <u>to live</u> in.

④ I decided <u>to study</u> Spanish.

⑤ It is very kind of you <u>to help</u> me.

21 다음 주어진 어구를 이용하여 〈보기〉와 같이 문장을 쓰시오.

> ┤ 보기 ├
>
> (boring / watch news on TV)
>
> ➡ It is boring to watch news on TV.

> (pleasant / listen to music)
>
> ➡ _____

22 다음 빈칸에 들어갈 말이 바르게 짝지어진 것은?

> • It's time for our children _____ to bed.
> • You don't have _____ an umbrella with you.

① go – take

② to go – taken

③ going – taking

④ going – to take

⑤ to go – to take

23 다음 문장에서 어법상 어색한 부분을 찾아 바르게 고쳐 쓰시오.

> It is necessary for you going there as soon as possible.

_____ ➡ _____

01 다음 두 문장의 뜻이 같도록 빈칸에 알맞은 말을 쓰시오.

> To cook French food is difficult.
> ➡ _____ is difficult _____ cook French food.

02 다음 빈칸에 공통으로 알맞은 말을 쓰시오.

> • Mike had no time _____ do his homework.
> • I'm going to buy some paper _____ write on.

03 다음 주어진 단어를 바르게 배열하여 문장을 완성하시오.

(1) (bake / is / cookies / to / it / easy)
➡ _____

(2) (a magazine / on / he / read / the train / bought / to)
➡ _____

04 다음 밑줄 친 단어를 알맞은 형태로 고쳐 쓰시오.

> It is strange for her receive fan letters.

➡ _____

05 다음 괄호 안에 주어진 말을 사용하여 우리말을 영작하시오. (가주어 – 진주어 구문을 사용할 것.)

(1) 주말마다 그를 방문하는 것은 쉽지 않았다.
(visit, easy, every)
➡ _____

(2) 다른 나라에서 사는 것은 재미있는 경험이다.
(it, exciting, live, another)
➡ _____

06 다음 괄호 안에 주어진 어구를 이용하여 우리말을 영어로 옮기시오.

(1) 그녀는 가수가 되려는 강한 욕망을 갖고 있다.
(strong desire, be, singer)
➡ _____

(2) 나는 이 문제를 해결하기 위해 모든 노력을 할 것이다. (every effort, solve)
➡ _____

(3) 우리는 이야기할 것이 있었다.
(something, talk about)
➡ _____

(4) 나는 쓸 종이를 한 장 원한다.
(want, write)
➡ _____

(5) 제게 뜨거운 마실 것을 좀 주십시오.
(please, something, drink)
➡ _____

07 다음 빈칸에 알맞은 말을 〈보기〉에서 골라 쓰시오. (중복해서 사용할 수 없음.)

┌─ 보기 ─┐
to   on   with   it

(1) _____ is hard to follow good advice.
(2) Do you have anything to write _____?
(3) I need a knife to cut the rope _____.
(4) I have a lot of things _____ do today.

08 다음 문장에서 어법상 어색한 것을 찾아 바르게 고쳐 쓰시오.

(1) He doesn't have time play with his friends.
_____ ➡ _____

(2) It is important of you to study hard.
_____ ➡ _____

[09~10] 다음 우리말을 참고하여 문장을 완성하시오.

09

이 도시에는 방문해야 할 장소가 많이 있다.
➡ There are many places _____ _____ in this city.

10

너는 공부를 열심히 하는 것이 중요하다.
➡ It is important _____ _____ to study hard.

11 다음 두 문장의 뜻이 같도록 빈칸에 알맞은 말을 쓰시오.

To learn to ride a bike was not difficult.
➡ _____ was not difficult _____ to ride a bike.

12 다음 빈칸에 공통으로 알맞은 말을 쓰시오.

• It's time for my brother _____ come home.
• You don't have _____ water the flowers.

13 다음 문장에서 어법상 어색한 것을 찾아 바르게 고쳐 쓰시오.

(1) It was stupid for you to believe the rumor.
_____ ➡ _____

(2) It isn't necessary of you to come here today.
_____ ➡ _____

14 다음 주어진 단어를 이용하여 우리말을 영어로 옮기시오.

그곳은 24시간 동안 많은 물건들을 파는 장소이다.
(it's / a place / to sell / things)

➡ _____

Reading

My Special Travel Journal

Hi, I am Lucy Hunter, and I live in London. Last week, my family went on a vacation for three days. During our trip, I made simple drawings in my journal. That was a great way to capture all the special moments.

August 5

At last, we set foot at Stonehenge, one of the most mysterious places on Earth. After a two-hour drive from our home in London, we finally got to Stonehenge. It was just amazing to see the ring of huge stones. How did those huge stones get there thousands of years ago? What were they for? I guess Stonehenge will remain a mystery for a long time.

Lucy's Drawing Tips

Don't try to make perfect drawing. A few colors will be enough.

August 6

In the morning, we walked around the Cotswolds. It started to rain in the afternoon, so we decided to stay indoors at our B&B. A B&B is a popular place to stay in England. It feels more like a home than a hotel.

---

go on a vacation 휴가를 가다
during ~ 중에
simple 간단한, 단순한
journal 일기
capture 담아내다, 포착하다
special 특별한
moment 순간
set 놓다, 두다
mysterious 신비스러운
amazing 놀라운
ring 반지, 고리
huge 거대한, 큰
thousands of 수천의
guess 추측하다, 생각하다
remain 남아 있다
mystery 미스터리, 신비
tip 충고
perfect 완전한
enough 충분한
decide 결정하다
feel like ~처럼 느껴지다

확인문제

● 다음 문장이 본문의 내용과 일치하면 T, 일치하지 않으면 F를 쓰시오.

1 Lucy's family went on a vacation last week. ☐

2 Lucy wrote interesting poems in her journal. ☐

3 Lucy's family went to Stonehenge. ☐

4 Stonehenge was an old temple. ☐

5 Lucy's family stayed indoors at their B&B on August 6. ☐

The owner invited us for afternoon tea today. The dining table was full of cookies, cake, bread, and cheese. While I was busy eating, Mom was admiring the beautiful cups and plates. I ate too much, so I couldn't eat anything for dinner.

Lucy's Drawing Tips

It is O.K to draw everyday objects like cups and plates in your journal.

August 7

Our last stop was Oxford. We first visited Christ Church College. It has become a world famous place to visit since it appeared in the *Harry Potter* movies. In the movies, Harry and everyone else eat dinner at the Hall of Christ Church. We also saw portraits of famous people who graduated from the college. When we were outside the building. I walked to the famous olive tree and touched it. "Because I touched this tree," I said, "I will get into Oxford University!" Then, my brother said to me with a smile, "I can't wait to see your portrait on the wall."

Lucy's Drawing Tips

Create your own avatar. Your drawing journal will become much more interesting.

owner 주인

invite 초대하다

be full of ~으로 가득 차다

while ~하는 동안

be busy -ing ~하느라 바쁘다

admire 감탄하며 바라보다

plate 접시

everyday 매일의, 일상적인,

object 사물

become ~이 되다

appear 나타나다, 출연하다

else 또 다른, 다른

portrait 초상화

graduate 졸업하다

college 대학

touch 만지다, 대다

smile 미소, 웃음

확인문제

● 다음 문장이 본문의 내용과 일치하면 T, 일치하지 않으면 F를 쓰시오.

1 Lucy's mom wanted to buy the beautiful cups and plates. ☐

2 Lucy's family visited Christ Church College. ☐

3 Christ Church College appeared in the *Harry Potter* movies. ☐

4 Lucy didn't touch the famous olive tree. ☐

● 우리말을 참고하여 빈칸에 알맞은 말을 쓰시오.

1 Hi, I am Lucy Hunter, and I _____ in London.

2 Last _____, my family went on a _____ for three days.

3 During our _____, I made simple drawings in my _____.

4 That was a great _____ to capture all the _____ moments.

5 At last, we _____ foot at Stonehenge, one of the most _____ places on _____.

6 After a two-hour _____ from our home in London, we _____ got to Stonehenge.

7 It was just _____ to see the _____ of huge stones.

8 How did those huge _____ get there _____ of years ago?

9 What were they _____?

10 I _____ Stonehenge will remain a _____ for a long time.

11 Don't try to make a _____ drawing.

12 A few _____ will be enough.

13 _____ the morning, we walked _____ the Cotswolds.

14 It _____ to rain in the afternoon, _____ we decided to stay indoors at our B&B.

15 A B&B is a _____ place to _____ in England.

1 안녕, 나는 Lucy Hunter이고 런던에 살아요.

2 지난주에 우리 가족은 3일 동안 휴가를 갔습니다.

3 여행 중에 나는 일기에 간단한 그림을 그렸어요.

4 그것은 모든 특별한 순간을 포착하는 훌륭한 방법이었어요.

5 마침내, 우리는 지구에서 가장 불가사의한 장소 중 하나인 스톤헨지에 발을 디뎠다.

6 런던에 있는 집에서 차로 두 시간을 달려서 우리는 마침내 스톤헨지에 도착했다.

7 원형으로 둘러서 있는 거대한 돌들을 보는 것은 정말 놀라웠다.

8 어떻게 그 거대한 돌들이 수천 년 전에 그곳에 도착했을까?

9 그것들은 무엇을 위한 것이었을까?

10 스톤헨지는 오랫동안 미스터리로 남을 것 같다.

11 완벽한 그림을 그리려고 하지 마세요.

12 몇 가지 색깔이면 충분할 것입니다.

13 아침에 우리는 코츠월드 언덕을 돌아다녔다.

14 오후에 비가 오기 시작해서, 우리는 B&B의 실내에서 머물기로 결정했다.

15 B&B는 영국에서 체류하는 곳으로 인기가 있다.

16 It feels more _____ a home than a hotel.

17 The owner _____ us for afternoon tea today.

18 The dining table was _____ of cookies, cake, bread, _____ cheese.

19 While I was _____ eating, Mom was _____ the beautiful cups and plates.

20 I ate too _____, so I couldn't eat _____ for dinner.

21 It is O.K. to _____ everyday objects _____ cups and plates in your journal.

22 Our last _____ was Oxford.

23 We first _____ Christ Church College.

24 It has _____ a world famous place to visit _____ it appeared in the *Harry Potter* movies.

25 In the _____, Harry and everyone _____ eat _____ at the Hall of Christ Church.

26 We _____ saw portraits of famous people _____ graduated from the college.

27 _____ we were _____ the building, I _____ to the famous olive tree and touched it.

28 "Because I _____ this tree," I said, "I will _____ into Oxford University!"

29 Then, my brother _____ to me with a _____, "I can't wait to see your _____ on the wall."

30 _____ your own avatar.

31 Your drawing _____ will become _____ more interesting.

16 그것은 호텔이라기보다는 집처럼 느껴진다.

17 주인은 오늘 오후의 다과회에 우리를 초대했다.

18 식탁에는 쿠키, 케이크, 빵, 그리고 치즈가 가득했다.

19 내가 먹느라고 바쁠 때, 엄마는 아름다운 컵과 접시를 감탄하며 바라보고 계셨다.

20 나는 너무 많이 먹어서 저녁으로 아무것도 먹을 수 없었다.

21 당신의 일기에 컵과 접시 같은 일상적인 물건들을 그려도 괜찮습니다.

22 우리가 마지막으로 머문 곳은 옥스퍼드였다.

23 우리는 먼저 Christ Church College를 방문했다.

24 이곳은 해리포터 영화에 등장한 이후 방문해야 할 세계적으로 유명한 장소가 되었다.

25 영화에서 Harry와 다른 모든 사람들이 Christ Church의 회관에서 저녁을 먹는다.

26 우리는 또한 그 대학을 졸업한 유명한 사람들의 초상화를 보았다.

27 우리가 건물 밖으로 나왔을 때, 나는 유명한 올리브 나무로 걸어가서 그것을 만졌다.

28 "이 나무를 만졌기 때문에, 난 옥스퍼드 대학교에 들어갈 거야!"라고 말했다.

29 그러자 오빠가 웃으면서 "벽에 걸린 네 초상화가 빨리 보고 싶어."라고 내게 말했다.

30 여러분 자신의 아바타를 만드세요.

31 그림일기가 훨씬 더 재미있을 거예요.

● 우리말을 참고하여 본문을 영작하시오.

1 안녕, 나는 Lucy Hunter이고 런던에 살아요.

➡ _____

2 지난주에 우리 가족은 3일 동안 휴가를 갔습니다.

➡ _____

3 여행 중에 나는 일기에 간단한 그림을 그렸어요.

➡ _____

4 그것은 모든 특별한 순간을 포착하는 훌륭한 방법이었어요.

➡ _____

5 마침내, 우리는 지구에서 가장 불가사의한 장소 중 하나인 스톤헨지에 발을 디뎠다.

➡ _____

6 런던에 있는 집에서 차로 두 시간을 달려서 우리는 마침내 스톤헨지에 도착했다.

➡ _____

7 원형으로 둘러서 있는 거대한 돌들을 보는 것은 정말 놀라웠다.

➡ _____

8 어떻게 그 거대한 돌들이 수천 년 전에 그곳에 도착했을까?

➡ _____

9 그것들은 무엇을 위한 것이었을까?

➡ _____

10 완벽한 그림을 그리려고 하지 마세요.

➡ _____

11 몇 가지 색깔이면 충분할 것입니다.

➡ _____

12 스톤헨지는 오랫동안 미스터리로 남을 것 같다.

➡ _____

13 아침에 우리는 코츠월드 언덕을 돌아다녔다.

➡ _____

14 오후에 비가 오기 시작해서, 우리는 B&B의 실내에서 머물기로 결정했다.

➡ _____

15 B&B는 영국에서 체류하는 곳으로 인기가 있다.

➡ _____

16 그것은 호텔이라기보다는 집처럼 느껴진다.

➡ _____

17 주인은 오늘 오후의 다과회에 우리를 초대했다.

➡ _____

18 식탁에는 쿠키, 케이크, 빵, 그리고 치즈가 가득했다.

➡ _____

19 내가 먹느라 바쁠 때, 엄마는 아름다운 컵과 접시를 감탄하며 바라보고 계셨다.

➡ _____

20 나는 너무 많이 먹어서 저녁으로 아무것도 먹을 수 없었다.

➡ _____

21 당신의 일기에 컵과 접시 같은 일상적인 물건들을 그려도 괜찮습니다.

➡ _____

22 우리가 마지막으로 머문 곳은 옥스퍼드였다.

➡ _____

23 우리는 먼저 Christ Church College를 방문했다.

➡ _____

24 이곳은 해리포터 영화에 등장한 이후 방문해야 할 세계적으로 유명한 장소가 되었다.

➡ _____

25 영화에서 Harry와 다른 모든 사람들이 Christ Church의 회관에서 저녁을 먹는다.

➡ _____

26 우리는 또한 그 대학을 졸업한 유명한 사람들의 초상화를 보았다.

➡ _____

27 우리가 건물 밖으로 나왔을 때, 나는 유명한 올리브 나무로 걸어가서 그것을 만졌다.

➡ _____

28 "이 나무를 만졌기 때문에, 난 옥스퍼드 대학교에 들어갈 거야!"라고 말했다.

➡ _____

29 그러자 오빠가 웃으면서 "벽에 걸린 네 초상화가 빨리 보고 싶어."라고 말했다.

➡ _____

30 여러분 자신의 아바타를 만드세요.

➡ _____

31 그림일기가 훨씬 더 재미있을 거예요.

➡ _____

[01~04] 다음 글을 읽고, 물음에 답하시오.

Hi, I am Lucy Hunter, and I live in London. Last week, my family went ___ⓐ___ a vacation ___ⓑ___ three days. ___ⓒ___ our trip, I made simple drawings in my journal. ⓓThat was a great way to capture all the special moments.

01 위 글의 빈칸 ⓐ에 알맞은 것은?

① on
② to
③ at
④ by
⑤ for

02 위 글의 빈칸 ⓑ와 ⓒ에 알맞은 말이 바르게 짝지어진 것은?

① on – During
② in – During
③ on – While
④ for – During
⑤ for – While

서답형

03 위 글의 밑줄 친 ⓓThat이 가리키는 것을 우리말로 쓰시오.

➡ _____

서답형

04 일기에 간단한 그림을 그리는 것의 장점을 우리말로 간단히 쓰시오.

➡ _____

[05~09] 다음 글을 읽고, 물음에 답하시오.

At last, we set foot at Stonehenge, one of the most mysterious places on Earth. (①) After a two-hour drive from our home in London, we finally got ___ⓐ___ Stonehenge. (②) It was just amazing to see the ring of huge stones. (③) What were they for? (④) I guess Stonehenge will remain a ___ⓑ___ for a long time. (⑤)
Lucy's Drawing Tips
Don't try to make a perfect drawing. ___ⓒ___ colors will be enough.

05 위 글의 ①~⑤ 중 주어진 문장이 들어갈 알맞은 곳은?

How did those huge stones get there thousands of years ago?

①   ②   ③   ④   ⑤

06 위 글의 빈칸 ⓐ에 알맞은 것은?

① at
② to
③ on
④ for
⑤ over

서답형

07 위 글의 빈칸 ⓑ에 다음 정의에 해당하는 단어를 주어진 철자로 시작하여 쓰시오.

something that is not understood or known about

➡ m_____

08 위 글의 빈칸 ⓒ에 알맞은 것은?

① Few   ② A few

③ Much   ④ Many

⑤ A little

09 위 글의 내용으로 보아 대답할 수 없는 질문은?

① Where did they go?

② Is Stonehenge a mysterious place?

③ How long did it take them to get to Stonehenge from their home?

④ What were the ring of huge stones for?

⑤ What is Lucy's drawing tip?

[10~15] 다음 글을 읽고, 물음에 답하시오.

(①) In the morning, we walked around the Cotswolds. (②) ⓐIt started to rain in the afternoon, so we decided to stay indoors at our B&B. A B&B is a popular place to stay in England. (③) The owner invited us for afternoon tea today. (④) The dining table was full ___ⓑ___ cookies, cake, bread, and cheese. (⑤) ___ⓒ___ I was busy eating, Mom was admiring the beautiful cups and plates. ⓓI ate too much, so I couldn't eat anything for dinner.   I = Lucy

10 위 글의 ①~⑤ 중 주어진 문장이 들어갈 알맞은 곳은?

It feels more like a home than a hotel.

①   ②   ③   ④   ⑤

11 위 글의 밑줄 친 ⓐ와 같은 용법으로 쓰이지 않은 것은?

① It's ten past twelve.

② It was raining this morning.

③ It is very dark in the room.

④ It's two miles to the beach from here.

⑤ It is in Mike's house.

12 위 글의 빈칸 ⓑ에 알맞은 것은?

① in   ② of

③ off   ④ with

⑤ from

13 위 글의 빈칸 ⓒ에 알맞은 것은?

① If   ② During

③ Since   ④ While

⑤ Though

서답형

14 위 글의 밑줄 친 ⓓ와 같은 뜻이 되도록 다음 문장의 빈칸에 알맞은 말을 쓰시오.

I couldn't eat anything _____ I ate too much.

15 위 글의 내용으로 보아 대답할 수 없는 질문은?

① Where did they walk?

② When did it begin to rain?

③ Where did they stay?

④ Why did the owner invite them for afternoon tea?

⑤ What was Lucy's mother admiring?

[16~20] 다음 글을 읽고, 물음에 답하시오.

(①) Our last stop was Oxford. (②) We first visited Christ Church College. (③) ⓐIt has become a world famous place to visit _____ ⓑ it appeared in the *Harry Potter* movies. (④) ⓒWe also saw portraits of famous people who graduated the college. (⑤)

16 위 글의 ①~⑤ 중 주어진 문장이 들어갈 알맞은 곳은?

In the movies, Harry and everyone else eat dinner at the Hall of Christ Church.

①   ②   ③   ④   ⑤

서답형

17 위 글의 밑줄 친 ⓐ가 가리키는 것을 영어로 쓰시오.

➡ _____

중요

18 위 글의 빈칸 ⓑ에 알맞은 것은?

① when   ② as
③ if   ④ while
⑤ since

서답형

19 위 글의 밑줄 친 ⓒ를 어법상 어색한 것을 고쳐 다시 쓰시오.

➡ _____
_____

20 위 글의 내용에서 언급되지 <u>않은</u> 것은?

① 우리가 마지막으로 들른 곳은 옥스퍼드였다.
② 우리는 Christ Church College를 방문했다.
③ Christ Church College는 영국에서 가장 인기 있는 관광지 중의 하나이다.
④ Christ Church College에서 Harry Potter 영화를 촬영했다.
⑤ Christ Church College에서 이 학교를 졸업한 유명 인사들의 초상화를 볼 수 있다.

[21~24] 다음 글을 읽고, 물음에 답하시오.

_____ ⓐ we were outside the building, I walked to the _____ ⓑ olive tree and touched it. "Because I touched this tree," I said, "I will get into Oxford University!" Then, my brother said to me with a smile, "I can't wait to see your portrait on the wall."
Lucy's Drawing Tips
Create your own avatar. Your drawing journal will become ⓒ*much more interesting.*

I = Lucy

21 위 글의 빈칸 ⓐ에 알맞은 것은?

① When   ② Though
③ If   ④ Because
⑤ Since

서답형

22 위 글의 빈칸 ⓑ에 다음 정의에 해당하는 말을 쓰시오.

very well known

➡ _____

23 위 글의 밑줄 친 ⓒ와 바꿔 쓸 수 없는 것은? (2개)

① many ② even
③ very ④ far
⑤ a lot

24 위 글의 내용과 일치하지 <u>않는</u> 것은?

① Lucy went out of the building.
② Lucy touched the olive tree.
③ Lucy wants to enter Oxford University.
④ Lucy's brother can see her portrait on the wall.
⑤ Lucy advises us to create our own avatar.

[25~30] 다음 글을 읽고, 물음에 답하시오.

Last winter, I went to Laos with my family. (①) We visited ⓐ<u>a lot of</u> beautiful temples and went to the night ⓑ ____ in Vientiane. (②) We also enjoyed their ⓒ<u>tradition</u> food. (③) ⓓ<u>It</u> was a lot of fun to try new things in a foreign country. (④) I hope I will have a chance to visit Laos again. (⑤)   I = Minsu

25 위 글의 ①~⑤ 중 주어진 문장이 들어갈 알맞은 곳은?

Then, we moved to Vang Vieng and went river tubing.

①　　　②　　　③　　　④　　　⑤

---

26 위 글의 밑줄 친 ⓐ와 바꿔 쓸 수 있는 것은?

① few ② many
③ much ④ a few
⑤ little

27 위 글의 빈칸 ⓑ에 다음 정의에 해당하는 단어를 쓰시오.

a place where goods are bought and sold, usually outdoors

➡ _____

28 위 글의 밑줄 친 ⓒ를 알맞은 어형으로 고치시오.

➡ _____

29 위 글의 밑줄 친 ⓓ가 가리키는 것을 우리말로 쓰시오.

➡ _____

30 위 글의 내용으로 보아 대답할 수 <u>없는</u> 질문은?

① Who did Minsu go to Laos with?
② Why did Minsu visit temples?
③ What did Minsu do at Vang Vieng?
④ What food did Minsu enjoy?
⑤ What does Minsu hope to do?

[01~05] 다음 글을 읽고, 물음에 답하시오.

August 5

　At last, we set ____ⓐ____ at Stonehenge, one of the most mysterious places on Earth. ____ⓑ____ a two-hour drive from our home in London, we finally got to Stonehenge. It was just ⓒ(amazed, amazing) to see the ring of huge stones. How did those huge stones get ⓓthere thousands of years ago? What were they for? I guess Stonehenge will remain a mystery for a long time.

Lucy's Drawing Tips
Don't try to make a perfect drawing. A few colors will be enough.

01 위 글의 빈칸 ⓐ에 다음 정의에 해당하는 단어를 쓰시오.

> the part of your body that is at the ends of your legs, and that you stand on

➡ _____

02 위 글의 빈칸 ⓑ에 알맞은 전치사를 쓰시오.

➡ _____

03 위 글의 괄호 ⓒ에서 알맞은 것을 고르시오.

➡ _____

04 위 글의 밑줄 친 ⓓ가 가리키는 것을 영어로 쓰시오.

➡ _____

05 What is Lucy's drawing tip? Answer in Korean.

➡ _____

[06~08] 다음 글을 읽고, 물음에 답하시오.

　Hi, I am Lucy Hunter, and I live in London. Last week, my family went ____ⓐ____ a vacation for three days. ⓑ(For, During) our trip, I made simple drawings in my journal. ⓒThat was a great way to capture the all special moments.

06 위 글의 빈칸 ⓐ에 알맞은 전치사를 쓰시오.

➡ _____

07 위 글의 괄호 ⓑ에서 알맞은 것을 고르시오.

➡ _____

08 위 글의 밑줄 친 ⓒ에서 어법상 어색한 것을 고쳐 다시 쓰시오.

➡ _____

[09~15] 다음 글을 읽고, 물음에 답하시오.

August 6

In the morning, we walked around the Cotswolds. It started to rain in the afternoon, so we decided ⓐ(staying, to stay) indoors at our B&B. A B&B is a popular place to stay in England. It feels more ___ⓑ___ a home than a hotel. The ⓒown invited us for afternoon tea today. ⓓThe dining table was full of cookies, cake, bread, and cheese. While I was busy eating, Mom was admiring the beautiful cups and plates. I ate too much, ⓔso I couldn't eat nothing for dinner.

Lucy's Drawing Tips
ⓕ*It is O.K. to draw everyday objects like cups and plates in your journal.*

09 위 글의 괄호 ⓐ에서 알맞은 것을 고르시오.

➡ _____

10 위 글의 빈칸 ⓑ에 알맞은 말을 쓰시오.

➡ _____

11 위 글의 밑줄 친 ⓒ를 알맞은 어형으로 고치시오.

➡ _____

12 위 글의 밑줄 친 ⓓ와 같은 뜻이 되도록 다음 문장의 빈칸에 알맞은 말을 쓰시오.

> The dining table was filled _____ cookies, cake, bread, and cheese.

13 위 글의 밑줄 친 ⓔ에서 어법상 어색한 것을 고치시오.

_____ ➡ _____

14 위 글의 밑줄 친 ⓕ를 우리말로 옮기시오.

➡ _____
_____

15 What was Lucy's mom doing when she was busy eating? Answer in English.

➡ _____

[16~18] 다음 글을 읽고, 물음에 답하시오.

We went on a field trip ___ⓐ___ Namhae last month. ⓑIt was just amazing to see so many beautiful islands. We also visited Namhae German Village. We'll never ⓒ(forget, remember) that trip.

16 위 글의 빈칸 ⓐ에 알맞은 말을 쓰시오.

➡ _____

17 위 글의 밑줄 친 ⓑ가 가리키는 내용을 우리말로 쓰시오.

➡ _____

18 위 글의 괄호 ⓒ에서 알맞은 것을 고르시오.

➡ _____

구석구석

Link - Share

We went on a field trip to Namhae last month. It was just amazing to see so
many beautiful islands. We also visited Namhae German Village. We'll never
forget that trip.

~로 현장 학습을 갔다 · 지난달 · 가주어 · 진주어
빈도부사는 일반동사 앞에 위치한다.

구문해설 · amazing: 놀라운 · island: 섬 · village: 마을 · trip: 여행

우리는 지난달에 남해로 현장 학습을 갔다. 그토록 아름다운 많은 섬들을 보는 것은 아주 놀라웠다. 우리는 남해 독일 마을도 방문했다. 우리는 그 여행을 절대 잊지 못할 것이다.

Write

Last winter, I went to Laos with my family. We visited a lot of beautiful
temples and went to the night market in Vientiane. Then, we moved to Vang
Vieng and went river tubing. We also enjoyed their traditional food. It was a
lot of fun to try new things in a foreign country. I hope I will have a chance to
visit Laos again.

~와 함께 · 많은(=lots of. many) · 야시장 · 가주어 =much · 진주어 · to부정사의 형용사적 용법(~할)

구문해설 · temple: 사원, 절 · traditional: 전통적인, 전통의 · foreign: 외국의 · country: 나라
· chance: 기회

지난 겨울, 나는 가족과 함께 라오스에 갔다. 우리는 아름다운 절들을 많이 방문했고 Vientiane의 야시장에 갔다. 그러고 나서, 우리는 Vang Vieng으로 옮겨서 강에 튜브를 타러 갔다. 우리는 또한 그들의 전통 음식을 즐겼다. 외국에서 새로운 것을 시도하는 것은 매우 재미있었다. 나는 라오스를 다시 방문할 기회가 있기를 바란다.

Culture Project

September 15, 1835

We finally arrived on this island. There are many animals to study here.
Today, I saw some strange turtles. It was amazing to watch them.

There are + 복수 명사 ~: ~가 있다 · to부정사의 형용사적 용법(~할)
가주어 · 진주어 = some strange turtles

구문해설 · finally: 마침내 · arrive: 도착하다 · strange: 이상한 · amazing: 놀라운

1835년 9월 15일
우리는 마침내 이 섬에 도착했다. 여기는 조사할 동물들이 많다. 오늘, 나는 몇몇 이상한 거북들을 보았다. 그들을 보는 것은 놀라웠다.

영역별 핵심문제

01 다음 중 짝지어진 단어의 관계가 나머지 넷과 <u>다른</u> 것은?

① final – finally
② slow – slowly
③ kind – kindly
④ friend – friendly
⑤ actual – actually

02 다음 빈칸에 들어갈 말로 적절하지 <u>않은</u> 것은?

- Did you _____ hear anything like that?
- Is there _____ room for me?
- What _____ did he say?
- Do you really _____ me to believe you?

① else
② ever
③ appear
④ expect
⑤ enough

03 다음 짝지어진 두 단어의 관계가 같도록 빈칸에 알맞은 말을 쓰시오.

cold : hot = same : _____

04 다음 빈칸에 들어갈 말이 바르게 짝지어진 것은?

- This is the line to get _____ the theater.
- Watch _____! There's a car coming!

① in – on
② to – off
③ into – out
④ to – after
⑤ into – for

05 다음 영영풀이에 해당하는 단어는?

a piece of land that is completely surrounded by water

① ground
② ocean
③ garden
④ earth
⑤ island

06 다음 문장의 밑줄 친 부분과 바꿔 쓸 수 있는 것은?

<u>At last</u>, the guests began to arrive.

① Usually
② Finally
③ Actually
④ Extremely
⑤ Especially

07 다음 우리말에 맞게 빈칸에 알맞은 말을 쓰시오.

그의 나이를 추측해 볼 수 있겠니?
➡ Can you _____ his age?

08 다음 중 의도하는 바가 나머지 넷과 <u>다른</u> 하나는?

① Have you seen the movie before?
② Have you had my spaghetti before?
③ Has our teacher gone home?
④ Have you ever been to China?
⑤ How many times have you been to the park?

[09~10] 다음 대화의 빈칸에 알맞은 것을 고르시오.

09

A: _____
B: It's raining.

① Do you like summer?
② Is it sunny today?
③ What's the weather like outside?
④ Do you like the windy weather?
⑤ Can you see the blue sky?

10

A: Have you ever tried Italian food?
B: _____ It was very tasty.

① Yes, I do.　　② Yes, I have.
③ No, I don't.　　④ No, I haven't.
⑤ Yes, I did.

11 다음 대화의 순서를 바르게 배열하시오.

(A) No, I haven't. How was it?
(B) Have you ever ridden a horse?
(C) Yes, I have. How about you?
(D) It was fun, but it was a little scary, too.

➡ _____

12 다음 빈칸에 들어갈 말로 적절하지 <u>않은</u> 것은?

A: How's the weather over there in London?
B: It's rainy. How about Seoul?
A: _____

① It's raining, too.
② It's sunny and warm.
③ It's windy and cloudy.
④ It's a beautiful city.
⑤ It's snowy and cold.

[13~16] 다음 대화를 읽고, 물음에 답하시오.

B: Mom, ⓐhow's the weather today? Do I need an umbrella? (①)
W: It's quite cloudy outside. (②)
B: Thank you, Mom. (③)
W: Well, ⓑit's not going to rain today. (④)
B: Good! Then, I don't need an umbrella today. (⑤)

13 위 대화의 ①~⑤ 중 다음 주어진 문장이 들어갈 알맞은 곳은?

I'll check the weather forecast.

①　　②　　③　　④　　⑤

14 위 대화의 밑줄 친 ⓐ와 바꿔 쓸 수 있는 것은?

① what's the weather today?
② what is it today?
③ how is it today?
④ what's the weather like today?
⑤ how's the weather like today?

15 위 대화의 밑줄 친 ⓑ와 같은 뜻이 되도록 다음 문장의 빈칸에 알맞은 말을 쓰시오.

it _____ rain today

16 Does the boy need an umbrella? Answer in English.

➡ _____

Grammar

[17~18] 다음 문장의 빈칸에 알맞은 것을 고르시오.

17

> It is very dangerous _____ climb the mountain.

① to ② in
③ of ④ for
⑤ with

18

> Do you have anything _____ tomorrow?

① do ② did
③ doing ④ to do
⑤ to doing

19 다음 빈칸에 공통으로 알맞은 것은?

> • It was stupid _____ you to believe him.
> • It is clever _____ him to solve the problem.

① at ② of
③ for ④ from
⑤ with

20 다음 대화의 빈칸에 알맞은 말을 쓰시오.

> A: I think _____ _____ difficult to find the things I want to buy.
> B: You know, they have information desks.

21 다음 중 어법상 어색한 것은?

① Jane kept her promise to enter a university.
② Kathy wants someone to travel with.
③ Mike wants interesting something to read.
④ Linda doesn't have a pen to write with.
⑤ She was the first woman to land on the moon.

22 다음 중 밑줄 친 부분의 쓰임이 〈보기〉와 다른 것은?

> ┤ 보기 ├
> Jake has a lot of homework to do today.

① I need somebody to talk to.
② Frank must be crazy to quit his job.
③ I don't have time to chat with you.
④ She couldn't find any chairs to sit on.
⑤ Do you know the way to get to City Hall?

23 다음 중 밑줄 친 부분의 쓰임이 나머지 넷과 다른 것은?

① It is necessary for you to study hard.
② It is too cold to go swimming in the lake.
③ It's good to try to solve the problem.
④ It is difficult for us to achieve the goal.
⑤ It is dangerous to walk alone at midnight.

24 다음 문장에서 어법상 어색한 부분을 바르게 고쳐 쓰시오.

> Kirk needs a ball pen to write.

_____ ➡ _____

25 다음 우리말을 영어로 바르게 옮긴 것은?

> 냉장고에는 먹을 음식이 많이 있다.

① There are a lot of food to eat in the refrigerator.
② There are a lot of food eating in the refrigerator.
③ There is a lot of food eating in the refrigerator.
④ There is a lot of foods to eat in the refrigerator.
⑤ There is a lot of food to eat in the refrigerator.

26 다음 단어를 바르게 배열하여 문장을 완성하시오.

> anything / myself / to make / slimmer / look

➡ I will do _____.

27 다음 두 문장이 같은 뜻이 되도록 빈칸에 알맞은 말을 쓰시오.

> To finish this work is very important.
> = _____ is very important _____ finish this work.

Reading

[28~31] 다음 글을 읽고, 물음에 답하시오.

> Last winter, I went to Laos with my family. (①) We visited ⓐa lot of beautiful temples and went to the night market in Vientiane. (②) Then, we moved to Vang Vieng and went river tubing. (③) We also enjoyed their traditional food. (④) I hope I will have a chance ⓑvisit Laos again. (⑤)　　　　I=Minsu

28 위 글의 ①~⑤ 중 다음 주어진 문장이 들어갈 알맞은 곳은?

> It was a lot of fun to try new things in a foreign country.

①　　②　　③　　④　　⑤

29 위 글의 밑줄 친 ⓐ 대신 쓸 수 있는 것은? (2개)

① many　　　② few
③ much　　　④ a little
⑤ lots of

30 위 글의 밑줄 친 ⓑ를 알맞은 형태로 고치시오.

➡ _____

31 위 글의 내용으로 보아 알 수 없는 것은?

① Minsu went to Laos last winter.
② Minsu's family visited beautiful temples.
③ Minsu did shopping at the night market in Vientiane.
④ Minsu's family went to Vang Vieng.
⑤ Minsu wishes to visit Laos again.

[32~37] 다음 글을 읽고, 물음에 답하시오.

August 7

Our last stop was Oxford. We first visited Christ Church College. It ___ⓐ___ a world famous place to visit since it appeared in the *Harry Potter* movies. In the movies, Harry and everyone else ⓑeat dinner at the Hall of Christ Church. We also saw portraits of famous people ___ⓒ___ graduated from the college. When we were outside the building, I walked to the famous olive tree and touched it. "ⓓBecause I touched this tree," I said, "I will get into Oxford University!" Then, my brother said to me with a smile, "I can't wait to see your portrait on the wall."

Lucy's Drawing Tips
Create your own avatar. Your drawing journal will become ⓔmuch *more interesting.*

32 위 글의 빈칸 ⓐ에 알맞은 것은?

① becomes   ② became
③ is becoming   ④ has become
⑤ had become

33 위 글의 밑줄 친 ⓑ 대신 쓸 수 있는 말을 쓰시오.

➡ _____

34 위 글의 빈칸 ⓒ에 알맞은 것은? (2개)

① whom   ② who
③ that   ④ what
⑤ which

35 위 글의 밑줄 친 ⓓ 대신 쓸 수 있는 것은?

① As   ② If
③ When   ④ Though
⑤ While

36 위 글의 밑줄 친 ⓔ 대신 쓸 수 <u>없는</u> 것은? (2개)

① far   ② very
③ even   ④ many
⑤ a lot

37 위 글의 내용으로 보아 대답할 수 <u>없는</u> 질문은?

① What was their last stop?
② Why is Christ Church College famous?
③ Who graduated from Christ Church College?
④ What did Lucy do when she was outside the building?
⑤ What did Lucy's brother say to her?

[38~39] 다음 글을 읽고, 물음에 답하시오.

September 15, 1835

We ⓐfinal arrived on this island. There are many animals to study here. Today, I saw some strange turtles. ⓑIt was amazing to watch them.

38 위 글의 밑줄 친 ⓐ를 알맞은 형으로 고치시오.

➡ _____

39 위 글의 밑줄 친 ⓑ가 가리키는 것을 우리말로 쓰시오.

➡ _____

01 출제율 90%

다음 중 짝지어진 단어의 관계가 나머지 넷과 다른 것은?

① warm : cool
② different : same
③ remember : forget
④ huge : large
⑤ indoors : outdoors

02 출제율 95%

다음 두 문장이 같은 뜻이 되도록 빈칸에 알맞은 것은?

A bus appeared around the corner.
= A bus showed _____ around the corner.

① in
② up
③ out
④ off
⑤ onto

03 출제율 90%

다음 짝지어진 두 단어의 관계가 같도록 빈칸에 알맞은 말을 쓰시오.

create : _____ = decide : decision

04 출제율 85%

다음 우리말에 맞게 빈칸에 알맞은 말을 쓰시오.

다른 누군가에게 도와 달라고 부탁해 봐.
➡ Ask somebody _____ to help you.

05 출제율 95%

다음 중 영영풀이가 잘못된 것은?

① earth: the planet on which we live
② invite: to ask someone to come to something such as a party
③ relax: to feel more calm and less worried or tense
④ travel: to go from one place to another, often to a place that is far away
⑤ carry: to put clothes and other things into a bag, because you are leaving a place

06 출제율 100%

다음 빈칸에 알맞은 것을 모두 고르시오.

A: _____
B: It's snowing.
A: Really? I should wear my snow boots. Thanks.

① How's the weather today?
② What weather do you like today?
③ What's the snowy weather today?
④ What's the weather like today?
⑤ What does the cloud look like?

07 출제율 95%

다음 대화의 빈칸에 알맞은 것은?

A: _____
B: No, I haven't, but I've heard of it many times.

① How often have you been to Namsan?
② Did you go to Namsan?
③ When did you go to Namsan?
④ Have you ever been to Namsan?
⑤ How many times did you visit Namsan?

[09~10] 다음 대화를 읽고, 물음에 답하시오.

Suho: Anna, have you ⓐbe to Australia before?

Anna: Yes, I have. Actually, I lived in Sydney for a year.

Suho: Great! How's the weather there in April? I'm going to visit Sydney on vacation next week.

Anna: April is a great time to visit Sydney. In April, it's autumn in Australia.

Suho: Good. ⓑI'm planning to spend some time on the beach and relax in the sun.

Anna: Well, it often rains in April, but you may have some sunny days.

Suho: I'll take my hat and pack an umbrella, too.

Anna: That's a good idea. Have a great time.

출제율 100%

08 위 대화의 밑줄 친 ⓐ를 알맞은 어형으로 고치시오.

➡ _____

출제율 90%

09 위 대화의 밑줄 친 ⓑ를 우리말로 옮기시오.

➡ _____
_____

출제율 95%

10 위 대화의 내용과 일치하지 <u>않는</u> 것은?

① Anna는 호주를 방문한 적이 있다.
② Anna는 시드니에서 1년간 산 적이 있다.
③ 수호는 다음 주에 시드니를 방문할 예정이다.
④ 4월에 호주의 날씨는 가을이다.
⑤ 4월의 시드니 날씨는 대체로 화창하다.

출제율 90%

11 다음 문장에서 어법상 <u>어색한</u> 부분을 바르게 고쳐 쓰시오.

> Mary needs some paper to write.

_____ ➡ _____

출제율 95%

12 다음 빈칸에 알맞은 말이 바르게 짝지어진 것은?

> • It was wise _____ you to agree to the proposal.
> • It is impossible _____ us to win the game.

① of – of
② of – for
③ for – for
④ for – of
⑤ for – with

출제율 100%

13 다음 빈칸에 들어갈 동사의 형태로 적절한 것은?

> It's necessary for you _____ the piano every day.

① practice
② practiced
③ practicing
④ to practice
⑤ to practicing

출제율 95%

14 다음 두 문장이 같은 뜻이 되도록 빈칸에 알맞은 말을 쓰시오.

> To solve this puzzle is very difficult.
> ➡ _____ is very difficult _____ solve this puzzle.

15 다음 중 〈보기〉의 밑줄 친 It과 쓰임이 같은 것은?

> ┤ 보기 ├
>
> It is very important to check the weather forecast every day.

① It is freezing here.

② It is not my lost puppy.

③ It was built by them.

④ It rained a lot yesterday morning.

⑤ It is fun to play soccer with my friends.

16 다음 중 어법상 어색한 문장은?

① I need a chair to sit.

② Columbus was the first man to discover the American Continent.

③ We have no house to live in.

④ He has a wish to become a pilot.

⑤ She forgot to bring something to write with.

17 다음 우리말을 영어로 바르게 옮긴 것은?

> 로마에는 방문할 장소가 많이 있다.

① There is many places visit in Rome.

② There are visiting many places in Rome.

③ There are many places visiting in Rome.

④ There are to visit many places in Rome.

⑤ There are many places to visit in Rome.

18 다음 중 밑줄 친 부분의 쓰임이 나머지 넷과 다른 하나는?

① He drove very quickly to get there on time.

② Katherine is coming to Seoul to visit us.

③ I'm going to the park to walk my dogs.

④ There's nothing to be afraid of any more.

⑤ I went to the post office to send the parcel.

[19~20] 다음 글을 읽고, 물음에 답하시오.

Hi, I am Lucy Hunter, and I live in London. Last week, my family went on a vacation ⓐ_____ three days. During our trip, I made simple drawings in my journal. That was a great way ⓑto capture all the special moments.

19 위 글의 빈칸 ⓐ에 알맞은 것은?

① in   ② for

③ to   ④ at

⑤ during

20 위 글의 밑줄 친 ⓑ와 같은 용법으로 쓰인 것은?

① We wished to reach the North Pole.

② He made a promise to come again.

③ He was excited to see the scenery.

④ The boy grew up to be a poet.

⑤ We decided to go fishing in the river.

[21~26] 다음 글을 읽고, 물음에 답하시오.

August 5

ⓐAt last, we set foot at Stonehenge, one of the most mysterious places on Earth. After a two-hour drive from our home in London, we finally ⓑgot to Stonehenge. It was just amazing to see the ring of huge stones. ⓒ How did those huge stones get there thousand of years ago? What were they for? I guess Stonehenge will ___ⓓ___ a mystery for a long time.

Lucy's Drawing Tips
Don't try ⓔ*(making, to make) a perfect drawing.*
A few colors will be enough.

출제율 95%

21 위 글의 밑줄 친 ⓐ 대신 쓸 수 있는 것은?

① In fact   ② In contrast
③ As a fact   ④ As a result
⑤ In the long run

출제율 100%

22 위 글의 밑줄 친 ⓑ 대신 쓸 수 있는 것은?

① arrived   ② reached
③ received   ④ appeared
⑤ happened

출제율 85%

23 위 글의 밑줄 친 ⓒ에서 어법상 어색한 것을 고치시오.

_____ ➡ _____

출제율 90%

24 위 글의 빈칸 ⓓ에 알맞은 것은?

① seem   ② look
③ remain   ④ appear
⑤ belong

출제율 95%

25 위 글의 괄호 ⓔ에서 알맞은 것을 고르시오

➡ _____

출제율 85%

26 위 글의 내용으로 보아 알 수 없는 것은? (2개)

① 스톤헨지는 세계에서 가장 신비한 곳들 중의 하나다.
② 런던의 집에서 스톤헨지까지 가는 데는 자동차로 두 시간 걸렸다.
③ 스톤헨지에서 거대한 돌들의 고리를 보았다.
④ Lucy는 그 거대한 돌들의 용도를 알았다.
⑤ 머지않아 스톤헨지의 미스터리가 풀릴 것이다.

[27~29] 다음 글을 읽고, 물음에 답하시오.

We went on a field trip to Namhae last month. ⓐIt was just amazing to see so many beautiful islands. We also visited Namhae German Village. We'll never forget that trip.

출제율 95%

27 위 글의 밑줄 친 ⓐ를 우리말로 옮기시오.

➡ _____

출제율 90%

28 When did they go to Namhae? Answer in English.

➡ _____

[01~03] 다음 대화를 읽고, 물음에 답하시오.

> W: ⓐ<u>Have you gone to any special places in Korea?</u>
> M: Yes, I have. I went to Ulleungdo last summer with my family.
> W: ⓑ<u>How was the weather there?</u>
> M: It was mostly sunny, ____ⓒ____ the weather changed often.

01 위 대화의 밑줄 친 ⓐ에서 어법상 어색한 것을 고치시오.

_____ ➡ _____

02 위 대화의 밑줄 친 ⓑ와 같은 뜻이 되도록 다음 문장의 빈칸에 알맞은 말을 쓰시오.

| _____ was the weather _____ there? |

03 위 대화의 빈칸 ⓒ에 알맞은 접속사를 쓰시오.

➡ _____

04 다음 대화의 순서를 바르게 배열하시오.

> (A) Mom, how's the weather today?
> (B) Thanks, Mom.
> (C) It's quite cloudy outside. I'll check the weather forecast.
> (D) Well, it's going to rain in the afternoon.

➡ _____

05 다음 우리말의 의미에 맞도록 주어진 어구를 이용하여 영작하시오.

(1) 매일 일기를 쓰는 것은 쉽지 않다.
(it, easy, keep, every)

➡ _____

(2) 나는 내 남동생이 찍는 사진들을 좋아한다.
(photographs, which, takes)

➡ _____
_____

06 다음 〈조건〉에 맞게 괄호 안의 단어를 이용하여 우리말을 영어로 옮기시오.

> ┌ 조건 ┐
> 1. 주어진 단어를 모두 이용할 것.
> 2. 필요시 관사를 붙이거나 단어를 추가 할 것.
> 3. It으로 시작할 것.
> 4. 대·소문자 및 구두점에 유의할 것.

(1) 내가 자동차를 주차하기는 어렵다.
(difficult, me, park, car)

➡ _____

(2) 헬멧을 쓰고 자전거를 타는 것이 안전하다.
(safe, ride, bike, with, helmet)

➡ _____

(3) 다른 나라에서 사는 것은 흥미진진한 경험이다.
(exciting, experience, live, another, country)

➡ _____
_____

07 다음 하루 일과표를 보고 빈칸에 알맞은 내용을 완성하시오.

8:00 a.m.	school
12:10 p.m.	lunch
5:00 p.m.	playground
6:30 p.m.	homework

(1) It's 8 a.m. It's time _____.

(2) It's 12:10 p.m. It's time _____.

(3) It's 5 p.m. It's time _____.

(4) It's 6:30 p.m. It's time _____.

[08~12] 다음 글을 읽고, 물음에 답하시오.

August 6

In the morning, we walked around the Cotswolds. ⓐIt started to rain in the afternoon, so we decided to stay indoors at our B&B. A B&B is a popular place to stay in England. ⓑIt feels more like a home than a hotel. The owner invited us for afternoon tea today. The dining table was full ⓒ_____ cookies, cake, bread, and cheese. While I was busy eating, Mom was admiring the beautiful cups and plates. I ate too much, so I couldn't eat ⓓ(something, anything) for dinner.

08 위 글의 밑줄 친 ⓐ와 같은 뜻이 되도록 빈칸에 알맞은 말을 쓰시오.

> We decided to stay indoors at our B&B _____ it started to rain in the afternoon.

09 위 글의 밑줄 친 ⓑ가 가리키는 것을 영어로 쓰시오.

➡ _____

10 위 글의 빈칸 ⓒ에 알맞은 전치사를 쓰시오.

➡ _____

11 위 글의 괄호 ⓓ에서 알맞은 것을 고르시오.

➡ _____

12 What did they do in the morning? Answer in English.

➡ _____

[13~15] 다음 글을 읽고, 물음에 답하시오.

Last winter, I went to Laos with my family. We visited ⓐa lot of beautiful temples and went to the night market in Vientiane. Then, we moved to Vang Vieng and went river tubing. We also enjoyed their traditional food. It was a lot of fun to try new things in a foreign country. ⓑI hope I will have a chance to visit Laos again.

13 위 글의 밑줄 친 ⓐ를 한 단어로 바꿔 쓰시오.

➡ _____

14 위 글의 밑줄 친 ⓑ를 우리말로 옮기시오.

➡ _____

15 Who did the writer go to Laos with? Answer in English.

➡ _____

창의사고력 서술형 문제

01 다음 주어진 상황에 맞게 〈to부정사〉와 괄호 안의 단어를 이용하여 〈보기〉처럼 문장을 완성하시오.

╺ 보기 ╺

I'm hungry. I need some food to eat. (eat)

(1) I'm very thirsty. _____ (drink)

(2) There's no chair here. _____ (sit)

(3) Tony feels lonely. _____ (talk)

02 다음 어구들을 연결하여 〈보기〉와 같이 한 문장으로 쓰시오.

• impossible • kind • difficult • stupid • possible • necessary	• him • foreigners • us • her • you • me	• to visit • to watch • to agree • to finish • to help • to learn	• his hometown • Korean • the work on time • the poor • to the proposal • the game

╺ 보기 ╺

It is impossible for him to visit his hometown.

(1) _____

(2) _____

(3) _____

(4) _____

(5) _____

03 다음 Jessica의 이번 주 일정표를 보고, 내용에 맞도록 문장을 완성하시오.

Mon.	Tue.	Wed.	Thu.	Fri.
movie / watch	a piano lesson / take	a baseball game / watch	a piano lesson / take	four comic books / read

(1) Jessica has _____ _____ _____ _____ this Monday.

(2) Jessica has _____ _____ _____ _____ _____ on TV this Wednesday.

(3) Jessica has _____ _____ _____ _____ _____ on Tuesday and Thurday.

(4) Jessica has _____ _____ _____ _____ _____ on Friday.

단원별 모의고사

01 다음 영영풀이에 해당하는 단어로 알맞은 것은?

> to cause something to happen or exist

① make ② repair ③ fix
④ create ⑤ prepare

02 다음 중 우리말 뜻이 <u>잘못된</u> 것은?

① at last: 마침내
② a little: 좀, 약간; 약간의
③ right now: 잠시
④ a lot of: 많은
⑤ set foot at: ~에 발을 디디다

03 다음 빈칸에 공통으로 알맞은 것은?

> • The bathtub was full _____ hot water.
> • Tom is fond _____ Kathy.

① at ② to ③ for
④ of ⑤ with

04 다음 짝지어진 두 단어의 관계가 같도록 빈칸에 알맞은 말을 쓰시오.

> arrive : arrival = decide : _____

05 다음 빈칸에 공통으로 들어갈 말을 쓰시오.

> • Mary didn't show _____ for the meeting yesterday.
> • I'm planning to clean _____ the park with my dad.

[06~08] 다음 대화의 빈칸에 알맞은 것을 고르시오.

06

> A: Have you ever caught a big fish?
> B: _____ I wish to catch it someday.

① Yes, I have.
② No, I haven't.
③ I caught a big fish.
④ Yes, my uncle caught a big fish.
⑤ I caught it and put it back.

07

> A: _____
> B: No, I haven't.

① Do you have a sister?
② Does he live with his grandparents?
③ Have you ever seen a bear?
④ Which country have you travelled?
⑤ Are you happy with the new class?

08

> A: What's the weather like there?
> B: _____

① I like hot summer.
② I got a bad cold.
③ I enjoy skiing here.
④ I should wear a coat.
⑤ It's cold and sometimes it snows a lot.

[09~10] 다음 대화를 읽고, 물음에 답하시오.

G: Bill, have you ever gone bungee jumping?
B: No, I haven't. ___ⓐ___ about you, Katie?
G: When I visited New Zealand, I tried bungee jumping once.
B: Wasn't it scary?
G: No, I liked it. I want to do it again.

09 위 대화의 빈칸 ⓐ에 알맞은 것은? (2개)

① How   ② Who
③ What   ④ Why
⑤ Which

10 위 대화의 내용으로 보아 알 수 없는 것은?

① Bill은 번지 점프를 해 본 적이 없다.
② Katie는 뉴질랜드를 방문한 적이 있다.
③ Katie는 번지 점프를 해 본 적이 있다.
④ Bill은 두려워서 번지 점프를 시도해 보지 않았다.
⑤ Katie는 다시 번지 점프를 하기를 원한다.

[11~13] 다음 문장의 빈칸에 알맞은 것을 고르시오.

11

My brother has many things _____ tonight.

① do   ② does
③ doing   ④ to do
⑤ to be doing

12

Kate is looking for a friend to travel _____.

① at   ② in   ③ with
④ on   ⑤ for

13

Alice and Ken are going to enter Berkeley. They need a dormitory _____.

① live   ② to live
③ to live in   ④ to live with
⑤ to living

14 다음 빈칸에 주어진 단어의 알맞은 형태를 쓰시오.

Is it possible _____ the project by tomorrow? (finish)

15 다음 밑줄 친 부분의 쓰임이 〈보기〉와 같은 것은?

┤ 보기 ├
I have nothing special to eat in my bag.

① She packed her bag to go home.
② I was happy to find my cell phone.
③ The man needs someone to look after his cat.
④ To eat breakfast is good for your brain.
⑤ We went to the school store to buy some snacks.

[16~17] 다음 중 어법상 알맞지 <u>않은</u> 문장을 고르시오.

16
① The man needs a piece of paper to write on.
② Amy has no house to live in.
③ There's nothing to worry about.
④ Give me a pen to write with.
⑤ You seem to have important something to tell me.

17
① It's hard to climb the tree.
② It's great fun skate on ice.
③ It's fun to watch a baseball game.
④ It's important for us to study English.
⑤ It's interesting to take a trip to strange lands.

18 다음 괄호 안의 단어 형태가 바르게 짝지어진 것은?

> • I have something (tell) you.
> • Do you have anything (read)?

① tell – read
② tell – to read
③ to tell – read
④ telling – read
⑤ to tell – to read

19 다음 밑줄 친 ⓐ, ⓑ를 어법상 올바른 형태로 쓰시오.

> I think shopping on the Internet is good. It's easy ⓐfind the things I want to buy. It's also easy ⓑfind good prices.

ⓐ _____ ⓑ _____

[20~23] 다음 글을 읽고, 물음에 답하시오.

> Our ①last stop was Oxford. We ②first visited Christ Church College. It has become a world famous place to visit ___ⓐ___ it appeared in the *Harry Potter* movies. In the movies, Harry and everyone ③other eat dinner ④at the Hall of Christ Church. We ⑤also saw portraits of famous people ___ⓑ___ graduated from the college.

20 위 글의 밑줄 친 ①~⑤ 중 어법상 어색한 것은?

① ② ③ ④ ⑤

21 위 글의 빈칸 ⓐ에 알맞은 것은?

① for ② when
③ during ④ since
⑤ while

22 위 글의 빈칸 ⓑ에 알맞은 것은?

① who ② that
③ what ④ whom
⑤ which

23 위 글의 내용으로 보아 알 수 <u>없는</u> 것은?

① 우리가 마지막으로 들른 곳은 옥스퍼드였다.
② 우리는 Christ Church College를 방문했다.
③ Christ Church College는 Harry Potter 영화에 나왔다.
④ Harry Potter는 Christ Church College의 학생이다.
⑤ 우리는 Christ Church College를 졸업한 유명한 사람들의 초상화를 보았다.

[24~27] 다음 글을 읽고, 물음에 답하시오.

> _____ ⓐ _____ we were outside the building, I walked to the famous olive tree and touched it. " _____ ⓑ _____ I touched this tree," I said, "I will get into Oxford University!" Then, my brother said to me with a smile, "I can't wait to see your _____ ⓒ _____ on the wall."
>
> _Lucy's Drawing Tips_
> _Create your own avatar. Your drawing journal will become _____ ⓓ _____ more interesting._

24 위 글의 빈칸 ⓐ와 ⓑ에 알맞은 말이 바르게 짝지어진 것은?

① If – Because   ② As – Though
③ When – Because   ④ Since – Because
⑤ When – While

25 위 글의 빈칸 ⓒ에 다음 정의에 해당하는 단어를 쓰시오.

> a painting, drawing, or photograph of a particular person

➡ _____

26 위 글의 빈칸 ⓓ에 알맞지 <u>않은</u> 것은?

① very   ② far
③ even   ④ much
⑤ a lot

27 Why is the olive tree famous? Answer in Korean.

➡ _____

[28~30] 다음 글을 읽고, 물음에 답하시오.

> Last winter, I went to Laos with my family. (①) We visited <u>a lot of</u> beautiful temples and went to the night market in Vientiane. (②) We also enjoyed their traditional food. (③) It was a lot of fun to try new things in a foreign country. (④) I hope I will have a chance to visit Laos again. (⑤)
>
> I=Minsu

28 위 글의 ①~⑤ 중 다음 주어진 문장이 들어갈 알맞은 곳은?

> Then, we moved to Vang Vieng and went river tubing.

①   ②   ③   ④   ⑤

29 위 글의 밑줄 친 부분을 한 단어로 쓰시오.

➡ _____

30 위 글의 내용으로 보아 대답할 수 <u>없는</u> 질문은?

① Where did Minsu go last winter?
② Where did Minsu go in Vientiane?
③ Was it a lot of fun to try new things in a foreign country?
④ What was their traditional food?
⑤ Does Minsu wish to visit Laos again?

INSIGHT
on the textbook

교과서 파헤치기

※ 다음 영어를 우리말로 쓰시오.

01 real	22 someone
02 tooth	23 practice
03 unique	24 ranger
04 vote	25 cloudy
05 wrong	26 activity
06 president	27 coworker
07 cartoonist	28 adventurous
08 recycle	29 decide
09 danger	30 awesome
10 push-up	31 skill
11 funny	32 skip stones
12 husband	33 cheerfully
13 janitor	34 speech
14 joke	35 be good at
15 jump rope	36 make one's day
16 listener	37 do a good job
17 nervous	38 fall asleep
18 once	39 give away
19 character	40 be good for
20 become	41 say hello to
21 superhero	42 such as
	43 be afraid of

※ 다음 우리말을 영어로 쓰시오.

01 기량, 기술 _____

02 실제로 _____

03 진정한, 진짜의 _____

04 이, 이빨 _____

05 여행하다 _____

06 독특한 _____

07 슈퍼히어로 _____

08 대통령, 회장 _____

09 물수제비뜨다 _____

10 투표하다 _____

11 연설, 담화 _____

12 틀린, 잘못된 _____

13 연습하다 _____

14 위험 _____

15 ~할 만큼 (충분히) _____

16 소설 _____

17 모험성이 강한 _____

18 문지기, 수위 _____

19 결정하다 _____

20 우스운 _____

21 만화가 _____

22 재활용[재생]하다 _____

23 남편 _____

24 대단한, 굉장히 좋은 _____

25 줄넘기를 하다 _____

26 기분 좋게 _____

27 불안해[초조해] 하는 _____

28 그림, 데생 _____

29 농담 _____

30 밖에(서) _____

31 각[매], ~당[마다] _____

32 공원[삼림] 관리원 _____

33 요리책 _____

34 동료 _____

35 ~와 같은 _____

36 ~에 좋다 _____

37 있잖아, 알겠니? _____

38 ~을 잘하다 _____

39 ~을 두려워하다 _____

40 잠들다 _____

41 마침내, 드디어 _____

42 ~을 보다 _____

43 조심하다 _____

※ 다음 영영풀이에 알맞은 단어를 <보기>에서 골라 쓴 후, 우리말 뜻을 쓰시오.

1 _____ : something that is said or done to make you laugh, for example a funny story: _____

2 _____ : the possibility that you will be hurt or killed: _____

3 _____ : a person who is making a speech or giving a talk: _____

4 _____ : a person whose job is to look after a building: _____

5 _____ : to be present at a meeting or event: _____

6 _____ : the hard white object in your mouth, which you use for biting and chewing: _____

7 _____ : a person whose job is to draw cartoons for newspapers and magazines: _____

8 _____ : a short period when you stop doing something before continuing: _____

9 _____ : the ability to speak or the act of speaking: _____

10 _____ : frightened or worried about something that is happening or might happen: _____

11 _____ : a long written story about imaginary people and events: _____

12 _____ : a small light motorcycle which has a low seat: _____

13 _____ : one of the sixty parts that a minute is divided into: _____

14 _____ : a restaurant where you choose your food from a counter and take it to your table after paying for it: _____

15 _____ : the people you work with, especially people on the same job or project as you: _____

16 _____ : to process things that have already been used, such as bottles or sheets of paper so that they can be used again: _____

보기			
scooter	cartoonist	attend	joke
cafeteria	danger	recycle	speaker
coworker	novel	speech	janitor
tooth	second	pause	nervous

※ 다음 우리말과 일치하도록 빈칸에 알맞은 말을 쓰시오.

Listen & Speak 1 A. Listen and Check

1. B: What _____ you _____, Nami?

   G: I'm _____ a smart phone case _____ _____ my old jeans.

   B: Wow! You're _____ _____ _____ old things.

   G: Thanks. I _____ _____. It's fun, and it's also _____ _____ our Earth.

2. B: Hello, everyone. I'm Kim Yujin. I want _____ _____ your _____ president. I'm a good _____ and always _____ _____ _____ others. I'm also _____ _____ _____ fun school activities. I'll _____ _____ for our class, so please _____ _____ me. Thank you _____ _____!

Listen & Speak 2 A. Listen and Check

1. B: Hi, Cindy. _____ something _____?

   G: I _____ _____ give a speech _____ _____ _____ the whole school. I'm so _____.

   B: _____ worry. You're a very _____ _____. I'm _____ you'll _____ _____ _____ _____.

   G: Thanks, Minho. I _____ _____ _____ now.

2. G: Tomorrow is _____ _____ birthday. What _____ I do _____ her?

   B: _____ _____ _____ bake a cake for her? You're _____ _____ _____.

   G: That's a good _____. I hope my mom _____ _____ my cake.

   B: _____ _____ your mom _____ _____ it.

1. B: 나미야, 뭐 하고 있니?
   G: 오래된 청바지로 스마트폰 케이스를 만들고 있어.
   B: 와! 너 오래된 것들을 재활용하는 것을 잘하는구나.
   G: 고마워. 나는 재활용하는 것을 좋아해. 그것은 재미있고, 우리의 지구에도 좋아.

2. B: 여러분, 안녕하세요. 저는 김유진입니다. 저는 여러분의 반 학급회장이 되고 싶습니다. 저는 남의 말을 잘 경청하고 항상 다른 사람들을 도우려고 노력합니다. 저는 재미있는 학교 활동 계획도 잘합니다. 저는 우리 반을 위해 열심히 일하겠으니 저에게 투표해 주세요. 들어주셔서 감사합니다!

1. B: 안녕, Cindy. 무슨 일 있니?
   G: 난 학교 전체 학생 앞에서 연설을 해야 해. 아주 긴장이 돼.
   B: 걱정하지 마. 너는 말을 아주 잘하잖아. 분명히 잘할 거야.
   G: 고마워, 민호야. 이제 기분이 훨씬 좋아졌어.

2. G: 내일은 우리 엄마의 생일이야. 내가 엄마를 위해 무엇을 해야 할까?
   B: 너의 엄마를 위해 케이크를 굽는 건 어때? 넌 빵을 잘 굽잖아.
   G: 좋은 생각이야. 엄마가 내 케이크를 좋아하셨으면 좋겠다.
   B: 너의 엄마는 분명히 아주 좋아하실 거야.

Communicate A. Listen and Answer

1. **Yuri:** What _____ you _____, Jaden?

   Jaden: I'm _____ _____.

   Yuri: Really? _____ I _____ a look _____ them?

   Jaden: No, _____ _____.

   Yuri: Why _____? You can show me a few, _____ _____?

   Jaden: Well, I _____ so.

   Yuri: (*pause*) Ha, ha, ha! _____! I like your cartoons. You're really _____ _____ _____.

   Jaden: Do you _____ _____? I want _____ _____ a cartoonist, but I don't think my _____ _____ are good _____.

   Yuri: Your cartoons are really _____, and you have _____ _____. I'm _____ you'll be a great _____.

   Jaden: Thank you, Yuri. You just _____ my day.

2. **A:** Why _____ you join our musical theater club? You're _____ _____ singing.

   B: Well, I'd _____ _____, but I don't think I'm good at _____ or _____.

   A: _____ worry. We can _____ _____. I'm sure you'll learn _____. Just _____ _____.

   B: O.K. I'll _____ _____ it.

Progress Check

1. **B:** _____ are you _____?

   G: I'm _____ _____ for dinner.

   B: Wow! You're really _____ _____ cooking!

   G: Thanks.

2. **B:** _____ something _____?

   G: I have to _____ _____ _____ in English. I'm so _____.

   B: Don't _____. Practice your speech _____ _____ _____ your family. I'm sure you'll do a _____ _____.

   G: Thank you. I'll _____.

3. **W:** Everybody _____ _____ _____ something. _____ people are good at drawing. _____ people are good at singing. What _____ you _____ _____?

1. 유리: 너 뭐 하고 있니, Jaden?
   Jaden: 만화를 그리고 있어.
   유리: 정말? 내가 그것들을 봐도 되니?
   Jaden: 아니, 아직은 아니야.
   유리: 왜 안 되는데? 몇 개 보여줄 수 있지, 안 그래?
   Jaden: 음, 그럴 수 있지.
   유리: (멈춤) 하, 하, 하! 대단해! 너의 만화가 마음에 들어. 넌 그림을 정말 잘 그리는구나.
   Jaden: 그렇게 생각하니? 나는 만화가가 되고 싶지만, 내 그림 그리는 기술이 충분히 능숙하지 않다고 생각해.
   유리: 네 만화들은 정말 재미있고, 독특한 캐릭터를 가지고 있어. 나는 네가 훌륭한 만화가가 될 거라고 확신해.
   Jaden: 고마워, 유리야. 넌 날 행복하게 해줬어.

2. A: 우리 뮤지컬 연극 동아리에 가입하는 게 어때? 노래를 잘하는구나.
   B: 음, 그러고 싶지만, 연기나 춤을 잘 못해.
   A: 걱정하지 마. 우리가 가르쳐 줄 수 있어. 나는 네가 빨리 배울 거라고 확신해. 그냥 우리와 함께 해.
   B: 좋아. 생각해 볼게.

1. B: 너 뭐 하고 있니?
   G: 저녁으로 피자를 만들고 있어.
   B: 와! 넌 요리를 정말 잘하는구나!
   G: 고마워.

2. B: 무슨 문제 있어?
   G: 영어로 연설을 해야 해. 아주 긴장이 돼.
   B: 걱정하지 마. 가족 앞에서 연설을 연습해 봐. 넌 분명히 잘할 거야.
   G: 고마워. 그렇게 해볼게.

3. W: 모든 사람은 잘하는 것이 있습니다. 어떤 사람들은 그림을 잘 그립니다. 또 어떤 사람들은 노래를 잘 부릅니다. 당신은 무엇을 잘합니까?

※ 다음 우리말에 맞도록 대화를 영어로 쓰시오.

Listen & Speak 1 A. Listen and Check

1. B: _____

   G: _____

   B: _____

   G: _____

2. B: _____

   _____

   _____

   _____

Listen & Speak 2 A. Listen and Check

1. B: _____

   G: _____

   B: _____

   G: _____

2. G: _____

   B: _____

   G: _____

   B: _____

1. B: 나미야, 뭐 하고 있니?
   G: 오래된 청바지로 스마트폰 케이스를 만들고 있어.
   B: 와! 너 오래된 것들을 재활용하는 것을 잘하는구나.
   G: 고마워. 나는 재활용하는 것을 좋아해. 그것은 재미있고, 우리의 지구에도 좋아.

2. B: 여러분, 안녕하세요. 저는 김유진입니다. 저는 여러분의 반 학급회장이 되고 싶습니다. 저는 남의 말을 잘 경청하고 항상 다른 사람들을 도우려고 노력합니다. 저는 재미있는 학교 활동 계획도 잘합니다. 저는 우리 반을 위해 열심히 일하겠으니 저에게 투표해 주세요. 들어주셔서 감사합니다!

1. B: 안녕, Cindy. 무슨 일 있니?
   G: 난 학교 전체 학생 앞에서 연설을 해야 해. 아주 긴장이 돼.
   B: 걱정하지 마. 너는 말을 아주 잘하잖아. 분명히 잘할 거야.
   G: 고마워, 민호야. 이제 기분이 훨씬 좋아졌어.

2. G: 내일은 우리 엄마의 생일이야. 내가 엄마를 위해 무엇을 해야 할까?
   B: 너의 엄마를 위해 케이크를 굽는 건 어때? 넌 빵을 잘 굽잖아.
   G: 좋은 생각이야. 엄마가 내 케이크를 좋아하셨으면 좋겠다.
   B: 너의 엄마는 분명히 아주 좋아하실 거야.

Communicate A. Listen and Answer

1. Yuri: _____

   Jaden: _____

   Yuri: _____

   Jaden: _____

   Yuri: _____

   Jaden: _____

   Yuri: _____
   _____

   Jaden: _____
   _____

   Yuri: _____
   _____

   Jaden: _____

2. A: _____

   B: _____

   A: _____

   B: _____

Progress Check

1. B: _____

   G: _____

   B: _____

   G: _____

2. B: _____

   G: _____

   B: _____
   _____

   G: _____

3. W: _____
   _____

1. 유리: 너 뭐 하고 있니, Jaden?
   Jaden: 만화를 그리고 있어.
   유리: 정말? 내가 그것들을 봐도 되니?
   Jaden: 아니, 아직은 아니야.
   유리: 왜 안 되는데? 몇 개 보여줄 수 있지, 안 그래?
   Jaden: 음, 그럴 수 있지.
   유리: (멈춤) 하, 하, 하! 대단해! 너의 만화가 마음에 들어. 넌 그림을 정말 잘 그리는구나.
   Jaden: 그렇게 생각하니? 나는 만화가가 되고 싶지만, 내 그림 그리는 기술이 충분히 능숙하지 않다고 생각해.
   유리: 네 만화들은 정말 재미있고, 독특한 캐릭터를 가지고 있어. 나는 네가 훌륭한 만화가가 될 거라고 확신해.
   Jaden: 고마워, 유리야. 넌 날 행복하게 해줬어.

2. A: 우리 뮤지컬 연극 동아리에 가입하는 게 어때? 노래를 잘하는구나.
   B: 음, 그러고 싶지만, 연기나 춤을 잘 못해.
   A: 걱정하지 마. 우리가 가르쳐 줄 수 있어. 나는 네가 빨리 배울 거라고 확신해. 그냥 우리와 함께 해.
   B: 좋아. 생각해 볼게.

1. B: 너 뭐 하고 있니?
   G: 저녁으로 피자를 만들고 있어.
   B: 와! 넌 요리를 정말 잘하는구나!
   G: 고마워.

2. B: 무슨 문제 있어?
   G: 영어로 연설을 해야 해. 아주 긴장이 돼.
   B: 걱정하지 마. 가족 앞에서 연설을 연습해 봐. 넌 분명히 잘할 거야.
   G: 고마워. 그렇게 해볼게.

3. W: 모든 사람은 잘하는 것이 있습니다. 어떤 사람들은 그림을 잘 그립니다. 또 어떤 사람들은 노래를 잘 부릅니다. 당신은 무엇을 잘합니까?

※ 다음 우리말과 일치하도록 빈칸에 알맞은 것을 골라 쓰시오.

1 _____ name is Hojin, and I _____ to make graphic _____.
A. novels   B. like   C. my

2 _____ I was _____ home from school last week, I _____ a woman _____ a scooter.
A. saw   B. on   C. walking   D. while

3 She _____ really _____, and her scooter was very _____.
A. unique   B. cool   C. looked

4 "Are you _____ home, Hojin?" she _____ to me _____.
A. suddenly   B. said   C. going

5 "Yes, _____ do I know you?" I _____.
A. asked   B. but

6 "Of _____," she _____.
A. answered   B. course

7 "I _____ you at the school _____ _____ day."
A. cafeteria   B. every   C. see

8 _____, she was one _____ the cafeteria _____ at school.
A. workers   B. of   C. surprisingly

9 "Amazing! She looks so _____ _____ the school," I _____.
A. outside   B. thought   C. different

10 "I _____ write a _____ novel about _____."
A. her   B. graphic   C. should

11 _____ I _____ home, I _____ to write a new graphic novel, *Lunch Lady Begins*.
A. began   B. got   C. after

12 _____ it, Lunch Lady is a _____.
A. superhero   B. in

13 She _____ a _____ scooter _____ can fly.
A. that   B. super   C. rides

14 She _____ people from _____ _____ the world.
A. danger   B. saves   C. around

15 She also makes 100 cookies _____ _____ and gives them _____ to hungry children.
A. away   B. second   C. per

1 내 이름은 호진이고, 만화 소설 쓰는 것을 좋아한다.

2 지난주에 나는 학교에서 집으로 걸어가던 중에 스쿠터에 탄 여자를 보았다.

3 그녀는 정말 멋져 보였고 그녀의 스쿠터는 매우 독특했다.

4 "호진아, 너 집에 가는 중이니?" 그녀가 갑자기 나에게 말했다.

5 "네, 그런데 저를 아시나요?" 나는 물었다.

6 "물론이지."라고 그녀가 대답했다.

7 "난 매일 학교 식당에서 너를 본단다."

8 놀랍게도, 그녀는 학교 식당 직원 중 한 명이었다.

9 "놀라워! 그녀는 학교 밖에서는 아주 달라 보여."라고 나는 생각했다.

10 "그녀에 대한 만화 소설을 써야겠다."

11 집에 도착한 후, 나는 〈런치 레이디 탄생하다〉라는 새로운 만화 소설을 쓰기 시작했다.

12 그 소설에서 런치 레이디는 슈퍼히어로이다.

13 그녀는 날 수 있는 슈퍼 스쿠터를 탄다.

14 그녀는 전 세계의 위험에 빠진 사람들을 구한다.

15 그녀는 또한 1초에 100개의 쿠키를 만들어 배고픈 아이들에게 나누어 준다.

16 A _____ days _____ , I showed my _____ novel to my friends.

A. graphic   B. later   C. few

17 "_____ ! I love this _____ . She's so _____ ," said all my friends.

A. cool   B. superhero   C. awesome

18 "_____ what? I modeled her _____ Ms. Lee, one of our cafeteria _____ ," I told them.

A. on   B. guess   C. workers

19 I showed _____ book _____ Ms. Lee.

A. to   B. my

20 She _____ it, _____ .

A. too   B. loved

21 She _____ told me about her _____ who had special _____ .

A. talents   B. coworkers   C. also

22 Ms. Park, _____ cafeteria worker, _____ a _____ contest.

A. dancing   B. won   C. another

23 Mr. Kim, the _____ at our school, was once an _____ park _____ .

A. ranger   B. adventurous   C. janitor

24 "I'd _____ to write _____ stories about them. Do you _____ they'll like that?" I _____ Ms. Lee.

A. think   B. superhero   C. asked   D. like

25 "Of _____ they will," she said _____ .

A. cheerfully   B. course

26 "Let's _____ and say _____ to _____ new superhero friends."

A. our   B. hello   C. go

16 며칠 후에 나는 나의 만화 소설을 친구들에게 보여 주었다.

17 "멋져! 나는 이 슈퍼히어로가 너무 좋아. 그녀는 아주 멋져."라고 내 모든 친구들이 말했다.

18 "있잖아. 나는 그녀를 우리 식당 직원 중 한 명인 이 여사를 모델로 했어."라고 나는 친구들에게 말했다.

19 나는 이 여사에게 내 책을 보여 주었다.

20 그녀도 그것을 아주 좋아했다.

21 그녀는 또한 나에게 특별한 재능을 가진 그녀의 동료들에 대해 말해 주었다.

22 또 다른 식당 직원인 박 여사는 댄스 경연대회에서 우승했다.

23 우리 학교의 관리인인 김 선생님은 한때 모험적인 공원 관리원이었다.

24 "저는 그들에 대한 슈퍼히어로 이야기를 쓰고 싶어요. 그분들이 그걸 좋아할 것 같아요?" 나는 이 여사한테 물어보았다.

25 "물론 그럴 거야."라고 그녀가 기분 좋게 말했다.

26 "가서 우리의 새 슈퍼히어로 친구들에게 인사하자."

※ 다음 우리말과 일치하도록 빈칸에 알맞은 말을 쓰시오.

1 _____ _____ is Hojin, and I like to make _____ _____.

2 _____ I was _____ _____ from school last week, I _____ a woman _____ a scooter.

3 She _____ really _____, and her scooter was very _____.

4 "Are you _____ _____, Hojin?" she _____ to me _____.

5 "Yes, _____ do I know you?" I _____.

6 "Of _____," she _____.

7 "I see you _____ the school cafeteria _____ _____."

8 _____, she was _____ _____ the cafeteria _____ at school.

9 "Amazing! She _____ so _____ outside the school," I _____.

10 "I _____ _____ a graphic novel about her."

11 _____ I _____ _____, I began to write a new _____ _____, *Lunch Lady Begins*.

12 _____ it, Lunch Lady is a _____.

13 She _____ a super scooter that _____ _____.

14 She _____ people from danger _____ _____ _____.

15 She also makes 100 cookies _____ _____ and _____ them _____ to hungry children.

1 내 이름은 호진이고, 만화 소설 쓰는 것을 좋아한다.

2 지난주에 나는 학교에서 집으로 걸어가던 중에 스쿠터에 탄 여자를 보았다.

3 그녀는 정말 멋져 보였고 그녀의 스쿠터는 매우 독특했다.

4 "호진아, 너 집에 가는 중이니?" 그녀가 갑자기 나에게 말했다.

5 "네, 그런데 저를 아시나요?" 나는 물었다.

6 "물론이지."라고 그녀가 대답했다.

7 "난 매일 학교 식당에서 너를 본단다."

8 놀랍게도, 그녀는 학교 식당 직원 중 한 명이었다.

9 "놀라워! 그녀는 학교 밖에서는 아주 달라 보여."라고 나는 생각했다.

10 "그녀에 대한 만화 소설을 써야겠다."

11 집에 도착한 후, 나는 〈런치 레이디 탄생하다〉라는 새로운 만화 소설을 쓰기 시작했다.

12 그 소설에서 런치 레이디는 슈퍼히어로이다.

13 그녀는 날 수 있는 슈퍼 스쿠터를 탄다.

14 그녀는 전 세계의 위험에 빠진 사람들을 구한다.

15 그녀는 또한 1초에 100개의 쿠키를 만들어 배고픈 아이들에게 나누어 준다.

16 A _____ _____ _____, I _____ my graphic novel
_____ my friends.

17 "_____! I love this superhero. She's so _____," said
_____ _____ friends.

18 "_____ what? I _____ her _____ Ms. Lee, _____
_____ our cafeteria _____," I told them.

19 I _____ my book _____ Ms. Lee.

20 She _____ it, _____.

21 She _____ told me about her _____ who had _____
_____.

22 Ms. Park, _____ cafeteria _____, _____ a dancing contest.

23 Mr. Kim, the _____ at our school, was _____ an _____
park _____.

24 "I'd _____ _____ _____ superhero stories about them. Do
you _____ they'll like that?" I _____ Ms. Lee.

25 "_____ _____ they will," she said _____.

26 "_____ go and _____ _____ _____ our new superhero
friends."

16 며칠 후에 나는 나의 만화 소설
을 친구들에게 보여 주었다.

17 "멋져! 나는 이 슈퍼히어로가 너
무 좋아. 그녀는 아주 멋져."라
고 내 모든 친구들이 말했다.

18 "있잖아, 나는 그녀를 우리 식당
직원 중 한 명인 이 여사를 모델
로 했어."라고 나는 친구들에게
말했다.

19 나는 이 여사에게 내 책을 보여
주었다.

20 그녀도 그것을 아주 좋아했다.

21 그녀는 또한 나에게 특별한 재
능을 가진 그녀의 동료들에 대
해 말해 주었다.

22 또 다른 식당 직원인 박 여사는
댄스 경연대회에서 우승했다.

23 우리 학교의 관리인인 김 선생
님은 한때 모험적인 공원 관리
원이었다.

24 "저는 그들에 대한 슈퍼히어로
이야기를 쓰고 싶어요. 그분들
이 그걸 좋아할 것 같아요?" 나
는 이 여사한테 물어보았다.

25 "물론 그럴 거야."라고 그녀가
기분 좋게 말했다.

26 "가서 우리의 새 슈퍼히어로 친
구들에게 인사하자."

※ 다음 문장을 우리말로 쓰시오.

1　My name is Hojin, and I like to make graphic novels.

➡ _____

2　While I was walking home from school last week, I saw a woman on a scooter.

➡ _____

3　She looked really cool, and her scooter was very unique.

➡ _____

4　"Are you going home, Hojin?" she said to me suddenly.

➡ _____

5　"Yes, but do I know you?" I asked.

➡ _____

6　"Of course," she answered.

➡ _____

7　"I see you at the school cafeteria every day."

➡ _____

8　Surprisingly, she was one of the cafeteria workers at school.

➡ _____

9　"Amazing! She looks so different outside the school," I thought.

➡ _____

10　"I should write a graphic novel about her."

➡ _____

11　After I got home, I began to write a new graphic novel, *Lunch Lady Begins*.

➡ _____

12　In it, Lunch Lady is a superhero.

➡ _____

13　She rides a super scooter that can fly.

➡ _____

14　She saves people from danger around the world.

➡ _____

15　She also makes 100 cookies per second and gives them away to hungry children.

➡ _____

16 A few days later, I showed my graphic novel to my friends.

➡ _____

17 "Awesome! I love this superhero. She's so cool," said all my friends.

➡ _____

18 "Guess what? I modeled her on Ms. Lee, one of our cafeteria workers," I told them.

➡ _____

19 I showed my book to Ms. Lee.

➡ _____

20 She loved it, too.

➡ _____

21 She also told me about her coworkers who had special talents.

➡ _____

22 Ms. Park, another cafeteria worker, won a dancing contest.

➡ _____

23 Mr. Kim, the janitor at our school, was once an adventurous park ranger.

➡ _____

24 "I'd like to write superhero stories about them. Do you think they'll like that?" I asked Ms. Lee.

➡ _____

25 "Of course they will," she said cheerfully.

➡ _____

26 "Let's go and say hello to our new superhero friends."

➡ _____

※ 다음 괄호 안의 단어들을 우리말에 맞도록 바르게 배열하시오.

1 (name / Hojin, / my / is / and / to / graphic / I / make / novels. / like)
➡ _____

2 (was / home / I / while / walking / last / school / from / week, / a / saw / I / on / scooter / a / woman)
➡ _____

3 (really / she / cool, / looked / and / scooter / very / her / unique. / was)
➡ _____

4 (going / "are / Hojin?" / you / home, / to / she / suddenly. / said / me)
➡ _____

5 (but / know / "yes, / I / do / you?" / asked. / I)
➡ _____

6 (answered. / "of / she / course,")
➡ _____

7 (you / see / the / I / at / school / day." / cafeteria / every)
➡ _____

8 (she / surprisingly, / of / was / one / workers / the / school. / at / cafeteria)
➡ _____

9 (she / "amazing! / so / different / looks / the / outside / school," / thought. / I)
➡ _____

10 (write / I / a / novel / write / graphic / should / her. / about)
➡ _____

11 (got / I / after / home, / began / I / write / to / novel, / a / graphic / new / Begins. / Lady / Lunch)
➡ _____

12 (it, / Lady / in / is / superhero. / Lunch / a)
➡ _____

13 (rides / scooter / she / super / a / fly. / can / that)
➡ _____

14 (people / she / danger / from / saves / world. / the / around)
➡ _____

15 (also / she / cookies / makes / second / per / 100 / and / to / them / away / children. / give / hungry)
➡ _____

1 내 이름은 호진이고, 만화 소설 쓰는 것을 좋아한다.

2 지난주에 나는 학교에서 집으로 걸어가던 중에 스쿠터에 탄 여자를 보았다.

3 그녀는 정말 멋져 보였고 그녀의 스쿠터는 매우 독특했다.

4 "호진아, 너 집에 가는 중이니?" 그녀가 갑자기 나에게 말했다.

5 "네, 그런데 저를 아시나요?" 나는 물었다.

6 "물론이지."라고 그녀가 대답했다.

7 "난 매일 학교 식당에서 너를 본단다."

8 놀랍게도, 그녀는 학교 식당 직원 중 한 명이었다.

9 "놀라워! 그녀는 학교 밖에서는 아주 달라 보여."라고 나는 생각했다.

10 "그녀에 대한 만화 소설을 써야겠다."

11 집에 도착한 후, 나는 〈런치 레이디 탄생하다〉라는 새로운 만화 소설을 쓰기 시작했다.

12 그 소설에서 런치 레이디는 슈퍼히어로이다.

13 그녀는 날 수 있는 슈퍼 스쿠터를 탄다.

14 그녀는 전 세계의 위험에 빠진 사람들을 구한다.

15 그녀는 또한 1초에 100개의 쿠키를 만들어 배고픈 아이들에게 나누어 준다.

16 (later, / days / few / a / my / graphic / I / novel / showed / friends. / to / my)

➡ _____

17 (love / I / this / "awesome! / superhero. / so / she's / cool," / friends. / my / all / said)

➡ _____

18 (what? / "guess / her / modeled / I / Ms. / Lee, / on / workers," / of / cafeteria / one / our / them. / I / told)

➡ _____
_____

19 (I / my / showed / Ms. / to / Lee. / book)

➡ _____

20 (too. / she / it, / loved)

➡ _____

21 (also / she / told / about / me / who / coworkers / her / talents. / had / special)

➡ _____

22 (Park, / another / Ms. / worker, / cafeteria / contest. / won / a / dancing)

➡ _____

23 (the / Mr. / Kim, / at / janitor / school, / our / once / was / ranger. / an / park / adventurous)

➡ _____

24 (like / I'd / superhero / write / stories / to / them. / about / think / like / they'll / do / you / that?" / I / Lee. / asked / Ms.)

➡ _____
_____

25 (they / "of / will, / course / cheerfully. / said / she)

➡ _____

26 (go / "let's / say / and / to / our / hello / friends." / superhero / new)

➡ _____

16 며칠 후에 나는 나의 만화 소설을 친구들에게 보여 주었다.

17 "멋져! 나는 이 슈퍼히어로가 너무 좋아. 그녀는 아주 멋져."라고 내 모든 친구들이 말했다.

18 "있잖아. 나는 그녀를 우리 식당 직원 중 한 명인 이 여사를 모델로 했어."라고 나는 친구들에게 말했다.

19 나는 이 여사에게 내 책을 보여 주었다.

20 그녀도 그것을 아주 좋아했다.

21 그녀는 또한 나에게 특별한 재능을 가진 그녀의 동료들에 대해 말해 주었다.

22 또 다른 식당 직원인 박 여사는 댄스 경연대회에서 우승했다.

23 우리 학교의 관리인인 김 선생님은 한때 모험적인 공원 관리원이었다.

24 "저는 그들에 대한 슈퍼히어로 이야기를 쓰고 싶어요. 그분들이 그걸 좋아할 것 같아요?" 나는 이 여사한테 물어보았다.

25 "물론 그럴 거야."라고 그녀가 기분 좋게 말했다.

26 "가서 우리의 새 슈퍼히어로로 친구들에게 인사하자."

※ 다음 우리말을 영어로 쓰시오.

1 내 이름은 호진이고, 만화 소설 쓰는 것을 좋아한다.

➡ _____

2 지난주에 학교에서 집으로 걸어가던 중에 스쿠터에 탄 여자를 보았다.

➡ _____

3 그녀는 정말 멋져 보였고 그녀의 스쿠터는 매우 독특했다.

➡ _____

4 "호진아, 너 집에 가는 중이니?" 그녀가 갑자기 나에게 말했다.

➡ _____

5 "네, 그런데 저를 아시나요?" 나는 물었다.

➡ _____

6 "물론이지," 그녀가 대답했다.

➡ _____

7 "난 매일 학교 식당에서 너를 본단다."

➡ _____

8 놀랍게도, 그녀는 학교 식당 직원 중 한 명이었다.

➡ _____

9 "놀라워! 그녀는 학교 밖에서는 아주 달라 보여."라고 나는 생각했다.

➡ _____

10 "그녀에 대한 만화 소설을 써야겠다."

➡ _____

11 집에 도착한 후, 나는 〈런치 레이디 탄생하다〉라는 새로운 만화 소설을 쓰기 시작했다.

➡ _____

12 그 소설에서 런치 레이디는 슈퍼히어로이다.

➡ _____

13 그녀는 날 수 있는 슈퍼 스쿠터를 탄다.

➡ _____

14 그녀는 전 세계의 위험에 빠진 사람들을 구한다.

➡ _____

15 그녀는 또한 1초에 100개의 쿠키를 만들어 배고픈 아이들에게 나누어 준다.

➡ _____

16 ▶ 며칠 후에 나는 나의 만화 소설을 친구들에게 보여 주었다.

➡ _____

17 ▶ "멋져! 나는 이 슈퍼히어로가 너무 좋아. 그녀는 아주 멋져."라고 내 모든 친구들이 말했다.

➡ _____

18 ▶ "있잖아, 나는 그녀를 우리 식당 직원 중 한 명인 이 여사를 모델로 했어."라고 나는 친구들에게 말했다.

➡ _____

19 ▶ 나는 이 여사에게 내 책을 보여 주었다.

➡ _____

20 ▶ 그녀도 그것을 아주 좋아했다.

➡ _____

21 ▶ 그녀는 또한 나에게 특별한 재능을 가진 그녀의 동료들에 대해 말해 주었다.

➡ _____

22 ▶ 또 다른 식당 직원인 박 여사는 댄스 경연대회에서 우승했다.

➡ _____

23 ▶ 우리 학교의 관리인인 김 선생님은 한때 모험적인 공원 관리원이었다.

➡ _____

24 ▶ "저는 그들에 대한 슈퍼히어로 이야기를 쓰고 싶어요. 그분들이 그걸 좋아할 것 같아요?"
나는 이 여사한테 물어보았다.

➡ _____

25 ▶ "물론 그럴 거야."라고 그녀가 기분 좋게 말했다.

➡ _____

26 ▶ "가서 우리의 새 슈퍼히어로 친구들에게 인사하자."

➡ _____

※ 다음 우리말과 일치하도록 빈칸에 알맞은 말을 쓰시오.

Language Arts

1. Two boys are _____ in a _____.
2. There _____ a _____.
3. The boys _____ get _____.
4. Lunch Lady _____ on her scooter and _____ them.

1. 두 소년이 도서관에서 공부하고 있다.
2. 불이 났다.
3. 그 소년들은 나갈 수 없다.
4. Lunch Lady는 스쿠터를 타고 날아와서 그들을 구한다.

Write

1. My _____ is my _____ model.
2. She is _____, strong, and _____.
3. _____ her 30s, she _____ to 70 _____ countries.
4. _____ she was _____, she made friends from all _____ the world.
5. I want to _____ someone who is not _____ of _____ new things just _____ her.

1. 나의 이모는 내 롤 모델이다.
2. 그녀는 똑똑하고, 강하고, 모험심이 강하다.
3. 30대 때, 그녀는 70개국을 여행했다.
4. 여행을 하는 동안, 그녀는 전 세계의 친구들을 사귀었다.
5. 나는 그녀처럼 새로운 것을 시도하는 것을 두려워하지 않는 사람이 되고 싶다.

Culture Project - Share

1. Julia Child was a person _____ found her _____ talent _____ her 30s.
2. _____ age 36, she _____ _____ Paris with her _____.
3. She _____ a _____ cooking school there.
4. _____ she was studying, she _____ _____ write a cookbook.
5. That book _____ a big _____.

1. Julia Child는 30대에 그녀의 진정한 재능을 발견한 사람이었다.
2. 36살 때, 그녀는 남편과 함께 파리로 이사를 했다.
3. 그녀는 그곳에서 유명한 요리 학교에 다닌다.
4. 그녀는 공부하는 동안 요리책을 쓰기로 결심했다.
5. 그 책은 큰 인기를 끌었다.

※ 다음 우리말을 영어로 쓰시오.

Language Arts

1. 두 소년이 도서관에서 공부하고 있다.

➡ _____

2. 불이 났다.

➡ _____

3. 그 소년들은 나갈 수 없다.

➡ _____

4. Lunch Lady는 스쿠터를 타고 날아와서 그들을 구한다.

➡ _____

Write

1. 나의 이모는 내 롤 모델이다.

➡ _____

2. 그녀는 똑똑하고, 강하고, 모험심이 강하다.

➡ _____

3. 30대 때, 그녀는 70개국을 여행했다.

➡ _____

4. 여행을 하는 동안, 그녀는 전 세계의 친구들을 사귀었다.

➡ _____

5. 나는 그녀처럼 새로운 것을 시도하는 것을 두려워하지 않는 사람이 되고 싶다.

➡ _____

Culture Project - Share

1. Julia Child는 30대에 그녀의 진정한 재능을 발견한 사람이었다.

➡ _____

2. 36살 때, 그녀는 남편과 함께 파리로 이사를 했다.

➡ _____

3. 그녀는 그곳에서 유명한 요리 학교에 다닌다.

➡ _____

4. 그녀는 공부하는 동안 요리책을 쓰기로 결심했다.

➡ _____

5. 그 책은 큰 인기를 끌었다.

➡ _____

※ 다음 영어를 우리말로 쓰시오.

01 wind

02 fine dust

03 sometimes

04 build

05 goat

06 decide

07 since

08 else

09 southern

10 entrance

11 forest

12 cave

13 fresh

14 airplane-shaped

15 become

16 gate

17 century

18 practice

19 stone

20 harmony

21 cone

22 information

23 meal

24 kind

25 lovely

26 tour

27 enemy

28 storage

29 low

30 wooden

31 piano-shaped

32 mall

33 dining room

34 ocean

35 look for

36 be afraid of

37 watch out for

38 give it a try

39 upside down

40 in harmony with

41 pile up

42 take down

43 be good at

※ 다음 우리말을 영어로 쓰시오.

01 구내식당 _____

02 씌우다, 덮다 _____

03 디자인, 설계 _____

04 자연 _____

05 다섯 번째의 _____

06 마루, 바닥 _____

07 환영하다 _____

08 방지하다, 피하다 _____

09 대양, 바다 _____

10 1,000, 천 _____

11 ~ 없이 _____

12 적 _____

13 지불하다 _____

14 징수원 _____

15 식물 _____

16 경관, 전망 _____

17 게스트하우스 _____

18 보호하다 _____

19 화장실, 세면실 _____

20 둥근, 동그란 _____

21 ~의 모양[형태]의 _____

22 세금 _____

23 유일무이한, 독특한 _____

24 풀, 잔디 _____

25 마을 _____

26 미세먼지 _____

27 때때로 _____

28 염소 _____

29 숲, 삼림 _____

30 동굴 _____

31 입구, 문 _____

32 저장, 보관 _____

33 나무로 된 _____

34 조화, 화합 _____

35 ~을 보다 _____

36 ~ 옆에 _____

37 ~을 조심하다 _____

38 ~와 조화를 이루어 _____

39 ~을 잘하다 _____

40 쌓아 올리다 _____

41 거꾸로, 뒤집혀 _____

42 (구조물을 해체하여) 치우다 _____

43 한번 해 보다 _____

※ 다음 영영풀이에 알맞은 단어를 <보기>에서 골라 쓴 후, 우리말 뜻을 쓰시오.

1 _____ : the number 1,000: _____

2 _____ : made of wood: _____

3 _____ : someone who hates you or wants to harm you: _____

4 _____ : a large hole in the side of a cliff or hill, or one that is under the ground: _____

5 _____ : facts about someone or something: _____

6 _____ : a period of a hundred years that is used when stating a date: _____

7 _____ : someone whose job is to collect taxes or debts etc.: _____

8 _____ : a large area where trees grow close together: _____

9 _____ : a current of air that is moving across the earth's surface: _____

10 _____ : a restaurant where you choose your food from a counter and take it to your table after paying for it: _____

11 _____ : to prevent someone or something from being harmed or damaged: _____

12 _____ : a room with a toilet for customers to use: _____

13 _____ : an amount of money that you have to pay to the government so that you can use public services: _____

14 _____ : to take action in order to prevent something unpleasant from happening: _____

15 _____ : a private home or boarding house offering accommodation to travellers: _____

16 _____ : a living thing that grows in the earth and has a stem, leaves, and roots, especially one that is smaller than a tree or bush: _____

보기			
forest	cave	plant	restroom
wooden	protect	cafeteria	avoid
enemy	collector	century	guesthouse
information	thousand	tax	wind

※ 다음 우리말과 일치하도록 빈칸에 알맞은 말을 쓰시오.

해석

Listen & Speak 1 A. Listen and Check

1. **B:** Hey, _____ _____ this house in the picture. It _____ _____ a big shoe!

   G: Oh, it's very _____, but I don't want _____ _____ _____ a shoe.

   B: _____ _____ of house do you want to _____ _____?

   G: Well, I _____ _____ live in an _____ house.

2. **M:** _____ me, is _____ a restaurant in this mall?

   W: Yes. What _____ of food _____ you _____?

   M: I'd _____ _____ food.

   W: _____ is a great restaurant _____ the _____ _____.

   M: Thank you.

Listen & Speak 2 A. Listen and Write

1. **W:** _____ me, _____ can I _____ women's shoes?

   M: You can find them on the _____ _____. They're _____ _____ the elevator.

   W: _____ you.

   M: You're _____.

2. **W:** _____ I _____ you?

   M: I'm _____ _____ watches. Where _____ _____ _____ them?

   W: They're _____ the _____ floor, _____ _____ the restroom.

   M: Thank _____.

Communicate A. Listen and Answer

Woman: _____ _____ Jeonju Hanok Guesthouse. _____ _____ _____ you?

Man: Yes, I'd _____ a room _____ two nights.

Woman: Well, what _____ _____ room would you _____?

Man: Do you have a room _____ a garden _____? You have a _____ garden.

Woman: Yes, we do. _____ room in our house _____ a garden _____, but there _____ _____ beds in the rooms.

Man: Do I _____ _____ sleep on the _____?

Woman: Yes, you _____.

Man: O.K. I'll _____ it a _____. Where can I _____ _____?

Woman: You _____ have breakfast in the _____ _____, _____ _____ the kitchen.

Man: I _____.

Woman: O.K. You're _____ the Nabi room. _____ your _____.

Man: _____ you.

W: 네, 그렇습니다.
M: 알았습니다. 한번 시도해 볼게요. 아침 식사는 어디서 해요?
W: 아침 식사는 부엌 옆에 있는 식당에서 할 수 있어요.
M: 알겠습니다.
W: 좋아요, 나비 방에 들어가세요. 여기 당신의 열쇠가 있습니다.
M: 고맙습니다.

Progress Check

1. **B:** Hey, look at this _____ house in the picture. It's _____ _____.

   G: Oh, it _____ _____, but I think it's _____ of _____.

   B: _____ _____ _____ house do you want to _____ _____?

   G: I like music, _____ I want to live _____ a _____ house.

2. **W:** _____ me, where can I find _____ _____?

   M: You _____ _____ them on the _____ _____. They're _____ _____ the elevator.

   W: _____ you.

   M: You're _____.

3. **M:** Excuse me, _____ can I _____ men's hats?

   W: You can find them _____ _____ _____ _____. They're _____ _____ the elevator.

   M: _____ you.

   W: You're _____.

1. B: 이봐, 사진 속의 이 독특한 집을 봐. 집이 거꾸로 있어.
   G: 아, 재미있어 보이지만, 좀 이상한 것 같아.
   B: 넌 어떤 집에서 살고 싶니?
   G: 나는 음악을 좋아해서 피아노 모양의 집에서 살고 싶어.
2. W: 실례합니다. 여자 청바지는 어디에 있나요?
   M: 2층에서 찾을 수 있어요. 엘리베이터 옆에 있어요.
   W: 감사합니다.
   M: 천만에요.
3. M: 실례합니다. 남성용 모자는 어디에 있나요?
   W: 2층에서 찾을 수 있어요. 엘리베이터 옆에 있어요.
   M: 감사합니다.
   W: 천만에요.

Work -Act

A: _____ _____ of house do you want _____ _____?

B: I want to build a _____ house that _____ _____ a boat.

A: _____ is the _____?

B: It's _____ _____ _____ _____.

A: 넌 어떤 집을 짓고 싶어?
B: 보트처럼 생긴 2층짜리 집을 짓고 싶어.
A: 부엌이 어디 있어?
B: 2층에 있어.

※ 다음 우리말에 맞도록 대화를 영어로 쓰시오.

Listen & Speak 1 A. Listen and Check

1. B: _____
   G: _____
   B: _____
   G: _____

2. M: _____
   W: _____
   M: _____
   W: _____
   M: _____

Listen & Speak 2 A. Listen and Write

1. W: _____
   M: _____
   W: _____
   M: _____

2. W: _____
   M: _____
   W: _____
   M: _____

Communicate A. Listen and Answer

Woman: _____

Man: _____

Woman: _____

Man: _____

Woman: _____

Man: _____

 해석

1. B: 어이, 이 사진 속의 집을 봐. 그것은 큰 신발처럼 보여!
   G: 오, 아주 독특하긴 하지만, 난 신발 속에서 살고 싶지 않아.
   B: 넌 어떤 종류의 집에서 살고 싶니?
   G: 음, 나는 비행기 모양의 집에서 살고 싶어.

2. M: 실례합니다, 이 쇼핑몰에 식당이 있나요?
   W: 네. 어떤 음식을 드시겠어요?
   M: 중국 음식을 먹고 싶어요.
   W: 5층에 멋진 식당이 있어요.
   M: 감사합니다.

1. W: 실례합니다, 여자 신발은 어디에 있어요?
   M: 2층에서 찾을 수 있어요. 엘리베이터 옆에 있어요.
   W: 감사합니다.
   M: 천만에요.

2. W: 뭘 도와드릴까요?
   M: 시계를 찾고 있어요. 어디에서 찾을 수 있습니까?
   W: 3층에, 화장실 옆에 있어요.
   M: 감사합니다.

W: 전주 한옥 게스트하우스에 오신 걸 환영합니다. 무엇을 도와드릴까요?
M: 네, 이틀 밤 묵을 방을 원해요.
W: 음, 어떤 방을 원하세요?
M: 정원이 보이는 방이 있어요? 정원이 아름답군요.
W: 네, 그렇습니다. 우리 집 모든 방에서는 정원이 보입니다. 하지만 방에는 침대가 없어요.
M: 바닥에서 자야 합니까?

Woman: _____

Man: _____

Woman: _____

Man: _____

Woman: _____

Man: _____

W: 네, 그렇습니다.
M: 알았습니다. 한번 시도해 볼게요. 아침 식사는 어디서 해요?
W: 아침 식사는 부엌 옆에 있는 식당에서 할 수 있어요.
M: 알겠습니다.
W: 좋아요, 나비 방에 들어가세요. 여기 당신의 열쇠가 있습니다.
M: 고맙습니다.

Progress Check

1. B: _____

   G: _____

   B: _____

   G: _____

2. W: _____

   M: _____

   W: _____

   M: _____

3. M: _____

   W: _____

   M: _____

   W: _____

1. B: 이봐, 사진 속의 이 독특한 집을 봐. 집이 거꾸로 있어.
   G: 아, 재미있어 보이지만, 좀 이상한 것 같아.
   B: 넌 어떤 집에서 살고 싶니?
   G: 나는 음악을 좋아해서 피아노 모양의 집에서 살고 싶어.

2. W: 실례합니다. 여자 청바지는 어디에 있나요?
   M: 2층에서 찾을 수 있어요. 엘리베이터 옆에 있어요.
   W: 감사합니다.
   M: 천만에요.

3. M: 실례합니다. 남성용 모자는 어디에 있나요?
   W: 2층에서 찾을 수 있어요. 엘리베이터 옆에 있어요.
   M: 감사합니다.
   W: 천만에요.

Work -Act

A: _____

B: _____

A: _____

B: _____

A: 넌 어떤 집을 짓고 싶어?
B: 보트처럼 생긴 2층짜리 집을 짓고 싶어.
A: 부엌이 어디 있어?
B: 2층에 있어.

※ 다음 우리말과 일치하도록 빈칸에 알맞은 것을 골라 쓰시오.

1 _____ you ever _____ a goat on the _____ of a house?
A. roof　　　　B. seen　　　　C. have

2 _____ Norway, we can _____ animals _____ roofs.
A. on　　　　B. see　　　　C. in

3 Norway has _____ _____.
A. forests　　　　B. large

4 In _____ with _____, people have built _____ houses for a long time.
A. wooden　　　　B. harmony　　　　C. nature

5 To _____ strong and warm houses, they _____ their roofs _____ grass.
A. with　　　　B. cover　　　　C. build

6 The grass roofs _____ them _____ the long cold winters and strong _____.
A. winds　　　　B. from　　　　C. protect

7 _____, trees or plants grow _____ of the grass _____, and some animals enjoy their _____ there.
A. roofs　　　　B. meals　　　　C. out　　　　D. sometimes

8 A roof is an _____ part of a house, but long _____ some people _____ roofs only to take them _____ easily.
A. ago　　　　B. down　　　　C. built　　　　D. essential

9 _____ ago in _____ Italy, people who had a house _____ a roof _____ lower taxes.
A. paid　　　　B. southern　　　　C. without　　　　D. centuries

10 To _____ high _____ on their houses, some people built _____ roofs by _____ up stones.
A. piling　　　　B. taxes　　　　C. cone-shaped　　　　D. avoid

1 여러분은 집의 지붕 위에 있는 염소를 본 적이 있는가?

2 노르웨이에서, 우리는 지붕 위에 있는 동물들을 볼 수 있다.

3 노르웨이는 큰 숲을 가지고 있다.

4 자연과 조화를 이루면서, 사람들은 오랫동안 나무로 집을 지었다.

5 강하고 따뜻한 집을 만들기 위해, 그들은 지붕을 잔디로 덮는다.

6 잔디 지붕은 길고 추운 겨울과 강한 바람으로부터 그들을 보호한다.

7 때때로, 나무나 식물들이 잔디 지붕에서 자라며, 어떤 동물들은 거기서 식사를 즐긴다.

8 지붕은 집의 필수적인 부분이지만, 오래 전에 어떤 사람들은 오직 지붕을 쉽게 철거하기 위해 지었다.

9 수세기 전 남부 이탈리아에서는 지붕 없는 집을 가진 사람들이 더 적은 세금을 냈다.

10 그들의 집에 부과되는 높은 세금을 피하기 위해, 어떤 사람들은 돌을 쌓아 올려 원뿔 모양의 지붕을 만들었다.

11 _____ tax _____ came to the town, people _____ their roofs _____ quickly.

A. down   B. when   C. took   D. collectors

12 After the _____ collectors _____, they _____ up the stones again.

A. piled   B. left   C. tax

13 _____ the sky in a _____ of _____ China, you can see round roofs that look _____ big doughnuts.

A. like   B. from   C. southern   D. part

14 They are the _____ of the big _____ houses of the Hakka _____.

A. people   B. round   C. roofs

15 They _____ lived in houses _____ these for _____ a thousand years to protect _____ from enemies.

A. like   B. themselves   C. about   D. have

16 The houses have _____ one gate _____ any windows _____ the first floor.

A. on   B. without   C. only

17 _____ house is big _____ for a _____ village.

A. whole   B. enough   C. each

18 It _____ has four _____.

A. stories   B. usually

19 It has kitchens on the first floor, _____ rooms on the _____ floor, and _____ rooms and bedrooms on the third and _____ floors.

A. fourth   B. second   C. living   D. storage

---

11 세금 징수원들이 마을에 오면, 사람들은 재빨리 지붕을 철거했다.

12 세금 징수원들이 떠난 후 그들은 다시 돌을 쌓아 올렸다.

13 중국 남부의 일부 지역의 하늘에서 보면, 여러분은 큰 도넛처럼 생긴 둥근 지붕들을 볼 수 있다.

14 그것들은 하카족의 크고 둥근 집들의 지붕이다.

15 그들은 적으로부터 스스로를 보호하기 위해 약 천 년 동안 이런 집에서 살아왔다.

16 그 집들에는 1층에 창문이 하나도 없고 문이 하나만 있다.

17 각각의 집은 전체 마을이 들어갈 만큼 크다.

18 그 집은 보통 4개의 층을 가지고 있다.

19 1층에는 주방, 2층에는 창고, 3층과 4층에는 거실과 침실이 있다.

※ 다음 우리말과 일치하도록 빈칸에 알맞은 말을 쓰시오.

1 _____ you ever _____ a goat _____ _____ _____ of a house?

2 _____ Norway, we _____ see animals _____ _____.

3 Norway _____ large _____.

4 _____ _____ _____ nature, people _____ _____ wooden houses _____ a long time.

5 _____ _____ strong and warm houses, they _____ their roofs _____ grass.

6 The grass roofs _____ them _____ the long _____ winters and _____ winds.

7 Sometimes, trees or plants _____ _____ _____ the grass roofs, and some animals _____ their _____ there.

8 A roof is an _____ _____ of a house, but _____ _____ some people built roofs only to _____ them _____ easily.

9 _____ _____ in southern Italy, people _____ had a house without a roof _____ lower _____.

10 _____ _____ high taxes on their houses, some people _____ cone-shaped roofs by _____ _____ stones.

1 여러분은 집의 지붕 위에 있는 염소를 본 적이 있는가?

2 노르웨이에서, 우리는 지붕 위에 있는 동물들을 볼 수 있다.

3 노르웨이는 큰 숲을 가지고 있다.

4 자연과 조화를 이루면서, 사람들은 오랫동안 나무로 집을 지었다.

5 강하고 따뜻한 집을 만들기 위해, 그들은 지붕을 잔디로 덮는다.

6 잔디 지붕은 길고 추운 겨울과 강한 바람으로부터 그들을 보호한다.

7 때때로, 나무나 식물들이 잔디 지붕에서 자라며, 어떤 동물들은 거기서 식사를 즐긴다.

8 지붕은 집의 필수적인 부분이지만, 오래 전에 어떤 사람들은 오직 지붕을 쉽게 철거하기 위해 지었다.

9 수세기 전 남부 이탈리아에서는 지붕 없는 집을 가진 사람들이 더 적은 세금을 냈다.

10 그들의 집에 부과되는 높은 세금을 피하기 위해, 어떤 사람들은 돌을 쌓아 올려 원뿔 모양의 지붕을 만들었다.

11 When _____ _____ came to the town, people _____ their roofs _____ quickly.

12 _____ the tax collectors _____, they _____ _____ the stones again.

13 _____ the sky in a part of _____ China, you can see _____ _____ that _____ _____ big doughnuts.

14 They are the _____ of the _____ _____ _____ of the Hakka people.

15 They _____ _____ in houses like these for about a _____ _____ to _____ themselves _____ enemies.

16 The houses have _____ one gate _____ any windows on the _____ _____.

17 _____ house is _____ _____ for a _____ _____.

18 It _____ has _____ _____.

19 It has kitchens on the _____ floor, _____ rooms on the _____ floor, and _____ _____ and bedrooms on the _____ and _____ floors.

11 세금 징수원들이 마을에 오면, 사람들은 재빨리 지붕을 철거했다.

12 세금 징수원들이 떠난 후 그들은 다시 돌을 쌓아 올렸다.

13 중국 남부의 일부 지역의 하늘에서 보면, 여러분은 큰 도넛처럼 생긴 둥근 지붕들을 볼 수 있다.

14 그것들은 하카족의 크고 둥근 집들의 지붕이다.

15 그들은 적으로부터 스스로를 보호하기 위해 약 천 년 동안 이런 집에서 살아왔다.

16 그 집들에는 1층에 창문이 하나도 없고 문이 하나만 있다.

17 각각의 집은 전체 마을이 들어갈 만큼 크다.

18 그 집은 보통 4개의 층을 가지고 있다.

19 1층에는 주방, 2층에는 창고, 3층과 4층에는 거실과 침실이 있다.

※ 다음 문장을 우리말로 쓰시오.

1 Have you ever seen a goat on the roof of a house?

➡ _____

2 In Norway, we can see animals on roofs.

➡ _____

3 Norway has large forests.

➡ _____

4 In harmony with nature, people have built wooden houses for a long time.

➡ _____

5 To build strong and warm houses, they cover their roofs with grass.

➡ _____

6 The grass roofs protect them from the long cold winters and strong winds.

➡ _____

7 Sometimes, trees or plants grow out of the grass roofs, and some animals enjoy their meals there.

➡ _____

8 A roof is an essential part of a house, but long ago some people built roofs only to take them down easily.

➡ _____

9 Centuries ago in southern Italy, people who had a house without a roof paid lower taxes.

➡ _____

10 To avoid high taxes on their houses, some people built cone-shaped roofs by piling up stones.

➡ _____

11 When tax collectors came to the town, people took their roofs down quickly

➡ _____

12 After the tax collectors left, they piled up the stones again.

➡ _____

13 From the sky in a part of southern China, you can see round roofs that look like big doughnuts.

➡ _____

14 They are the roofs of the big round houses of the Hakka people.

➡ _____

15 They have lived in houses like these for about a thousand years to protect themselves from enemies.

➡ _____

16 The houses have only one gate without any windows on the first floor.

➡ _____

17 Each house is big enough for a whole village.

➡ _____

18 It usually has four stories.

➡ _____

19 It has kitchens on the first floor, storage rooms on the second floor, and living rooms and bedrooms on the third and fourth floors.

➡ _____

※ 다음 괄호 안의 단어들을 우리말에 맞도록 바르게 배열하시오.

1 (you / seen / ever / have / on / goat / a / house? / the / of / roof / a)

➡ _____

2 (Norway, / we / in / see / can / roofs. / on / animals)

➡ _____

3 (has / forests. / Norway / large)

➡ _____

4 (with / harmony / nature, / in / people / wooden / built / have / for / houses / time. / long / a)

➡ _____

5 (warm / to / and / build / houses, / strong / they / roofs / grass. / with / their / cover)

➡ _____

6 (roofs / the / protect / grass / from / long / them / cold / the / winters / winds. / and / strong)

➡ _____
_____

7 (trees / sometimes, / or / grow / plants / of / grass / out / the / roofs, / and / enjoy / there. / animals / some / meals / their)

➡ _____
_____

8 (is / an / roof / part / a / essential / house, / a / of / but / ago / long / roofs / people / only / some / to / built / them / easily. / down / take)

➡ _____
_____

9 (ago / Italy, / centuries / in / southern / who / people / house / a / had / taxes. / without / paid / a / lower / roof)

➡ _____
_____

10 (taxes / to / their / avoid / on / high / houses, / people / some / cone-shaped / by / built / piling / stones. / roofs / by / up)

➡ _____
_____

1 여러분은 집의 지붕 위에 있는 염소를 본 적이 있는가?

2 노르웨이에서, 우리는 지붕 위에 있는 동물들을 볼 수 있다.

3 노르웨이는 큰 숲을 가지고 있다.

4 자연과 조화를 이루면서, 사람들은 오랫동안 나무로 집을 지었다.

5 강하고 따뜻한 집을 만들기 위해, 그들은 지붕을 잔디로 덮는다.

6 잔디 지붕은 길고 추운 겨울과 강한 바람으로부터 그들을 보호한다.

7 때때로, 나무나 식물들이 잔디 지붕에서 자라며, 어떤 동물들은 거기서 식사를 즐긴다.

8 지붕은 집의 필수적인 부분이지만, 오래 전에 어떤 사람들은 오직 지붕을 쉽게 철거하기 위해 지었다.

9 수세기 전 남부 이탈리아에서는 지붕 없는 집을 가진 사람들이 더 적은 세금을 냈다.

10 그들의 집에 부과되는 높은 세금을 피하기 위해, 어떤 사람들은 돌을 쌓아 올려 원뿔 모양의 지붕을 만들었다.

11 (tax / came / when / the / collectors / down, / to / people / quickly. / roofs / took / their / down)

➡ _____

_____

12 (the / collectors / after / tax / left, / piled / they / stones / again. / the / up)

➡ _____

13 (the / from / sky / part / in / a / of / China, / southern / can / you / round / see / look / that / roofs / doughnuts. / big / like)

➡ _____

_____

14 (the / are / roofs / they / the / of / round / big / Hakka / the / people. / of / houses)

➡ _____

15 (lived / they / houses / in / have / these / like / about / a / for / years / thousand / to / enemies. / from / themselves / protect)

➡ _____

_____

16 (houses / the / only / gate / one / have / without / the / floor. / windows / any / on / first)

➡ _____

17 (house / each / enough / big / is / village. / whole / a / for)

➡ _____

18 (has / usually / stories. / it / four)

➡ _____

19 (has / kitchens / first / it / on / the / floor, / rooms / storage / the / floor, / second / on / and / rooms / living / bedrooms / on / and / fourth / the / floors. / and / third)

➡ _____

_____

11 세금 징수원들이 마을에 오면, 사람들은 재빨리 지붕을 철거했다.

12 세금 징수원들이 떠난 후 그들은 다시 돌을 쌓아 올렸다.

13 중국 남부의 일부 지역의 하늘에서 보면, 여러분은 큰 도넛처럼 생긴 둥근 지붕들을 볼 수 있다.

14 그것들은 하카족의 크고 둥근 집들의 지붕이다.

15 그들은 적으로부터 스스로를 보호하기 위해 약 천 년 동안 이런 집에서 살아왔다.

16 그 집들에는 1층에 창문이 하나도 없고 문이 하나만 있다.

17 각각의 집은 전체 마을이 들어갈 만큼 크다.

18 그 집은 보통 4개의 층을 가지고 있다.

19 1층에는 주방, 2층에는 창고, 3층과 4층에는 거실과 침실이 있다.

※ 다음 우리말을 영어로 쓰시오.

1 여러분은 집의 지붕 위에 있는 염소를 본 적이 있는가?

➡ _____

2 노르웨이에서, 우리는 지붕 위에 있는 동물들을 볼 수 있다.

➡ _____

3 노르웨이는 큰 숲을 가지고 있다.

➡ _____

4 자연과 조화를 이루면서, 사람들은 오랫동안 나무로 집을 지었다.

➡ _____

5 강하고 따뜻한 집을 만들기 위해, 그들은 지붕을 잔디로 덮는다.

➡ _____

6 잔디 지붕은 길고 추운 겨울과 강한 바람으로부터 그들을 보호한다.

➡ _____

7 때때로, 나무나 식물들이 잔디 지붕에서 자라며, 어떤 동물들은 거기서 식사를 즐긴다.

➡ _____

8 지붕은 집의 필수적인 부분이지만, 오래 전에 어떤 사람들은 오직 지붕을 쉽게 철거하기 위해 지었다.

➡ _____

9 수세기 전 남부 이탈리아에서는 지붕 없는 집을 가진 사람들이 더 적은 세금을 냈다.

➡ _____

10 그들의 집에 부과되는 높은 세금을 피하기 위해, 어떤 사람들은 돌을 쌓아 올려 원뿔 모양의 지붕을 만들었다.

➡ _____

11 세금 징수원들이 마을에 오면, 사람들은 재빨리 지붕을 철거했다.

➡ _____

12 세금 징수원들이 떠난 후 그들은 다시 돌을 쌓아 올렸다.

➡ _____

13 중국 남부의 일부 지역의 하늘에서 보면, 여러분은 큰 도넛처럼 생긴 둥근 지붕들을 볼 수 있다.

➡ _____

14 그것들은 하카족의 크고 둥근 집들의 지붕이다.

➡ _____

15 그들은 적으로부터 스스로를 보호하기 위해 약 천 년 동안 이런 집에서 살아왔다.

➡ _____

16 그 집들에는 1층에 창문이 하나도 없고 문이 하나만 있다.

➡ _____

17 각각의 집은 전체 마을이 들어갈 만큼 크다.

➡ _____

18 그 집은 보통 4개의 층을 가지고 있다.

➡ _____

19 1층에는 주방, 2층에는 창고, 3층과 4층에는 거실과 침실이 있다.

➡ _____

_____

※ 다음 우리말과 일치하도록 빈칸에 알맞은 말을 쓰시오.

Link

1. I can't open windows _____ _____ the fine dust _____ _____.

2. How _____ _____ a small garden on the _____?

3. _____ _____ has _____ a big problem in the spring.

4. We _____ a roof _____ has a small garden _____ trees and many _____ plants.

5. This garden will _____ us _____ air.

1. 나는 요즘 미세먼지 때문에 창문을 열 수가 없어요.
2. 지붕에 작은 정원을 만드는 것은 어떨까요?
3. 봄에는 미세먼지가 큰 문제가 되어 왔다.
4. 우리는 나무와 다른 많은 식물들이 있는 작은 정원을 가진 지붕을 설계했다.
5. 이 정원은 우리에게 신선한 공기를 줄 것이다.

Write

1. Sejong _____ Library is _____ Sejong, Korea.

2. It is a _____ building that _____ _____ an open book.

3. It has _____ 400 thousand books on the first and _____ _____ and a large cafeteria on the _____ floor.

4. It _____ _____ 2013.

5. _____ then, many people have _____ this _____ building.

1. 국립 세종 도서관은 한국의 세종시에 있다.
2. 그것은 펴놓은 책처럼 보이는 4층 건물이다.
3. 1층과 2층에는 약 40만 권의 책이 있고, 맨 위층에는 큰 구내식당이 있다.
4. 그것은 2013년에 문을 열었다.
5. 그 이후로, 많은 사람들이 이 독특한 건물을 방문했다.

Culture Project

1. _____ Granada, Spain, some people have _____ in cave houses _____ a long time.

2. The _____ in this place is very _____ in the summer and _____ in the winter.

3. It's not _____ cold or hot in _____ houses.

1. 스페인의 그라나다에서는, 몇몇 사람들이 오랫동안 동굴 집에서 살아왔다.
2. 이곳의 날씨는 여름에는 매우 덥고 겨울에는 춥다.
3. 동굴 집은 너무 춥거나 덥지도 않다.

※ 다음 우리말을 영어로 쓰시오.

Link

1. 나는 요즘 미세먼지 때문에 창문을 열 수가 없어요.

   ➡ _____

2. 지붕에 작은 정원을 만드는 것은 어떨까요?

   ➡ _____

3. 봄에는 미세먼지가 큰 문제가 되어 왔다.

   ➡ _____

4. 우리는 나무와 다른 많은 식물들이 있는 작은 정원을 가진 지붕을 설계했다.

   ➡ _____

5. 이 정원은 우리에게 신선한 공기를 줄 것이다.

   ➡ _____

Write

1. 국립 세종 도서관은 한국의 세종시에 있다.

   ➡ _____

2. 그것은 펴놓은 책처럼 보이는 4층 건물이다.

   ➡ _____

3. 1층과 2층에는 약 40만 권의 책이 있고, 맨 위층에는 큰 구내식당이 있다.

   ➡ _____

   _____

4. 그것은 2013년에 문을 열었다.

   ➡ _____

5. 그 이후로, 많은 사람들이 이 독특한 건물을 방문했다.

   ➡ _____

Culture Project

1. 스페인의 그라나다에서는, 몇몇 사람들이 오랫동안 동굴 집에서 살아왔다.

   ➡ _____

2. 이곳의 날씨는 여름에는 매우 덥고 겨울에는 춥다.

   ➡ _____

3. 동굴 집은 너무 춥거나 덥지도 않다.

   ➡ _____

※ 다음 영어를 우리말로 쓰시오.

01 perfect _____

02 amazing _____

03 become _____

04 capture _____

05 seafood _____

06 travel _____

07 simple _____

08 bungee jumping _____

09 forecast _____

10 earth _____

11 else _____

12 famous _____

13 portrait _____

14 finally _____

15 food _____

16 graduate _____

17 chance _____

18 island _____

19 remain _____

20 weather _____

21 guess _____

22 market _____

23 foreign _____

24 mystery _____

25 freezing _____

26 actually _____

27 expect _____

28 journal _____

29 scary _____

30 indoors _____

31 create _____

32 university _____

33 vacation _____

34 appear _____

35 get to _____

36 be full of _____

37 get into _____

38 right now _____

39 a lot of _____

40 such as _____

41 set foot at[in] _____

42 a little _____

43 show up _____

※ 다음 우리말을 영어로 쓰시오.

01	만지다	
02	접시, 그릇	
03	살피다, 점검하다	
04	흐린	
05	(짐을) 싸다	
06	결정하다	
07	~ 동안[내내]	
08	외국의	
09	~ 둘레에, ~ 주위에	
10	(차량을) 몰다	
11	바람이 많이 부는	
12	초대하다	
13	큰, 거대한	
14	화신	
15	현장 학습	
16	물건, 물체	
17	전문학교	
18	날씨	
19	잠깐, 잠시	
20	휴식을 취하다	
21	그림, 소묘	

22	여행	
23	거북	
24	시장	
25	존경하다, 감탄하며 바라보다	
26	수첩, 일기	
27	완전한	
28	예상[기대]하다	
29	포착하다, 담아내다	
30	졸업하다	
31	꽁꽁 얼게[너무나] 추운	
32	무서운, 겁나는	
33	간단한	
34	섬	
35	소수의, 약간의	
36	지금, 당장	
37	~에 도착하다	
38	~으로 가득 차다	
39	마침내	
40	나타나다	
41	~에 발을 들여놓다	
42	~에 들어가다, ~에 타다	
43	~와 같은	

※ 다음 영영풀이에 알맞은 단어를 <보기>에서 골라 쓴 후, 우리말 뜻을 쓰시오.

1 _____ : what people and animals eat: _____

2 _____ : the possibility that something will happen: _____

3 _____ : a piece of land that is completely surrounded by water: _____

4 _____ : a place where goods are bought and sold, usually outdoors: _____

5 _____ : to like and respect someone or something very much: _____

6 _____ : a picture made with a pencil or pen: _____

7 _____ : very surprising and making you feel pleasure, approval, or wonder:
_____

8 _____ : an area of sand or stones beside the sea: _____

9 _____ : to cause something to happen or exist: _____

10 _____ : to ask someone to come to something such as a party: _____

11 _____ : something that is not understood or known about: _____

12 _____ : unusual or unexpected, and making you feel slightly nervous or afraid:
_____

13 _____ : to go from one place to another, often to a place that is far away:
_____

14 _____ : to choose to do something, usually after you have thought carefully about the other possibilities: _____

15 _____ : to spend time resting or doing something enjoyable especially after you have been doing work: _____

16 _____ : to put clothes and other things into a bag, because you are leaving a place: _____

보기			
create	chance	mystery	market
admire	invite	travel	pack
island	decide	food	drawing
amazing	strange	relax	beach

※ 다음 우리말과 일치하도록 빈칸에 알맞은 말을 쓰시오.

Listen & Speak 1 A. Listen and Check

1. **G:** _____ you ever _____ Indian food?

   B: Yes, I _____, but I've _____ _____ Indian curry.

   G: _____ was _____?

   B: It was really _____, _____ I loved it.

2. **G:** Bill, _____ you ever _____ bungee jumping?

   B: _____, I _____. _____ _____ you, Katie?

   G: _____ I _____ New Zealand, I _____ bungee jumping _____.

   B: _____ it _____?

   G: No, I liked it. I _____ _____ do it _____.

Listen & Speak 2 A. Listen and Answer

1. **B:** Mom, _____ the _____ today? Do I _____ an umbrella?

   W: It's quite _____ _____. I'll _____ the weather _____.

   B: _____ you, Mom.

   W: Well, it's not _____ _____ _____ today.

   B: Good! Then, I _____ _____ an umbrella today.

2. **W:** Good morning, and _____ _____ the weather forecast. It's _____ _____, but we're _____ some rain in the afternoon. _____ _____ home _____ your umbrella. That's the _____ _____ for today. _____ a nice day.

1. G: 너 인도 음식을 먹어 본 적이 있니?
   B: 응, 있어, 하지만 인도 카레만 먹어 봤어.
   G: 어땠어?
   B: 정말 매웠지만, 아주 좋았어.

2. G: Bill, 번지 점프하러 가 본 적 있니?
   B: 아니, 없어. Katie, 넌 어때?
   G: 뉴질랜드를 방문했을 때, 번지 점프를 한 번 해봤어.
   B: 무섭지 않았어?
   G: 아니, 좋았어. 또 하고 싶어.

1. B: 엄마, 오늘 날씨 어때요? 우산이 필요한가요?
   W: 바깥 날씨가 아주 흐려. 일기예보를 확인해 볼게.
   B: 고마워요, 엄마.
   W: 음, 오늘은 비가 안 올 거야.
   B: 좋아요! 그럼, 오늘은 우산이 필요 없어요.

2. W: 좋은 아침입니다, 일기예보에 오신 것을 환영합니다. 밖은 화창하지만 오후에는 약간의 비가 예상됩니다. 우산 없이 집을 나서지 마세요. 오늘의 일기예보입니다. 좋은 하루 되세요.

Communicate A~B

A. **Suho** Anna, _____ you _____ _____ Australia before?

  Anna: Yes, I _____ . Actually, I _____ in Sydney _____ a year.

  Suho: Great! _____ the weather _____ in April? I'm _____ _____ visit Sydney _____ _____ next week.

  Anna: April is a great time _____ _____ Sydney. In April, it's _____ in Australia.

  Suho: Good. I'm _____ _____ _____ some time on the beach and _____ in the sun.

  Anna: Well, it _____ _____ in April, but you _____ have some _____ _____ .

  Suho: I'll _____ my hat and _____ an umbrella, _____ .

  Anna: That's a _____ _____ . _____ a great time.

B. **A:** _____ you _____ _____ any special _____ in Korea?

  B: Yes, I _____ . I _____ _____ Ulleungdo _____ summer _____ my family.

  A: _____ was the _____ there?

  B: It was _____ _____ , but the weather _____ often.

Progress Check

1. **G:** _____ you ever _____ a horse?

  B: Yes, I _____ . _____ _____ you?

  G: No, I _____ . _____ was it?

  B: It was _____ , but it was _____ _____ scary, _____ .

2. **B:** Mom, how's the _____ today?

  W: It's quite _____ _____ . I'll _____ the weather _____ .

  B: Thanks, Mom.

  W: Well, it's _____ _____ _____ in the afternoon.

3. **M:** Good evening, and _____ _____ the weather forecast. It's _____ _____ _____ , but we're _____ a sunny day tomorrow. Don't _____ home tomorrow _____ your hat.

A. 수호: Anna, 너 전에 호주에 가본 적 있어?

  Anna: 응, 있어. 사실, 나는 시드니에서 1년 동안 살았어.

  수호: 멋지다! 그곳의 4월 날씨는 어때? 난 다음 주 방학 때 시드니에 갈 거야.

  Anna: 4월은 시드니를 방문하기에 좋은 시기야. 4월에, 호주는 가을이야.

  수호: 좋아. 나는 해변에서 시간을 좀 보내고 햇빛을 쐬며 휴식을 취할 계획이야.

  Anna: 음, 4월에는 종종 비가 오지만, 맑은 날도 좀 있을 거야.

  수호: 나도 모자를 가져가고 우산도 챙길 거야.

  Anna: 좋은 생각이야. 좋은 시간 보내.

B. A: 넌 한국의 어느 특별한 장소들을 가본 적이 있니?

  B: 응, 있어. 나는 작년 여름에 가족과 울릉도에 갔어.

  A: 거기 날씨는 어땠어?

  B: 대체로 맑았지만, 날씨가 자주 바뀌었어.

1. G: 너 말을 타본 적 있니?

  B: 응, 있어. 너는 어때?

  G: 아니, 난 없어. 말 타는 거 어땠어?

  B: 재미있었지만, 조금 무섭기도 했어.

2. B: 엄마, 오늘 날씨 어때요?

  W: 바깥 날씨가 꽤 흐려. 일기예보를 확인해 볼게.

  B: 고마워요, 엄마.

  W: 음, 오후에 비가 올 거야.

3. M: 안녕하세요, 일기예보에 오신 것을 환영합니다. 지금은 비가 오지만 내일은 화창한 날씨가 예상됩니다. 내일 모자를 쓰지 않고 집을 나서지 마세요.

※ 다음 우리말에 맞도록 대화를 영어로 쓰시오.

Listen & Speak 1 A. Listen and Check

1. G: _____

   B: _____

   G: _____

   B: _____

2. G: _____

   B: _____

   G: _____

   B: _____

   G: _____

Listen & Speak 2 A. Listen and Answer

1. B: _____

   W: _____

   B: _____

   W: _____

   B: _____

2. W: _____

   _____

   _____

해석

1. G: 너 인도 음식을 먹어 본 적이 있니?
   B: 응, 있어. 하지만 인도 카레만 먹어봤어.
   G: 어땠어?
   B: 정말 매웠지만, 아주 좋았어.

2. G: Bill, 번지 점프하러 가 본 적 있니?
   B: 아니, 없어. Katie, 넌 어때?
   G: 뉴질랜드를 방문했을 때, 번지 점프를 한 번 해봤어.
   B: 무섭지 않았어?
   G: 아니, 좋았어. 또 하고 싶어.

1. B: 엄마, 오늘 날씨 어때요? 우산이 필요한가요?
   W: 바깥 날씨가 아주 흐려. 일기예보를 확인해 볼게.
   B: 고마워요, 엄마.
   W: 음, 오늘은 비가 안 올 거야.
   B: 좋아요! 그럼, 오늘은 우산이 필요 없어요.

2. W: 좋은 아침입니다. 일기예보에 오신 것을 환영합니다. 밝은 화창하지만 오후에는 약간의 비가 예상됩니다. 우산 없이 집을 나서지 마세요. 오늘의 일기예보입니다. 좋은 하루 되세요.

Communicate A~B

A. Suho _____

Anna: _____

Suho: _____

_____

Anna: _____

Suho: _____

Anna: _____

Suho: _____

Anna: _____

B. A: _____

B: _____

A: _____

B: _____

Progress Check

1. G: _____

B: _____

G: _____

B: _____

2. B: _____

W: _____

B: _____

W: _____

3. M: _____

_____

_____

A. 수호: Anna, 너 전에 호주에 가본 적 있어?

Anna: 응, 있어. 사실, 나는 시드니에서 1년 동안 살았어.

수호: 멋지다! 그곳의 4월 날씨는 어때? 난 다음 주 방학 때 시드니에 갈 거야.

Anna: 4월은 시드니를 방문하기에 좋은 시기야. 4월에, 호주는 가을이야.

수호: 좋아. 나는 해변에서 시간을 좀 보내고 햇빛을 쐬며 휴식을 취할 계획이야.

Anna: 음, 4월에는 종종 비가 오지만, 맑은 날도 좀 있을 거야.

수호: 나도 모자를 가져가고 우산도 챙길 거야.

Anna: 좋은 생각이야. 좋은 시간 보내.

B. A: 넌 한국의 어느 특별한 장소들을 가본 적이 있니?

B: 응, 있어. 나는 작년 여름에 가족과 울릉도에 갔어.

A: 거기 날씨는 어땠어?

B: 대체로 맑았지만, 날씨가 자주 바뀌었어.

1. G: 너 말을 타본 적 있니?

B: 응, 있어. 너는 어때?

G: 아니, 난 없어. 말 타는 거 어땠어?

B: 재미있었지만, 조금 무섭기도 했어.

2. B: 엄마, 오늘 날씨 어때요?

W: 바깥 날씨가 꽤 흐려. 일기예보를 확인해 볼게.

B: 고마워요, 엄마.

W: 음, 오후에 비가 올 거야.

3. M: 안녕하세요, 일기예보에 오신 것을 환영합니다. 지금은 비가 오지만 내일은 화창한 날씨가 예상됩니다. 내일 모자를 쓰지 않고 집을 나서지 마세요.

※ 다음 우리말과 일치하도록 빈칸에 알맞은 것을 골라 쓰시오.

1 Hi, I _____ Lucy Hunter, and I _____ _____ London.

    A. in   B. am   C. live

2 _____ week, my family went _____ a vacation _____ three days.

    A. for   B. last   C. on

3 _____ our trip, I made _____ drawings in my _____.

    A. journal   B. simple   C. during

4 That was a great _____ to _____ all the _____ moments.

    A. special   B. capture   C. way

5 At _____, we _____ foot at Stonehenge, one of the most _____ places on Earth.

    A. mysterious   B. set   C. last

6 _____ a two-hour _____ from our home in London, we _____ got to Stonehenge.

    A. finally   B. drive   C. after

7 It was just _____ to see the _____ of _____ stones.

    A. huge   B. ring   C. amazing

8 How did those huge _____ get there _____ of years _____?

    A. ago   B. thousands   C. stones

9 _____ were they _____?

    A. for   B. what

10 I _____ Stonehenge will _____ a _____ for a long time.

    A. remain   B. guess   C. mystery

11 Don't _____ to make a _____ drawing.

    A. perfect   B. try

12 A _____ colors will be _____.

    A. enough   B. few

13 _____ the morning, we walked _____ the Cotswolds.

    A. around   B. in

14 It _____ to rain in the afternoon, _____ we _____ to stay indoors at our B&B.

    A. decided   B. started   C. so

15 A B&B is a _____ place to _____ in England.

    A. stay   B. popular

---

1 안녕, 나는 Lucy Hunter이고 런던에 살아요.

2 지난주에 우리 가족은 3일 동안 휴가를 갔습니다.

3 여행 중에 나는 일기에 간단한 그림을 그렸어요.

4 그것은 모든 특별한 순간을 포착하는 훌륭한 방법이었어요.

5 마침내, 우리는 지구에서 가장 불가사의한 장소 중 하나인 스톤헨지에 발을 디뎠다.

6 런던에 있는 집에서 차로 두 시간을 달려서 우리는 마침내 스톤헨지에 도착했다.

7 원형으로 둘러서 있는 거대한 돌들을 보는 것은 정말 놀라웠다.

8 어떻게 그 거대한 돌들이 수천 년 전에 그곳에 도착했을까?

9 그것들은 무엇을 위한 것이었을까?

10 스톤헨지는 오랫동안 미스터리로 남을 것 같다.

11 완벽한 그림을 그리려고 하지 마세요.

12 몇 가지 색깔이면 충분할 것입니다.

13 아침에 우리는 코츠월드 언덕을 돌아다녔다.

14 오후에 비가 오기 시작해서, 우리는 B&B의 실내에서 머물기로 결정했다.

15 B&B는 영국에서 체류하는 곳으로 인기가 있다.

16 It feels more _____ a home _____ a hotel.
A. than   B. like

17 The owner _____ us _____ afternoon tea today.
A. for   B. invited

18 The _____ table was _____ of cookies, cake, bread, _____ cheese.
A. and   B. full   C. dining

19 While I was _____ eating, Mom was _____ the beautiful cups and _____.
A. plates   B. admiring   C. busy

20 I ate too _____, so I couldn't eat _____ for dinner.
A. anything   B. much

21 It is O.K. to _____ everyday objects _____ cups and plates in your _____.
A. journal   B. like   C. draw

22 _____ last _____ was Oxford.
A. stop   B. our

23 We first _____ Christ Church _____.
A. College   B. visited

24 It has _____ a world famous place to visit _____ it _____ in the *Harry Potter* movies.
A. appeared   B. since   C. become

25 In the _____, Harry and everyone _____ eat _____ at the Hall of Christ Church.
A. dinner   B. else   C. movies

26 We _____ saw _____ of famous people who _____ from the college.
A. graduated   B. portraits   C. also

27 When we were _____ the building, I _____ to the famous olive tree and _____ it.
A. touched   B. outside   C. walked

28 "_____ I _____ this tree," I said, "I will _____ into Oxford University!"
A. get   B. touched   C. because

29 Then, my brother _____ to me with a _____, "I can't _____ to see your portrait on the wall."
A. wait   B. smile   C. said

30 _____ your _____ avatar.
A. own   B. create

31 Your _____ journal will become _____ more _____.
A. interesting   B. much   C. drawing

16 그것은 호텔이라기보다는 집처럼 느껴진다.

17 주인은 오늘 오후의 다과회에 우리를 초대했다.

18 식탁에는 쿠키, 케이크, 빵, 그리고 치즈가 가득했다.

19 내가 먹느라고 바쁠 때, 엄마는 아름다운 컵과 접시를 감탄하며 바라보고 계셨다.

20 나는 너무 많이 먹어서 저녁으로 아무것도 먹을 수 없었다.

21 당신의 일기에 컵과 접시 같은 일상적인 물건들을 그려도 괜찮습니다.

22 우리가 마지막으로 머문 곳은 옥스퍼드였다.

23 우리는 먼저 Christ Church College를 방문했다.

24 이곳은 해리포터 영화에 등장한 이후 방문해야 할 세계적으로 유명한 장소가 되었다.

25 영화에서 Harry와 다른 모든 사람들이 Christ Church의 회관에서 저녁을 먹는다.

26 우리는 또한 그 대학을 졸업한 유명한 사람들의 초상화를 보았다.

27 우리가 건물 밖으로 나왔을 때, 나는 유명한 올리브 나무로 걸어가서 그것을 만졌다.

28 "이 나무를 만졌기 때문에, 난 옥스퍼드 대학교에 들어갈 거야!"라고 말했다.

29 그러자 오빠가 웃으면서 "벽에 걸린 네 초상화가 빨리 보고 싶어."라고 내게 말했다.

30 여러분 자신의 아바타를 만드세요.

31 그림일기가 훨씬 더 재미있을 거예요.

※ 다음 우리말과 일치하도록 빈칸에 알맞은 말을 쓰시오.

1 Hi, I _____ Lucy Hunter, and I _____ _____ London.

2 _____ _____, my family _____ _____ a vacation _____ three days.

3 _____ our trip, I made simple _____ in my _____.

4 That was a great way _____ _____ all the _____ _____.

5 At last, we _____ _____ _____ Stonehenge, _____ _____ the most mysterious _____ on Earth.

6 _____ a two-hour _____ _____ our home in London, we finally _____ _____ Stonehenge.

7 It was just _____ to see the _____ of huge stones.

8 How did those _____ _____ get there _____ of years _____?

9 _____ were they _____?

10 I _____ Stonehenge will _____ a mystery _____ a long time.

11 _____ _____ to make a _____ drawing.

12 _____ _____ colors will be _____.

13 _____ the morning, we _____ _____ the Cotswolds.

14 It started _____ _____ in the afternoon, so we _____ _____ _____ indoors at our B&B.

15 A B&B is a _____ place to _____ _____ England.

1 안녕, 나는 Lucy Hunter이고 런던에 살아요.

2 지난주에 우리 가족은 3일 동안 휴가를 갔습니다.

3 여행 중에 나는 일기에 간단한 그림을 그렸어요.

4 그것은 모든 특별한 순간을 포착하는 훌륭한 방법이었어요.

5 마침내, 우리는 지구에서 가장 불가사의한 장소 중 하나인 스톤헨지에 발을 디뎠다.

6 런던에 있는 집에서 차로 두 시간을 달려서 우리는 마침내 스톤헨지에 도착했다.

7 원형으로 둘러서 있는 거대한 돌들을 보는 것은 정말 놀라웠다.

8 어떻게 그 거대한 돌들이 수천 년 전에 그곳에 도착했을까?

9 그것들은 무엇을 위한 것이었을까?

10 스톤헨지는 오랫동안 미스터리로 남을 것 같다.

11 완벽한 그림을 그리려고 하지 마세요.

12 몇 가지 색깔이면 충분할 것입니다.

13 아침에 우리는 코츠월드 언덕을 돌아다녔다.

14 오후에 비가 오기 시작해서, 우리는 B&B의 실내에서 머물기로 결정했다.

15 B&B는 영국에서 체류하는 곳으로 인기가 있다.

16 It _____ more _____ a home _____ a hotel.

17 The _____ _____ us for afternoon tea today.

18 The _____ table _____ _____ _____ cookies, cake, bread, and cheese.

19 While I was _____ _____, Mom was _____ the beautiful cups and _____.

20 I _____ too much, _____ I _____ _____ anything for dinner.

21 It is O.K. _____ _____ everyday objects _____ cups and plates in your _____.

22 Our _____ _____ was Oxford.

23 We _____ _____ Christ Church College.

24 It _____ _____ a world _____ _____ to visit _____ it appeared in the *Harry Potter* movies.

25 In the movies, Harry and _____ else _____ _____ at the Hall of Christ Church.

26 We also _____ _____ of famous people who _____ _____ the college.

27 _____ we were _____ the building, I _____ _____ the famous olive tree and _____ it.

28 "_____ I _____ this tree," I said, "I will _____ _____ Oxford University!"

29 Then, my brother said to me _____ _____ _____, "I _____ _____ _____ see your portrait on the wall."

30 _____ your own _____.

31 Your _____ _____ will become _____ _____ interesting.

16 그것은 호텔이라기보다는 집처럼 느껴진다.

17 주인은 오늘 오후의 다과회에 우리를 초대했다.

18 식탁에는 쿠키, 케이크, 빵, 그리고 치즈가 가득했다.

19 내가 먹느라고 바쁠 때, 엄마는 아름다운 컵과 접시를 감탄하며 바라보고 계셨다.

20 나는 너무 많이 먹어서 저녁으로 아무것도 먹을 수 없었다.

21 당신의 일기에 컵과 접시 같은 일상적인 물건들을 그려도 괜찮습니다.

22 우리가 마지막으로 머문 곳은 옥스퍼드였다.

23 우리는 먼저 Christ Church College를 방문했다.

24 이곳은 해리포터 영화에 등장한 이후 방문해야 할 세계적으로 유명한 장소가 되었다.

25 영화에서 Harry와 다른 모든 사람들이 Christ Church의 회관에서 저녁을 먹는다.

26 우리는 또한 그 대학을 졸업한 유명한 사람들의 초상화를 보았다.

27 우리가 건물 밖으로 나왔을 때, 나는 유명한 올리브 나무로 걸어가서 그것을 만졌다.

28 "이 나무를 만졌기 때문에, 난 옥스퍼드 대학교에 들어갈 거야!"라고 말했다.

29 그러자 오빠가 웃으면서 "벽에 걸린 네 초상화가 빨리 보고 싶어."라고 내게 말했다.

30 여러분 자신의 아바타를 만드세요.

31 그림일기가 훨씬 더 재미있을 거예요.

※ 다음 문장을 우리말로 쓰시오.

1   Hi, I am Lucy Hunter, and I live in London.

➡ _____

2   Last week, my family went on a vacation for three days.

➡ _____

3   During our trip, I made simple drawings in my journal.

➡ _____

4   That was a great way to capture all the special moments.

➡ _____

5   At last, we set foot at Stonehenge, one of the most mysterious places on Earth.

➡ _____

6   After a two-hour drive from our home in London, we finally got to Stonehenge.

➡ _____

7   It was just amazing to see the ring of huge stones.

➡ _____

8   How did those huge stones get there thousands of years ago?

➡ _____

9   What were they for?

➡ _____

10   Don't try to make a perfect drawing.

➡ _____

11   A few colors will be enough.

➡ _____

12   I guess Stonehenge will remain a mystery for a long time.

➡ _____

13   In the morning, we walked around the Cotswolds.

➡ _____

14   It started to rain in the afternoon, so we decided to stay indoors at our B&B.

➡ _____

15   A B&B is a popular place to stay in England.

➡ _____

16 It feels more like a home than a hotel.

➡ _____

17 The owner invited us for afternoon tea today.

➡ _____

18 The dining table was full of cookies, cake, bread, and cheese.

➡ _____

19 While I was busy eating, Mom was admiring the beautiful cups and plates.

➡ _____

20 I ate too much, so I couldn't eat anything for dinner.

➡ _____

21 It is O.K. to draw everyday objects like cups and plates in your journal.

➡ _____

22 Our last stop was Oxford.

➡ _____

23 We first visited Christ Church College.

➡ _____

24 It has become a world famous place to visit since it appeared in the *Harry Potter* movies.

➡ _____

25 In the movies, Harry and everyone else eat dinner at the Hall of Christ Church.

➡ _____

26 We also saw portraits of famous people who graduated from the college.

➡ _____

27 When we were outside the building, I walked to the famous olive tree and touched it.

➡ _____

28 "Because I touched this tree," I said, "I will get into Oxford University!"

➡ _____

29 Then, my brother said to me with a smile, "I can't wait to see your portrait on the wall."

➡ _____

30 Create your own avatar.

➡ _____

31 Your drawing journal will become much more interesting.

➡ _____

※ 다음 괄호 안의 단어들을 우리말에 맞도록 바르게 배열하시오.

1 (am / hi, / Hunter, / I / Lucy / and / London. / live / I / in)
➡ _____

2 (week, / last / went / family / my / a / on / days. / three / for / vacation)
➡ _____

3 (our / during / trip, / made / I / drawings / in / journal. / simple / my)
➡ _____

4 (was / a / that / great / way / capture / to / moments. / the / all / special)
➡ _____

5 (last, / at / foot / set / we / Stonehenge, / at / of / one / places / Earth. / most / the / on / mysterious)
➡ _____

6 (a / drive / after / two-hour / our / from / home / London, / in / we / Stonehenge. / to / finally / got)
➡ _____

7 (just / it / amazing / was / see / to / the / stones. / of / huge / ring)
➡ _____

8 (did / how / stones / huge / those / there / get / ago? / years / of / thousands)
➡ _____

9 (were / they / for? / what)
➡ _____

10 (try / don't / make / to / drawing. / perfect / a)
➡ _____

11 (few / a / colors / enough. / be / will)
➡ _____

12 (guess / I / Stonehenge / remain / will / a / time. / a / mystery / long / for)
➡ _____

13 (the / morning, / in / walked / the / we / Cotswolds. / around)
➡ _____

14 (to / started / rain / the / it / in / afternoon, / so / decided / we / to / at / indoors / B&B. / stay / our)
➡ _____
_____

15 (a / is / B&B / place / popular / a / stay / England. / to / in)
➡ _____

1 안녕, 나는 Lucy Hunter이고 런던에 살아요.

2 지난주에 우리 가족은 3일 동안 휴가를 갔습니다.

3 여행 중에 나는 일기에 간단한 그림을 그렸어요.

4 그것은 모든 특별한 순간을 포착하는 훌륭한 방법이었어요.

5 마침내. 우리는 지구에서 가장 불가사의한 장소 중 하나인 스톤헨지에 발을 디뎠다.

6 런던에 있는 집에서 차로 두 시간을 달려서 우리는 마침내 스톤헨지에 도착했다.

7 원형으로 둘러서 있는 거대한 돌들을 보는 것은 정말 놀라웠다.

8 어떻게 그 거대한 돌들이 수천 년 전에 그곳에 도착했을까?

9 그것들은 무엇을 위한 것이었을까?

10 스톤헨지는 오랫동안 미스터리로 남을 것 같다.

11 완벽한 그림을 그리려고 하지 마세요.

12 몇 가지 색깔이면 충분할 것입니다.

13 아침에 우리는 코츠월드 언덕을 돌아다녔다.

14 오후에 비가 오기 시작해서, 우리는 B&B의 실내에서 머물기로 결정했다.

15 B&B는 영국에서 체류하는 곳으로 인기가 있다.

16 (feels / it / like / a / more / hotel. / than / home / a)
➡ _____

17 (owner / the / us / invited / today. / for / tea / afternoon)
➡ _____

18 (dining / the / table / of / was / full / cookies, / bread, / and / cheese. / cake,)
➡ _____

19 (was / eating, / while / I / busy / was / Mom / admiring / the / plates. / cups / and / beautiful)
➡ _____

20 (ate / much, / I / too / so / I / eat / anything / couldn't / dinner. / for)
➡ _____

21 (is / to / O.K. / it / draw / objects / eveyday / cups / like / in / and / journal. / your / plates)
➡ _____

22 (last / our / was / Oxford. / stop)
➡ _____

23 (first / we / visited / College. / Church / Christ)
➡ _____

24 (it / become / has / a / place / famous / world / visit / to / in / since / appeared / it / movies. / the / Potter / Harry)
➡ _____

25 (the / in / movies, / and / everyone / Harry / eat / else / dinner / Church. / of / Hall / at / the / Christ)
➡ _____

26 (also / saw / we / portraits / people / of / famous / who / college. / the / from / graduated)
➡ _____

27 (were / we / when / the / building, / the / outside / I / walked / tree / the / olive / to / famous / and / it. / touched)
➡ _____

28 (I / tree," / touched / "because / this / I / said, / will / "I / into / University!" / get / Oxford)
➡ _____

29 (then, / brother / my / said / me / to / smile, / a / with / "I / wait / see / can't / to / on / wall." / the / portrait / your)
➡ _____

30 (your / avatar. / own / create)
➡ _____

31 (drawing / your / journal / become / will / more / interesting. / much)
➡ _____

16 그것은 호텔이라기보다는 집처럼 느껴진다.

17 주인은 오늘 오후의 다과회에 우리를 초대했다.

18 식탁에는 쿠키, 케이크, 빵, 그리고 치즈가 가득했다.

19 내가 먹느라고 바쁠 때, 엄마는 아름다운 컵과 접시를 감탄하며 바라보고 계셨다.

20 나는 너무 많이 먹어서 저녁으로 아무것도 먹을 수 없었다.

21 당신의 일기에 컵과 접시 같은 일상적인 물건들을 그려도 괜찮습니다.

22 우리가 마지막으로 머문 곳은 옥스퍼드였다.

23 우리는 먼저 Christ Church College를 방문했다.

24 이곳은 해리포터 영화에 등장한 이후 방문해야 할 세계적으로 유명한 장소가 되었다.

25 영화에서 Harry와 다른 모든 사람들이 Christ Church의 회관에서 저녁을 먹는다.

26 우리는 또한 그 대학을 졸업한 유명한 사람들의 초상화를 보았다.

27 우리가 건물 밖으로 나왔을 때, 나는 유명한 올리브 나무로 걸어가서 그것을 만졌다.

28 "이 나무를 만졌기 때문에, 난 옥스퍼드 대학교에 들어갈 거야!"라고 말했다.

29 그러자 오빠가 웃으면서 "벽에 걸린 네 초상화가 빨리 보고 싶어."라고 내게 말했다.

30 여러분 자신의 아바타를 만드세요.

31 그림일기가 훨씬 더 재미있을 거예요.

※ 다음 우리말을 영어로 쓰시오.

1 안녕, 나는 Lucy Hunter이고 런던에 살아요.

➡ _____

2 지난주에 우리 가족은 3일 동안 휴가를 갔습니다.

➡ _____

3 여행 중에 나는 일기에 간단한 그림을 그렸어요.

➡ _____

4 그것은 모든 특별한 순간을 포착하는 훌륭한 방법이었어요.

➡ _____

5 마침내, 우리는 지구에서 가장 불가사의한 장소 중 하나인 스톤헨지에 발을 디뎠다.

➡ _____

6 런던에 있는 집에서 차로 두 시간을 달려서 우리는 마침내 스톤헨지에 도착했다.

➡ _____

7 원형으로 둘러서 있는 거대한 돌들을 보는 것은 정말 놀라웠다.

➡ _____

8 어떻게 그 거대한 돌들이 수천 년 전에 그곳에 도착했을까?

➡ _____

9 그것들은 무엇을 위한 것이었을까?

➡ _____

10 완벽한 그림을 그리려고 하지 마세요.

➡ _____

11 몇 가지 색깔이면 충분할 것입니다.

➡ _____

12 스톤헨지는 오랫동안 미스터리로 남을 것 같다.

➡ _____

13 아침에 우리는 코츠월드 언덕을 돌아다녔다.

➡ _____

14 오후에 비가 오기 시작해서, 우리는 B&B의 실내에서 머물기로 결정했다.

➡ _____

15 B&B는 영국에서 체류하는 곳으로 인기가 있다.

➡ _____

16 그것은 호텔이라기보다는 집처럼 느껴진다.

➡ _____

17 주인은 오늘 오후의 다과회에 우리를 초대했다.

➡ _____

18 식탁에는 쿠키, 케이크, 빵, 그리고 치즈가 가득했다.

➡ _____

19 내가 먹느라 바쁠 때, 엄마는 아름다운 컵과 접시를 감탄하며 바라보고 계셨다.

➡ _____

20 나는 너무 많이 먹어서 저녁으로 아무것도 먹을 수 없었다.

➡ _____

21 당신의 일기에 컵과 접시 같은 일상적인 물건들을 그려도 괜찮습니다.

➡ _____

22 우리가 마지막으로 머문 곳은 옥스퍼드였다.

➡ _____

23 우리는 먼저 Christ Church College를 방문했다.

➡ _____

24 이곳은 해리포터 영화에 등장한 이후 방문해야 할 세계적으로 유명한 장소가 되었다.

➡ _____

25 영화에서 Harry와 다른 모든 사람들이 Christ Church의 회관에서 저녁을 먹는다.

➡ _____

26 우리는 또한 그 대학을 졸업한 유명한 사람들의 초상화를 보았다.

➡ _____

27 우리가 건물 밖으로 나왔을 때, 나는 유명한 올리브 나무로 걸어가서 그것을 만졌다.

➡ _____

28 "이 나무를 만졌기 때문에, 난 옥스퍼드 대학교에 들어갈 거야!"라고 말했다.

➡ _____

29 그러자 오빠가 웃으면서 "벽에 걸린 네 초상화가 빨리 보고 싶어."라고 말했다.

➡ _____

30 여러분 자신의 아바타를 만드세요.

➡ _____

31 그림일기가 훨씬 더 재미있을 거예요.

➡ _____

※ 다음 우리말과 일치하도록 빈칸에 알맞은 말을 쓰시오.

Link - Share

1. We _____ _____ a field trip to Namhae _____ month.

2. _____ was just _____ to see so many beautiful _____.

3. We _____ _____ Namhae German _____.

4. We'll _____ _____ that trip.

1. 우리는 지난달에 남해로 현장 학습을 갔다.
2. 그토록 아름다운 많은 섬들을 보는 것은 아주 놀라웠다.
3. 우리는 남해 독일 마을도 방문했다.
4. 우리는 그 여행을 절대 잊지 못할 것이다.

Write

1. _____ _____, I _____ to Laos _____ my family.

2. We visited a _____ of beautiful _____ and went to the night _____ in Vientiane.

3. Then, we _____ _____ Vang Vieng and _____ river tubing.

4. We also _____ their _____ food.

5. It was a _____ _____ fun _____ _____ new things in a _____ country.

6. I hope I will have a _____ _____ _____ Laos again.

1. 지난 겨울, 나는 가족과 함께 라오스에 갔다.
2. 우리는 아름다운 절들을 많이 방문했고 Vientiane의 야시장에 갔다.
3. 그리고 나서, 우리는 Vang Vieng으로 옮겨서 강에 튜브를 타러 갔다.
4. 우리는 또한 그들의 전통 음식을 즐겼다.
5. 외국에서 새로운 것을 시도하는 것은 매우 재미있었다.
6. 나는 라오스를 다시 방문할 기회가 있기를 바란다.

Culture Project

1. _____ 15, 1835

2. We finally _____ _____ this island.

3. There _____ many animals _____ _____ here.

4. Today, I _____ some _____ turtles.

5. It was _____ to _____ them.

1. 1835년 9월 15일
2. 우리는 마침내 이 섬에 도착했다.
3. 여기는 조사할 동물들이 많다.
4. 오늘, 나는 몇몇 이상한 거북들을 보았다.
5. 그들을 보는 것은 놀라웠다.

※ 다음 우리말을 영어로 쓰시오.

Link - Share

1. 우리는 지난달에 남해로 현장 학습을 갔다.

➡ _____

2. 그토록 아름다운 많은 섬들을 보는 것은 아주 놀라웠다.

➡ _____

3. 우리는 남해 독일 마을도 방문했다.

➡ _____

4. 우리는 그 여행을 절대 잊지 못할 것이다.

➡ _____

Write

1. 지난 겨울, 나는 가족과 함께 라오스에 갔다.

➡ _____

2. 우리는 아름다운 절들을 많이 방문했고 Vientiane의 야시장에 갔다.

➡ _____

3. 그리고 나서, 우리는 Vang Vieng으로 옮겨서 강에 튜브를 타러 갔다.

➡ _____

4. 우리는 또한 그들의 전통 음식을 즐겼다.

➡ _____

5. 외국에서 새로운 것을 시도하는 것은 매우 재미있었다.

➡ _____

6. 나는 라오스를 다시 방문할 기회가 있기를 바란다.

➡ _____

Culture Project

1. 1835년 9월 15일

➡ _____

2. 우리는 마침내 이 섬에 도착했다.

➡ _____

3. 여기는 조사할 동물들이 많다.

➡ _____

4. 오늘, 나는 몇몇 이상한 거북들을 보았다.

➡ _____

5. 그들을 보는 것은 놀라웠다.

➡ _____

MEMO

영어 기출 문제집

적중100

1학기

정답 및 해설

미래 | 최연희

중 2

영어 기출 문제집

적중100

1학기

정답 및 해설

미래 | 최연희

중 2

Great Things about Yourself

01 ②	02 ②	03 ④	04 wife
05 ①	06 danger	07 decide	08 ②

01 ①, ③, ④, ⑤의 -er은 동사의 행위자를 나타내는 말이고, ②는 '스쿠터'

02 in front of: ~ 앞에 / be good for: ~에 좋다

03 한 장소에서 다른 장소로, 종종 멀리 떨어진 장소로 가다: 여 행하다(travel)

04 남성명사-여성명사의 관계이다. 소년 : 소녀 = 남편 : 아내

05 say hello to: ~에게 인사하다

06 누군가 다치거나 죽을지도 모를 가능성: danger(위험)

07 decide: 결정하다

08 be afraid of: ~을 무서워하다 / a lot of: 많은

서술형 시험대비   p.09

01 (1) actor   (2) cartoonist   (3) inventor

02 (1) such as   (2) do a good job   (3) a look at

03 (1) fun   (2) give   (3) per   (4) unique

04 (1) cloudy   (2) nervous   (3) dangerous

05 (1) good at   (2) good for

    (3) give away   (4) fall asleep

06 (1) (h)unsband   (2) (d)ecide

01 (1), (3)은 '동사 : 행위자' 관계이고, (2)는 '명사 - 행위자' 관계이다.

02 (1) such as: ~과 같은 (2) do a good job: 잘하다 (3) take a look at: ~을 보다

03 (1) fun: 재미 (2) give a speech: 연설하다 (3) per: ~당[마다] (4) unique: 유일무이한, 독특한

04 (1) cloudy: 흐린 (2) nervous: 불안해[초조해] 하는 (3) dangerous: 위험한

05 (1) be good at: ~을 잘하다 (2) be good for: ~에 좋다 (3) give away: 나누어 주다 (4) fall asleep: 잠들다

06 (1) husband: 남편 (2) decide: 결정하다, 결심하다

교과서 Conversation

1 (1) good at
  (2) how to / poor at
  (3) how to swim

2 (1) am sure
  (2) Are, sure

교과서 대화문 익히기

1 F   2 T   3 F   4 T   5 T   6 F

교과서 확인학습   p.14~15

Listen & Speak 1 A. Listen and Check

1 What, doing / making, out / good, recycling / recycling, fun, good

2 everyone, be, president, listener, try, good, fun, work, class, vote, listening

Listen & Speak 2 A. Listen and Check

1 Hi, wrong / have, front, nervous / worry, speaker, sure, job / Thanks, better

2 birthday, should / don't, for, good / idea, hope, like / sure, love

Communicate A. Listen and Answer

1 What, doing / cartoons / Can, look / yet / not, show, can't / guess / cartoons, good, drawing / so, be, think, enough / funny, unique, sure, cartoonist / Thank, day

2 don't, musical, singing / like, think, good / worry, teach, sure, join / think

Progress Check

1 doing / making / really, at

2 wrong / give, in, nervous / worry, Practice, front, sure, job / try

3 something, Some, at, Other, good, What

시험대비 기본평가
p.16

01 ②　　　02 ①　　　03 ③　　　04 ①, ③

01 be good at: ~을 잘하다

02 I'm sure that ~, Surely, ~. 등은 확신을 말할 때 사용하는 표현이다.

03 능력을 나타낼 때는 조동사 can이나 be good at을 써서 표현할 수 있다.

04 B가 마지막 말에서 I'm sure ~.라고 했으므로 '확신하니?'라는 표현이 들어가야 한다.

시험대비 실력평가

p.17~18

01 ②　　　02 ③　　　03 sure[certain]
04 I am not good at playing the guitar.　05 ④
06 ④　　　07 ④　　　08 listen, well　09 ②
10 listening　11 ④　　　12 matter with
13 ③, ⑤　　　14 나는 네가 잘할 것이라고 확신해.

01 나미야, 뭐 해? - 오래된 청바지로 스마트폰 케이스를 만들고 있어 - 와! 너 오래된 것들을 재활용하는 것을 잘하는구나. - 고마워. 나는 재활용하는 것을 좋아해. 그것은 재미있고, 우리의 지구에도 좋아.

02 '~할 줄 아는지' 능력을 묻는 표현이다.

03 Are you sure[certain] (that)+주어+동사 ~?는 확신 여부를 묻는 표현이다.

04 능력을 부인하는 표현으로 I'm not good at을 사용할 수 있다.

05 I'm sure that ~.은 It's certain that ~. 표현과 같은 의미이다.

06 ④ A가 '너는 바이올린을 정말 아름답게 연주하는구나.'라고 칭찬을 했는데 B가 '나는 바이올린 연주하는 법을 몰라.'라고 대답하는 것은 어색하다.

07 ⓐ, ④ 명사적 용법 ①,③ 형용사적 용법 ②, ⑤ 부사적 용법

08 '형용사+명사' 구문은 '동사+부사' 구문으로 바꿔 쓸 수 있다.

09 be good at: ~을 잘하다

10 전치사의 목적어로는 동명사가 와야 한다.

11 김유진이 공부를 열심히 하는지는 위 담화문을 통해 알 수 없다.

12 Is something wrong?=What's the matter with you?: 무슨 좋지 않은 일이 있니?

13 give[make, deliver] a speech: 연설을 하다

14 do a good job: 잘하다

서술형 시험대비
p.19

01 (1) He is good at Chinese.
　(2) I'm sure (that) there are two boys in the room.

(3) Do you know how to make cookies?

02 I am not good at cooking. / I can't cook well.

03 (B) – (D) – (C) – (A)

04 I'm sure that he'll pass the exam.

05 about baking

06 at

07 소녀의 어머니를 위해 케이크를 굽는 것

01 (1) be good at: ~을 잘하다 (2) 「I'm sure that+주어+ 동사 ~」: 나는 ~을 확신한다. (3) how to ~: ~하는 방법

02 어떤 일을 할 능력이 없는 것을 나타낼 때 사용하는 표현을 쓴다.

03 너 뭐 하고 있니? - 저녁으로 피자를 만들고 있어. - 와! 넌 요리를 정말 잘하는구나! - 고마워.

04 I'm sure that+주어+동사 ~.: 나는 ~을 확신한다.

05 Why don't you ~?는 제안하는 표현으로 How[What] about -ing ~?로 바꿔 쓸 수 있다.

06 be good at: ~을 잘하다

07 that은 지시대명사로 앞에 나온 문장을 받는다.

교과서
Grammar
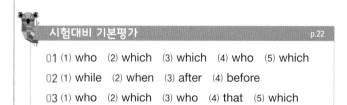

핵심 Check
p.20~21

1 (1) who　(2) which　(3) who　(4) which　(5) who
2 (1) while　(2) after　(3) Before

시험대비 기본평가
p.22

01 (1) who　(2) which　(3) which　(4) who　(5) which
02 (1) while　(2) when　(3) after　(4) before
03 (1) who　(2) which　(3) who　(4) that　(5) which

01 주격 관계대명사는 선행사가 사람일 경우 who, 사물일 경우 which를 쓴다.

02 (1) while: ~하는 동안 (2) when: ~할 때 (3) after: ~한 후에 (4) before: ~하기 전에

03 (1) 선행사가 사람(the girl)이므로 who를 쓴다. (2) 선행사가 사물(the dolls)이므로 which를 쓴다. (3) 선행사가 사람(a friend)이므로 who를 쓴다. (4) 선행사가 사람(the girl)이므로 that 을 쓴다. (5) 선행사가 사물(the river)이므로 which를 쓴다.

01 ⑤	02 ①	03 ⑤
04 (1) who[that] (2) that	05 ⑤	06 ②
07 ④	08 ⑤	09 ①	10 ①
11 ⑤	12 ②, ④	13 ⑤
14 which → that	15 ②	16 ④
17 I will ask him about it when he comes home.		
18 ②	19 ①	20 ①, ③

01 첫 번째 문장은 이유, 두 번째 문장은 때를 나타낸다.

02 ⓐ 선행사가 사람이고 주격이므로 who를 쓴다. ⓑ is의 보어이므로 동명사나 to부정사가 올 수 있다.

03 A before B(B를 하기 전에 A를 하다) = B after A(A를 하고 나서 B를 하다)

04 (1) 선행사가 사람(the boy)이므로 which 대신 who나 that을 써야 한다. (2) 선행사 앞에 최상급이 왔으므로 관계대명사 that을 쓴다.

05 before가 이끄는 때를 나타내는 부사절은 미래의 의미이더라도 현재시제로 써야 한다. will get → gets

06 선행사가 사람이고 주격이므로 관계대명사 who가 들어가야 알맞다.

07 선행사 the building이 사물이고 주격이므로 관계대명사 which가 들어가야 알맞다.

08 ①은 After, ②는 when, ③은 If, ④는 Though[Although] 를 쓸 수 있다.

09 첫 문장은 선행사가 사람이고 주격이므로 관계대명사 who가 들어가야 알맞다. 두 번째 문장은 선행사가 사물이고 주격이므로 관계대명사 which가 들어가야 알맞다.

10 ①은 '~인데 반해'의 뜻이고, 나머지는 '~하는 동안에'라는 뜻을 지닌 접속사이다.

11 선행사가 사물이고, 주격이므로 관계대명사 which가 알맞다.

12 선행사가 사물이고, 관계사절에서 The bus는 주격이므로 관계대명사 which나 that이 알맞다.

13 while: ~하는 동안 / put on: ~을 입다

14 선행사가 사람과 동물 둘 다 있을 때는 that을 사용한다.

15 while은 '~하는 동안'과 '~인 반면에'의 두 가지 뜻이 있다.

16 <보기>와 ④는 관계대명사, ①은 지시부사(그렇게), ②는 접속사, ③은 지시대명사, ⑤는 지시형용사로 쓰였다.

17 when이 이끄는 때를 나타내는 부사절은 미래의 일이라도 현재시제를 쓴다.

18 나머지는 after가 접속사로 쓰여, 뒤에 「주어+동사」로 구성된 절이 왔지만, ②는 전치사로 쓰였다.

19 ① 선행사가 사람이므로 which를 쓸 수 없다.

20 <보기> 접속사 ① 의문부사 ② 접속사 ③ 관계부사 ④ 접속사 ⑤ 접속사

01 that[which]
02 (1) I went shopping   (2) I had dinner
    (3) it started to rain.   (4) he looks around.
03 that
04 I will call you when I arrive.
05 (1) The young lady who is sitting on the bench is our music teacher.
    (2) We found a dog which was running toward us.
    (3) This is the firefighter that saved the baby from the burning building.
    (4) This is the only story that is interesting to read.
06 (1) before   (2) when   (3) after   (4) while
07 (1) I know the woman who[that] is standing by the car.
    (2) Did you see the car which[that] has only two doors?
    (3) This is a restaurant which[that] is famous for its spaghetti.
    (4) The lady who[that] lives next door is my English teacher.
08 While we are having dinner
09 which[that], was
10 Before they washed the dishes, they finished dinner. / They finished dinner before they washed the dishes.
11 before → while
12 I know the[a] doctor who[that] likes baseball.
13 They had a party after she arrived there. / After she arrived there, they had a party.

01 선행사가 동물(the cat)이므로 which 또는 that을 관계대명사로 쓴다.

02 after: ~한 후에 / before: ~하기 전에

03 선행사가 사람일 때와 사물일 때 모두 쓸 수 있는 관계대명사는 that이다.

04 때를 나타내는 부사절에서는 미래의 일을 현재시제로 나타낸다.

05 (1) The young lady를 선행사로 한다. (2) a dog를 선행사로 한다. (3) the firefighter를 선행사로 한다. (4) the only story를 선행사로 한다.

06 before: ~하기 전에 / when: ~할 때 / after: ~한 후에 / while: ~하는 동안

07 (1) 선행사가 the woman이므로 주격 관계대명사 who 또는 that으로 연결한다. (2) 선행사가 the car이므로 주격 관계대명사 which 또는 that으로 연결한다. (3) 선행사가 a restaurant 이므로 주격 관계대명사 which 또는 that으로 연결한다. (3) 선행사가 The lady이므로 주격 관계대명사 who 또는 that으

로 연결한다.

08 while은 '~하는 동안'의 의미를 지닌다.

09 선행사가 The traffic accident이므로 관계대명사는 which 또는 that이다. 또, 단수이므로 was가 알맞다.

11 엄마가 신을 벗을 동안 전화를 끊지 않고 기다려 주겠니? / hold the line: (전화를) 끊지 않고 기다리다

12 선행사가 사람이고 주격이므로 who나 that을 쓴다.

13 after가 이끄는 절은 주절의 앞이나 뒤에 위치할 수 있다.

Reading

확인문제 p.28

1 F 2 F 3 F 4 T 5 T

확인문제 p.29

1 T 2 F 3 F 4 T 5 T 6 F

교과서 확인학습 A p.30~31

01 name, like, novels
02 While, home, woman
03 lookesd, unique
04 going, suddenly   05 but, asked
06 course   07 see, every
08 Surprisingly, workers
09 different, thought   10 should, about
11 After, began   12 superhero   13 rides, that
14 saves, danger 15 also, per, hungry
16 later, graphic   17 superhero, cool
18 what, on, worker   19 showed, to
20 loved   21 also, who, talents
22 another, dancing
23 janitor, once, ranger
24 like, stories, think, asked
25 course, cheerfully
26 go, hello, superhero

교과서 확인학습 B p.32~33

1 My name is Hojin, and I like to make graphic novels.

2 While I was walking home from school last week, I saw a woman on a scooter.

3 She looked really cool, and her scooter was very unique.

4 "Are you going home, Hojin?" she said to me suddenly.

5 "Yes, but do I know you?" I asked.

6 "Of course," she answered.

7 "I see you at the school cafeteria every day."

8 Surprisingly, she was one of the cafeteria workers at school.

9 "Amazing! She looks so different outside the school," I thought.

10 "I should write a graphic novel about her."

11 After I got home, I began to write a new graphic novel, Lunch Lady Begins .

12 In it, Lunch Lady is a superhero.

13 She rides a super scooter that can fly

14 She saves people from danger around the world.

15 She also makes 100 cookies per second and gives them away to hungry children.

16 A few days later, I showed my graphic novel to my friends.

17 "Awesome! I love this superhero. She's so cool," said all my friends.

18 "Guess what? I modeled her on Ms. Lee, one of our cafeteria workers," I told them.

19 I showed my book to Ms. Lee.

20 She loved it, too.

21 She also told me about her coworkers who had special talents.

22 Ms. Park, another cafeteria worker, won a dancing contest.

23 Mr. Kim, the janitor at our school, was once an adventurous park ranger.

24 "I'd like to write superhero stories about them. Do you think they'll like that?" I asked Ms. Lee.

25 "Of course they will," she said cheerfully.

26 "Let's go and say hello to our new superhero friends."

시험대비 실력평가 p.34~37

01 ②   02 ③   03 suddenly   04 난 매일 학교 식당에서 너를 본다.   05 ③   06 ④

07 ⑤	08 (d)anger	09 ①	10 ②
11 later	12 ③	13 ④	14 He

modeled her on Ms. Lee, one of his cafeteria

workers. 15 ③ 16 ④

17 adventurous 18 그들에 대한 슈퍼히어로

이야기를 쓰는 것 19 ④ 20 (r)ole

(m)odel 21 ⑤ 22 that 23 ②

24 ①, ③ 25 (t)alent 26 ④ 27 ②

28 ③ 29 ② 30 but 31 ⑤

01 스쿠터를 타고 있는 여인에 대한 문장 다음인 ②에 와야 한다.

02 while: ~하는 동안에

03 sudden+-ly=suddenly

04 every day: 매일

05 ③ 호진이가 어디 사는지는 알 수 없다.

06 문맥상 '다른'이 알맞다.

07 문맥상 '집에 온 후'가 알맞다.

08 누군가를 다치게 하거나 해를 입히거나 죽일 수 있는 어떤 일이 일어날 가능성

09 per와 a는 '~당[마다]'의 뜻으로 쓰인다.

10 ② 호진은 그 여인을 구내식당에서 본 적이 있지만, 밖에서 보니까 다른 여인 같았다고 진술하고 있다.

11 a few days later: 며칠 후에

12 show는 간접목적어를 직접목적어 뒤로 보낼 때 전치사 to를 붙인다.

13 Guess what: 있잖아, 알겠니?, 맞혀 봐!

14 호진이는 그녀를 학교 식당 직원의 한 명인 이 씨를 모델로 했다.

15 주격 관계대명사 who 대신 that을 쓸 수 있다.

16 another+단수명사: 또 다른 ~

17 adventure의 형용사형이 알맞다.

18 that은 지시대명사로 앞에 나온 내용을 받는다.

19 ④ 박 여사가 언제 춤 경연 대회에서 우승했는지는 언급되지 않았다.

20 당신이 숭배하고 닮기를 원하는 사람: role model(역할 모델)

21 while: ~하는 동안

22 주격 관계대명사 who 대신 that을 쓸 수 있다.

23 ⓓ와 ②는 전치사로 쓰였고, 나머지는 모두 동사로 쓰였다.

24 선행사가 사람이고 주격이므로 관계대명사 who나 that을 쓸 수 있다.

25 어떤 것을 잘할 수 있는 타고난 능력: talent(재능)

26 attend: ~에 다니다

27 ⓓ, ② 명사적 용법 ①, ⑤ 형용사적 용법 ③, ④ 부사적 용법

28 liked의 보어로 형용사가 와야 한다. coolly → cool

29 '~을 타고'를 나타낼 때는 전치사 on을 쓴다.

30 문맥상 '그러나, 하지만'의 뜻이 알맞다.

31 ⑤ 그 여인이 식당에서 일하고 있는지는 위 글에서 알 수 없다.

서술형 시험대비

01 Surprisingly 02 different 03 which

04 from 05 100 cookies 06 Lunch

Lady는 초당 100개의 쿠키를 만든다. 07 to

08 (s)uperhero 09 나는 그녀를 우리 식당 직원 중 한 명인 이 여사를 모델로 했어. 10 to 11 that

12 other → another 13 특수한 재능을 가진 이

여사의 동료들 14 cheerfully 15 Yes, she was.

16 adventurous 17 a friend → friends

18 who[that] 19 of

01 surprising: 놀라운 / surprisingly: 놀랍게도

02 same: 같은 / different: 다른

03 선행사가 사물이고 주격이므로 which나 that을 쓸 수 있다.

04 save A from B: B로부터 A를 구하다

05 them은 인칭대명사로 앞에 나온 복수명사를 받는다.

07 show+직접목적어+to+간접목적어

08 만화나 영화에 나오는 특별한 힘을 가지고 악에 대항해 싸우는 등장인물: superhero(슈퍼영웅)

09 model: 모델로 하다

10 4형식의 문장을 3형식의 문장으로 바꿔 쓴다.

11 선행사가 사람이고 주격이므로 who나 that을 쓸 수 있다.

12 other 뒤에는 복수명사, another 뒤에는 단수명사가 온다.

14 동사 said를 수식하므로 cheerful의 부사형이 되어야 한다.

15 박 여사는 댄싱 대회에서 우승한 적이 있다고 했다.

16 adventure의 형용사형을 쓴다.

17 make friends: 친구를 사귀다

18 선행사가 사람이고 주격이므로 who나 that을 쓸 수 있다.

19 be afraid of: ~을 두려워하다

영역별 핵심문제

01 ④	02 ③	03 (w)rong	04 ③
05 ⑤	06 ①	07 enough	08 ②

09 No, you can't take a look at them yet. 10 ①

11 ③ 12 ④ 13 It, certain 14 ②

15 ④ 16 sure[certain] 17 ①

18 ④ 19 ② 20 He brushed his teeth

after he finished his dinner. 21 ⑤ 22 ③

23 ② 24 ① 25 ⑤ 26 What is

the name of the tallest boy that[who] just came in?

27 will see → sees 28 ② 29 Lunch

Lady Begins 30 She saves people from danger

around the world. 31 ⑤ 32 ④

33 ③ 34 workers 35 who 36 ranger

37 to 38 out 39 ④

01 동사에 -er이 붙어 행위자를 나타내는 경우인데, ④의 cooker 는 행위자의 뜻이 아니다.

02 • 그는 결혼식에 참석하려고 한다. • 날씨가 흐리고 가끔씩 소나기가 온다. • 그 여자는 결혼식 날에 초조했다. • 알루미늄 캔들은 재활용하기가 매우 쉽다.

03 반의어 관계이다. 싼 : 비싼 = 옳은 : 틀린

04 be afraid of: ~을 두려워하다 / be good for: ~에 좋다

05 어떤 모임이나 행사에 참석하다: attend(참석하다)

06 take a look at: ~을 보다

07 enough: ~에 필요한 만큼의, ~할 만큼 (충분히)

08 A가 '너는 높이 점프할 수 있니?'라고 물었는데 B가 할 수 있다고 대답했으므로 빈칸에는 '~을 잘하다'라는 의미의 good이 알맞다.

09 No, not yet.: 아니, 아직 아니야.

10 Why not?: 왜 안 되지?

11 be good at: ~을 잘하다

12 상반되는 내용의 두 개의 절을 연결하므로 but이 알맞다.

13 It is certain that ~: ~은 확실하다 / It is sure that ~도 쓰이지만, It is certain that ~을 더 많이 쓴다.

14 ② 유리가 왜 Jaden의 만화를 보고 싶어 하는지는 알 수 없다.

15 '~하는 방법을 알고 있다'의 뜻으로 능력을 표현한다.

16 Are you sure[certain] (that)+주어+동사 ~?는 확신 여부를 묻는 표현이다.

17 선행사가 사람(the girl)이고 주격이므로 who가 적절하다.

18 접속사 while은 '~하는 동안에'라는 의미를 지닌다.

19 선행사가 동물일 경우에는 관계대명사 which나 that 둘 다 쓸 수 있는데, 둘 중 어느 것을 더 좋아하냐고 물을 때는 의문사 which로 시작해야 하므로 ②가 정답이다.

20 after가 이끄는 절이 주절 앞에 올 수 있으므로 After he finished his dinner, he brushed his teeth.도 가능하다.

21 ⑤ 선행사 The men이 복수이므로 who 다음의 동사도 복수형 are로 바꾼다.

22 나머지는 before가 접속사로 쓰여, 뒤에 「주어+동사」가 오지만, ③은 전치사로 쓰였다.

23 나머지는 앞에 있는 명사를 수식하는 형용사절을 이끄는 주격 관계대명사인데, ②는 명사절을 이끄는 접속사이다.

24 관계대명사 that 다음에 be동사 were가 왔으므로 선행사로 복수명사가 와야 한다.

25 ⑤ 주절의 동사 arrived가 과거시제이므로, 종속절의 동사도 현재가 아닌 과거로 시제를 맞춘다. leaves → left

26 선행사가 사람이고 주격이므로 관계대명사 that이나 who를 써서 한 문장으로 만든다.

27 때를 나타내는 부사절(before ~)에서는 미래시제 대신 현재시제를 사용한다.

28 문맥상 '~한 후에'가 알맞다.

29 it은 인칭대명사로 앞에 나오는 단수명사를 받는다.

30 save A from B: A를 B에서 구하다 / around the world: 전 세계에서

31 give away: 거저 주다

32 a few days later: 며칠 후에

33 Guess what?: (대화를 시작할 때) 있잖아, 이봐

34 work: 일하다 / worker: 근로자, 일하는 사람

35 선행사가 사람이고 주격이므로 관계대명사 that이나 who를 쓸 수 있다.

36 하는 일이 숲이나 큰 공원을 돌보는 사람: ranger(공원[삼림/자연] 관리원

37 say hello to: ~에게 인사를 하다

38 break out: (화재가) 발생하다

39 get out: 나오다

단원별 예상문제   p.46~49

01 ④	02 ②	03 rainy	04 ⑤
05 away	06 ④	07 ⑤	08 ④
09 Why can't I take a look at them?			10 (that) I'm really good at drawing
11 너는 방금 나를 행복하게 했어.		12 ①	13 ③
14 is → was		15 before	16 ②	17 ①
18 ②	19 ⑤	20 ②	21 ③
22 try → trying		23 am → was	24 ①
25 (s)uddenly	26 Amazing	27 ③	28 ④
29 ⑤			

01 ④는 유의어 관계이고, 나머지는 반의어 관계이다.

02 out of: ~으로 / in front of: ~ 앞에

03 자연 현상을 나타내는 명사에 -y를 붙이면 형용사가 된다.

04 ⑤는 novel(소설)의 영영풀이이다.

05 give away: 거저 주다, 나누어 주다

06 Are you sure?는 상대방이 확신하고 있는지의 여부를 물 을 때 사용하는 표현이다.

07 문을 잠갔다고 하고 나서 가서 확인해 보겠다고 말하는 것은 어색하다.

08 take[have] a look at: ~을 보다

09 not은 앞에 언급된 부정의 문장을 받을 수 있다.

10 so는 앞에 언급된 긍정의 문장을 받을 수 있다.

11 make one's day: ~을 행복하게 하다

12 선행사가 사람(a girl)이고 주격이므로 관계대명사 who가 들어 가야 알맞다.

13 문맥상 '~하는 동안에'라는 의미를 지닌 시간을 나타내는 접속사 while이 적절하다.

14 주절의 동사가 과거이므로 관계사절의 동사도 과거가 되어야 한

다.

15 B after A = A before B

16 선행사가 사물일 때는 주격 관계대명사 which[that]를, 사람일 때는 주격 관계대명사 who[that]를 쓴다.

17 ①은 의문대명사이고, 나머지는 사물을 선행사로 하는 관계대명사 주격이다.

18 ②는 '~인 반면에'의 의미이고 나머지는 '~하는 동안'의 의미이다.

19 ⑤ a man이 선행사이고 관계사절에서 주어 역할을 하므로 who가 알맞다. whom → who

20 주어진 문장의 She는 My aunt를 받는다.

21 make friends: 친구를 사귀다

22 전치사 of의 목적어이므로 동명사로 고쳐야 한다.

23 전체 문장이 과거시제이므로 과거진행형으로 고쳐야 한다.

24 ⓑ, ① 2문형 ② 5문형 ③ 1문형 ④ 4문형 ⑤ 3문형

25 빨리 그리고 예기치 않게: suddenly(갑자기)

26 사람을 놀라게 하는 것이므로 현재분사형의 형용사로 고쳐야 한다.

27 ③ 호진이는 처음에 그 여인을 알아보지 못했다.

28 연령 앞에는 전치사 at을 쓴다.

29 become a hit: 히트를 치다, 성공하다

01 |모범답안| What's the matter (with you)? / What's wrong (with you)? / Is (there) something wrong with you?

02 nervous   03 나는 네가 잘할 것이라고 확신해.

04 (B)-(C)-(D)-(A)

05 (1) Dad cooks me a fried egg which[that] is my favorite.
   (2) I have an uncle who[that] is a math teacher.
   (3) She has a bird which[that] speaks English.

06 (1) Kathy went to bed after she took a bath.
   (2) Mr. Smith came to see you while you were out.
   (3) You should come back before it gets dark.

07 (1) is → are
   (2) who → which[that]
   (3) who → that

08 strong   09 (d)ifferent

10 나는 나의 이모처럼 새로운 것들을 시도하기를 두려워하지 않는 사람이 되고 싶다.

11 who[that]   12 age

13 She attended a famous cooking school there.

14 to write

---

01 상대방에게 좋지 않은 일이 있는지 물을 때 사용하는 표현에는 What's wrong with you? / What's the matter with you? / Is (there) something wrong with you? 등이 있다.

02 nerve의 형용사형 nervous가 알맞다.

03 do a good job: 잘하다

04 (B) 내일은 우리 엄마 생일이야. 내가 엄마를 위해 무엇을 해야 할까? - (C) 너의 엄마를 위해 케이크를 굽는 건 어때? 넌 빵을 잘 굽잖아. - (D) 좋은 생각이야. 엄마가 내 케이크를 좋아하셨으면 좋겠어. - (A) 너의 엄마는 분명히 좋아하실 거야.

05 (1) 선행사가 사물(a fried egg)이므로 which나 that을 쓴다. (2) 선행사가 사람이므로 who나 that을 쓴다. (3) 선행사가 동물(a bird)이므로 which나 that을 쓴다.

06 after: ~한 후에 / while: ~하는 동안 / before: ~하기 전에

07 (1) The animals가 복수이다. (2) 선행사가 the letter이므로 관계대명사는 which 또는 that을 쓴다. (3) 선행사가 사람과 동물이므로 관계대명사는 that을 쓴다.

08 weak: 약한 / strong: 강한

09 한 가지 또는 그 이상의 점에서 서로 같지 않은: different(다른)

10 someone: 어떤 사람 / like: ~처럼

11 선행사가 사람이고 주격이므로 who나 that을 쓸 수 있다.

12 당신이 살아온 해들의 수: age(나이, 연령)

13 attend는 타동사이므로 전치사 없이 목적어를 취한다.

14 decide는 to부정사를 목적어로 취한다.

창의사고력 서술형 문제 p.52

|모범답안|

01 (1) A waiter is someone who serves food in a restaurant.
   (2) A zookeeper is someone who looks after animals in the zoo.
   (3) Dessert is sweet food which is served after a meal.

02 (1) Before I leave this town, I'm going to visit my friend. / I'm going to visit my friend before I leave this town.
   (2) After I saw the advertisement on TV, I bought the PS4. / I bought the PS4 after I saw the advertisement on TV.
   (3) Before you go out, the rain will stop. / The rain will stop before you go out.
   (4) While I put on my coat, hold my bag, please. / Please hold my bag while I put on my coat.
   (5) After we eat something, we're going to see a movie. / We're going to see a movie after we eat something.
   (6) When I came home, my sister was watching TV. /

8   정답 및 해설

My sister was watching TV when I came home.

(7) Before you go out, you have to finish this. /
You have to finish this before you go out.

---

01 ①   02 ④   03 ④
04 cartoonist 05 at   06 Everybody is good at
something.   07 ②   08 matter   09 ③
10 speak, well 11 ③, ⑤   12 ①   13 tells →
tell   14 ④   15 ①   16 before
17 ②   18 ⑤   19 Before   20 ③
21 hairs → hair   22 ②   23 second
24 ④   25 ③   26 ⑤   27 He is
the janitor at the writer's school.   28 ⑤
29 그녀는 정말 멋져 보였고, 그녀의 스쿠터는 아주 독특했다.
30 ⑤

01 보통 다른 가능성들에 대해 주의 깊게 생각한 후에 어떤 것을 하
기로 선택하다: 결정하다(decide)

02 be good for: ~에 좋다

03 once: 한 번 / per: ~에 대하여, ~당

04 '명사 : 행위자' 관계이다. 예술, 미술 : 예술가, 미술가 / 만화 :
만화가

05 take a look at: ~을 보다 / be good at: ~을 잘하다

06 everybody는 단수동사로 받는다.

07 some ~, other ...: 어떤 사람들은 ~하고, 또 어떤 사람들은 …
하다

08 Is something wrong?=What's the matter with you?: 무
슨 일 있니?

09 많은 학생들 앞에서 연설을 해야 하므로 긴장될 것이다.

10 '형용사+명사' 구문은 '동사+부사' 구문으로 바꿔 쓸 수 있다.

11 확신을 나타낼 때는 I'm sure[certain] ~를 쓴다.

12 앞 문장의 빈칸에는 the famous singer를 선행사로 하는 주격
관계대명사 who가, 뒤 문장에는 a chair를 선행사로 하는 주격
관계대명사 which가 들어가야 알맞다.

13 선행사 three books가 복수이므로 that절의 동사는 복수 동사
tell이 되어야 한다.

14 '네가 조깅하는 동안에 ~'의 뒤에 어울리는 말을 찾아보자.

15 who는 관계대명사로 쓰일 수도 있지만 의문대명사로 쓰여 '누
구'의 의미를 나타낸다. ①은 의문대명사로 쓰고, 나머지는 관계
대명사로 쓴다.

16 첫 번째 문장에서는 부사로, 두 번째 문장에서는 접속사로 쓰인
다.

17 빈칸에는 a boy를 선행사로 하는 주격 관계대명사 who가 들어

가야 알맞다.

18 ⑤ 문장의 주어는 The man이고 who is sitting on the box
는 The man을 수식하는 관계대명사절이다. 따라서 동사는
have가 아니라 단수형인 has가 알맞다.

19 B after A(A를 하고 나서 B를 하다) =A before B(B를 하
기 전에 A를 하다)

20 be good at: ~에 능숙하다

21 hair는 머리카락 전체를 나타낼 때는 단수형을 취한다.

22 주어진 문장의 it은 Lunch Lady Begins를 받는다.

23 1분이 나뉘어지는 60개의 부분들 중의 하나: second(초)

24 ④ Lunch Lady가 어떻게 사람들을 위험으로부터 구하는 지는
알 수 없다.

25 ③ 뒤에 단수명사가 오므로 other를 another로 고쳐야 한다.

26 ⓐ, ⑤ 3형형 ① 4형형 ② 2형형 ③ 1형형 ④ 5형형

27 김 씨의 직업은 무엇인가? - 그는 글쓴이의 학교 수위이다

28 while: ~하는 동안

29 cool: 멋진 / unique: 독특한

30 ⑤ 호진이는 그 여인을 만난 기억이 없다.

Where Do People Live?

시험대비 실력평가   p.60

01 ②	02 ②	03 ④	04 high
05 ③	06 jeans	07 grass	08 ②

01 ①, ③, ④, ⑤는 모두 animal(동물)에 속한다.

02 kind of: 약간, 어느 정도 / look for: ~을 찾다

03 예를 들면 문이나 정문처럼 어떤 곳에 들어가는 길: entrances(입구, 문)

04 반의어의 관계이다. 싼 : 비싼 = 낮은 : 높은

05 upside down: 거꾸로

06 보통 데님이라고 불리는 질긴 파란색 면직물로 만들어진 캐주얼 바지: jeans(바지, 청바지)

07 grass: 풀, 잔디

08 out of: ~에서 / a lot of: 많은

서술형 시험대비   p.61

01 (1) second   (2) fifth   (3) ninth
02 (1) in harmony with   (2) next to   (3) look at
03 (1) avoid   (2) build   (3) protect   (4) entrance
04 (1) lovely   (2) southern   (3) wooden
05 (1) good at   (2) take down   (3) look for   (4) pile up
06 (1) (c)ollector   (2) (e)nemy

01 fifth, ninth는 기수에 th를 붙일 때 철자가 변한다.

02 (1) in harmony with: ~와 조화를 이루어 (2) next to: ~ 옆에 (3) look at: ~을 보다

03 (1) avoid: 피하다 (2) build: 짓다 (3) protect: 보호하다 (4) entrance: 입구, 문

04 (1) lovely: 사랑스러운 (2) southern: 남쪽의, 남부의 (3) wooden: 목제의

05 (1) be good at: ~을 잘하다 (2) take down: (구조물을 해체하여) 치우다 (3) look for: ~을 찾다 (4) pile up: (양이) 많아지다

06 (1) collector: 징수원 (2) enemy: 적

Conversation

핵심 Check   p.62~63

1 (1) kind, want / to live   (2) What, be, want to
2 (1) Where, find / next   (2) Where / behind
  (3) Where / in   (4) tell, where / front

교과서 대화문 익히기

Check(√) True or False   p.64

1 T   2 F   3 F   4 T   5 T   6 F

교과서 확인학습   p.66~67

Listen & Speak 1 A. Listen and Check

1 look, in, like / unique, want to / kind, live / to house
2 Excuse, there, mall / kind, would / like / There, on / Thank

Listen & Speak 2 A. Listen and Check

1 Excuse, find, can, second, next / you / welcome
2 help, for, can, on, next

Communicate A. Listen and Answer

Welcome, May / like, for / kind, like / with, view, garden / do, room, view, no / have, floor / do / give, try, Where, have / can, dining, to / see / in, Here's / Thank

Progress Check

1 at, in, down / look, but, kind / kind, want / so, live
2 Excuse, find / find, second, next / Thank / welcome
3 where, hats / can, floor, to / you / welcome

Work-Act

What, build / to, that, like / Where / second

시험대비 기본평가   p.68

01 want	02 ①, ③	03 ①	04 ④

01 want to: ~하기를 원하다

02 사고 싶은 물건이 있는 장소를 물을 때는 Where can I

find[buy] ~?나 Where is[are] ~?의 표현을 쓴다.

03 want to: ~하기를 원하다

04 A가 여성복 매장의 위치를 물었으므로 ④와 같이 답한다. ③은 주어가 단수이므로 옳지 않다.

시험대비 실력평가   p.69~70

01 ②	02 ④	03 Where	04 do
05 ③	06 ⑤	07 What can	08 ②
09 give	10 알겠습니다.	11 ④	12 at
13 ①			

01 어이, 이 사진 속의 집을 봐. 그것은 큰 신발처럼 보여! - 아, 아주 독특하긴 하지만, 난 신발 속에서 살고 싶지 않아. - 넌 어떤 종류의 집에서 살고 싶니? - 음, 나는 비행기 모양의 집에서 살고 싶어.

02 ④는 도움을 제안하는 표현이고, 나머지는 길이나 위치를 묻는 표현이다.

03 B가 2층에 있다고 말했으므로 남성복이 있는 위치(where)를 물었을 것이다.

04 I do. = I want to go on a picnic.

05 대화 내용상 찾고자 하는 물건의 위치를 확인하는 것이다.

06 ⑤의 Do you know where ~?에 대한 응답으로 Yes, that's right.는 어색하다.

07 May I help you?는 상점 등에서 점원이 손님에게 도와주겠다는 표현으로 What can I do for you?라고 할 때도 있다.

08 ⓑ와 ②는 '~을 가진, ~이 있는'의 뜻으로 소유를 나타낸다. ① ~와 함께 ③ ~으로 ④ ~에게 ⑤ ~에, ~에 관하여

09 give it a try: 시도해 보다

10 I see.: 알겠습니다.

11 ④ 남자는 침대가 없는 방에서 자 보기로 했다.

12 look at: ~을 보다

13 상반의 접속사 but이 알맞다.

서술형 시험대비   p.71

01 They're on the fourth floor.

02 What kind of pet do you want to have?

03 (C) – (D) – (B) – (A)

04 (B) – (D) – (A) – (C)

05 ⑤	06 kind	07 fifth
08 mention		

01 be on the fourth floor: 4층에 있다

02 What kind of ~?: 어떤 종류의 ~?

03 실례합니다, 여자 신발은 어디에 있어요? - 2층에서 찾을 수 있어

요. 엘리베이터 옆에 있어요. - 감사합니다. - 천만에요.

04 (B) 넌 어떤 집을 짓고 싶어? - (D) 보트처럼 생긴 2층짜리 집을 짓고 싶어. - (A) 부엌이 어디 있어? - (C) 2층에 있어.

05 모르는 사람에게 말을 걸 때 관용적으로 쓰는 표현은 Excuse me.이다.

06 What kind of ~?: 어떤 종류의 ~?

07 five에 -th를 붙여 서수를 만들 때는 철자의 변화에 유의해야 한다.

08 You're welcome.=Don't mention it.: 천만에요.

시험대비 기본평가   p.74

01 (1) has been   (2) been   (3) finished

    (4) has just finished   (5) arrived   (6) did you reach

02 (1) does   (2) has   (3) side

    (4) students   (5) boy   (6) are

03 (1) He has been sick in bed since last Friday.

    (2) How long have you known Miss Smith?

    (3) Have you ever read Christmas Carol?

    (4) My father hasn't read the newspaper yet.

01 (1) 부사구 since ~가 있으므로 현재완료가 맞다. (2) '~에 다녀오다'=have been to (3) two hours ago와 같이 명백한 과거 시점을 나타내는 부사구가 있으므로 현재완료가 아닌 과거시제로 써야 한다. (4) just와 함께 '이제 막 마쳤다'라는 의미이므로 현재완료가 맞다. (5) yesterday 와 같이 명백한 과거시점을 나타내는 부사가 있으므로 현재완료가 아닌 과거시제로 써야 한다. (6) 의문사 when은 특정 시점에 대해 묻는 의문사이므로 현재완료와 함께 쓸 수 없다.

02 (1), (2) each가 주어일 때는 단수 동사로 받는다. (3) each가 형용사로 쓰일 때는 뒤에 단수 명사가 온다. (4) each가 대명사로 쓰일 때 each of 뒤에는 복수 명사가 온다. (5) every 뒤에는 단수 명사가 온다. (6) 주어에 both가 있을 때는 복수 동사로 받는다.

03 (1) 계속 용법의 현재완료이다. (2) 계속 용법의 현재완료이다. (3) 경험 용법의 현재완료이다. (4) 완료 용법의 현재완료이다.

01 ⑤	02 ③	03 ④	04 Each
05 have	06 ①	07 ④	08 ④
09 ④	10 ④	11 not	12 ②
13 since	14 ④	15 ②	16 Each student, speaks
		17 ②	18 ④
19 ③	20 has been absent		21 yet
22 ③	23 ④		

01 계속을 나타내는 현재완료이다.

02 'each of+복수 명사'는 단수로 취급한다.

03 계속을 나타내는 현재완료이다.

04 each+단수 명사: 각각의 ~ /
each of+복수 명사: ~의 각각

05 「have+p.p.」로 현재완료 시제로 쓰인 문장이다.

06 ①은 '각자'라는 뜻의 부사이다. 나머지는 '각각의 ~'라는 뜻의
형용사이다.

07 현재완료의 경험 용법이 사용된 문장에서 빈도부사 never는
have와 been 사이에 위치해야 한다.

08 each other: 서로

09 계속을 나타내는 현재완료이다.

10 every minute / Both the brothers / All the eggs / each of
them

11 앞 문장이 현재완료 결과의 문장이므로 '나의 엄마는 쇼핑하러
가서 여기 없다.'의 뜻이 되어야 한다.

12 뒤에 단수 명사 boy가 온 것으로 보아 '각각의'라는 뜻의 each
가 적절하다.

13 '~한 이래로'는 since로 나타낸다.

14 ⓐ는 단수 명사가 이어지므로 each 또는 every가 적절하고, ⓑ
는 복수 명사가 이어지므로 all 또는 each of가 적절하다.

15 현재완료형으로 물었으므로 현재완료형으로 대답해야 한다.

16 '각 학생'은 'each+단수 명사'로 나타내고 동사는 3인칭 단수형
으로 쓴다.

17 ②는 대명사이고, 나머지는 모두 형용사이다.

18 ④와 같이 when ~이 명백한 과거의 시점을 나타낼 때는 현재
완료 시제는 쓸 수 없다. (has been → was)

19 ③에서 'each of+복수명사'는 단수로 취급한다. (have their
→ has its)

20 얼마나 오랫동안 결석했는지 물었으므로 현재완료(have+p.p.)
로 쓴다.

21 yet: 1. 이미, 벌써(의문문) 2. 아직(부정문)

22 ③에서 'each of+복수 대명사'는 단수 취급하므로 have를 has
로 고쳐야 한다.

23 ④의 has gone은 '~에 가고 없다'는 의미의 현재완료 결과 용
법이다. 나머지는 모두 현재완료 경험의 용법으로 쓰였다.

01 (1) have, started   (2) has not returned
    (3) has gone to

02 (1) each   (2) Both   (3) All   (4) each   (5) every

03 (1) has gone → went
    (2) already → yet

04 Each / each

05 (1) didn't see → have not[haven't] seen
    (2) is → has been

06 (1) He has been to Italy many times.
    (2) I have been very busy these days.
    (3) I have never visited Paris before.

07 (1) all   (2) every   (3) any
    (4) each   (5) some   (6) both

08 (1) I went to London four years ago.
    (2) When did you see a white lion?
    (3) I often played with her when I was a child.
    (4) He was ill in bed last month.

09 (1) Each of us has to finish our project.
    (2) There were four books on the table. Each
       book was in a different color.
    (3) Every driver should be careful.

10 (1) He has lived in New York since 1970.
    (2) Have you finished reading this story yet?
    (3) I have seen the movie once.

11 Each, has

01 (1) 현재완료 완료 용법 (2) yet은 과거에서 현재까지 아직 완료
되지 않은 상태를 말한다. (3) 현재완료 결과 용법

02 (1) '각각'이라는 의미를 나타내는 부사는 each이다. (2) both:
둘 다 (3) all: 모든 (4) each of+복수 명사: ~의 각각 (5) '모든
학생이 시험에 합격한 것은 아니었다.'의 뜻으로 부분부정이다.

03 (1) 과거를 나타내는 부사구가 있으므로 현재완료 시제가 아니라
과거시제를 써야 한다. (2) 부정문에서 '아직'의 뜻으로는 yet을
쓴다.

04 Each student: 각각의 학생 / each other: 서로

05 since는 현재완료 시제와 함께 쓰이므로 didn't see는 have
not[haven't] seen이 되어야 한다.

06 (1) 현재완료 경험 용법 (2) 일정한 기간을 나타내는 부사구
(these days)는 현재완료와 함께 쓰일 수 있다. (3) 현재완료 경
험 용법

07 (1) all+소유격+단수 명사 (2) every+단수 명사 (3) not ~
any: 조금도 ~ 않다 (4) each+of+복수 대명사 (5) some: (긍
정문에서) 약간의 (6) both+복수 명사

08 (1) 과거 시점을 나타내는 four years ago가 있으므로 과거시
제로 쓴다. (2) when은 과거의 특정 시점을 묻는 표현이므로

과거시제로 써야 한다. (3) when 이하의 절이 과거의 특정 시점을 나타내므로 과거시제로 쓴다. (4) '지난달 (last month)'이라는 명백한 과거 시점이 있으므로 과거시제로 나타낸다.

09 (1) 'each of+복수 대명사+단수 동사'(have → has) (2) 'There are+복수 명사'(book → books) (3) 'every+단수명사'로 사용 (drivers → driver)

10 (1) 현재완료 계속 용법 (2) 현재완료 완료 용법 (3) 현재완료 경험 용법

11 '각각의 학생'은 each+단수명사(student)로 나타낸다.

Reading

확인문제 p.80

1 T 2 F 3 T 4 T 5 F

확인문제 p.81

1 T 2 F 3 T 4 F 5 T

교과서 확인학습 A p.82~83

01 Have, seen, roof 02 see, on
03 forests 04 harmony, built, for
05 build, cover, with
06 protect, from, strong
07 grow, some, meals 08 part, ago, only
09 Centuries, who, paid
10 avoid, some, piling
11 When, town, took, down
12 After, piled, stone
13 stay, southern, round, like 14 roofs, people
15 have, about, themselves 16 only, without
17 is, whole 18 usually
19 first, second, living, fourth

교과서 확인학습 B p.84~85

1 Have you ever seen a goat on the roof of a house?
2 In Norway, we can see animals on roofs.
3 Norway has large forests.
4 In harmony with nature, people have built wooden houses for a long time.

5 To build strong and warm houses, they cover their roofs with grass.
6 The grass roofs protect them from the long cold winters and strong winds.
7 Sometimes, trees or plants grow out of the grass roofs, and some animals enjoy their meals there.
8 A roof is an essential part of a house, but long ago some people built roofs only to take them down easily.
9 Centuries ago in southern Italy, people who had a house without a roof paid lower taxes.
10 To avoid high taxes on their houses, some people built cone-shaped roofs by piling up stones.
11 When tax collectors came to the town, people took their roofs down quickly.
12 After the tax collectors left, they piled up the stones again.
13 From the sky in a part of southern China, you can see round roofs that look like big doughnuts.
14 They are the roofs of the big round houses of the Hakka people.
15 They have lived in houses like these for about a thousand years to protect themselves from enemies.
16 The houses have only one gate without any windows on the first floor.
17 Each house is big enough for a whole village.
18 It usually has four stories.
19 It has kitchens on the first floor, storage rooms on the second floor, and living rooms and bedrooms on the third and fourth floors.

시험대비 실력평가 p.86~89

01 ② 02 ③ 03 wooden 04 ④
05 ① 06 ④ 07 잔디 지붕 위에서
08 ⑤ 09 ④ 10 southern 11 ②
12 paid 13 ① 14 piling 15 ④
16 ③ 17 원뿔 모양의 지붕을 만들었다, 속히 지붕을 철거했다 18 sky 19 which 20 ①
21 ② 22 are → is 23 kitchens 24 ⑤
25 ⑤ 26 seen 27 ①, ④ 28 with
29 ⑤ 30 ④ 31 southern 32 ①, ④

01 지붕 위에 있는 염소를 본 적이 있느냐는 문장 다음인 ②에 와야 한다.

02 'in harmony with: ~와 조화롭게 / cover A with B: B로 A

13

를 덮다

03 wood(나무, 목재)+-en(형용사 어미)=wooden(목재의)

04 ⓒ, ④ 부사적 용법 ①, ⑤ 형용사적 용법 ②, ③ 명사적 용법

05 ① 노르웨이의 집들의 지붕 위에 염소가 올라가는지는 알 수 없다.

06 protect A from B: B로부터 A를 보호하다

07 there는 장소를 가리키는 부사이다.

08 상반의 접속사 but이 알맞다.

09 take down: 분해하다, 철거하다

10 south(남부)+-ern(형용사 어미)=southern(남부의)

11 선행사가 사람이고 주격이므로 who나 that을 쓸 수 있다.

12 pay의 과거형 paid를 써야 한다.

13 문맥상 '높은 세금을 피하기 위하여'가 알맞다.

14 'by+동명사' 구문이 알맞다.

15 '~할 때'의 뜻을 나타내는 접속사 when이 알맞다.

16 '~한 후에'의 뜻을 나타내는 접속사 after가 알맞다.

18 밖에 서서 위를 바라볼 때 볼 수 있는 지구 주위의 공간: sky(하늘)

19 선행사가 사물이고 주격이므로 which나 that을 쓸 수 있다.

20 ⓒ, ① 현재완료로 계속을 나타낸다. ②, ④ 경험 ③ 완료 ⑤ 결과

21 without any ~: ~이 하나도 없는

22 주어에 each가 있을 때는 단수 동사로 받는다.

23 요리와 식기를 씻는 것과 같은 집안일을 하기 위해 사용되는 방: kitchen(부엌)

24 ⑤ 4층에 얼마나 많은 침실이 있는지는 알 수 없다.

25 강하고 따뜻한 집을 짓기 위해 잔디로 지붕을 덮는다는 문장 다음에 와야 한다.

26 현재완료형이 되어야 하므로 과거분사 seen이 알맞다.

27 ⓑ, ①, ④ 계속 ② 경험 ③ 완료 ⑤ 결과

28 cover A with B: B로 A를 덮다

29 ⑤ 동물들이 지붕 위에서 산다는 말은 언급되지 않았다.

30 Centuries before → Centuries ago

31 south: 남쪽, 남부 southern: 남쪽의, 남부의

32 without : ~이 없는

서술형 시험대비   p.90~91

01 To avoid   02 by   03 As   04 down
05 세금 징수원들이 떠나간 후에 그들은 다시 돌을 쌓아올렸다.
06 which   07 doughnuts   08 have
lived   09 themselves   10 1층에는
창문이 하나도 없이   11 for   12 Each
house   13 third   14 They are on the
second floor. 15 in   16 four-stories → four-
story   17 Since   18 There are about 400
thousand books.   19 It opened in 2013.

---

01 문맥상 목적을 나타내는 부사적 용법의 to부정사가 되어야 한다.

02 by -ing: ~함으로써

03 when과 as는 '~할 때'의 뜻으로 때를 나타내는 접속사의 용법이 있다.

04 take down: ~을 철거하다

05 after: ~한 후에 / pile up: ~을 쌓아올리다

06 선행사가 사물이고 주격이므로 that이나 which를 쓸 수 있다.

07 뜨거운 기름으로 튀긴 달콤한 밀가루 반죽으로 만들어진 빵과 같은 케이크: doughnut(도넛)

08 과거에서 현재까지 계속된 일이므로 현재완료형을 써야 한다.

09 동사의 목적어가 주어 자신이므로 재귀대명사를 써야 한다.

10 without ~ 이하의 부대상황을 나타내는 부사구로 집의 상태를 나타낸다.

11 big enough for ~: ~에게 충분할 만큼 큰

12 It은 인칭대명사로 앞에 나온 단수 명사를 받는다.

13 three의 서수는 third이다.

14 저장실은 2층에 있다.

15 도시 앞에는 전치사 in을 쓴다.

16 '4층 건물'의 뜻으로 four-story가 building을 수식하므로 복수형인 stories는 틀린다.

17 '~부터'의 뜻이므로 since가 알맞다.

18 국립 세종 도서관에는 약 40만 권의 책이 있다고 언급되었다.

19 국립 세종 도서관은 2013년에 문을 열었다고 언급되었다.

영역별 핵심문제   p.93~97

01 ②, ④	02 ③	03 low	04 ④
05 ⑤	06 kind	07 give, a try	08 Where
09 to	10 ①, ④	11 lovely	12 have → has
13 ④	14 한번 시도해 보겠습니다.		
15 ④	16 ①	17 ③	18 ④
19 ④	20 each other	21 ③	22 ⑤
23 ④	24 ②	25 ③	26 ①
27 Each of their opinions are	28 ②	29 There	
30 ④	31 protect	32 ⑤	
33 ④	34 이곳의 날씨는 여름에는 아주 덥고 겨울에는 춥다.		
35 ①	36 동굴 집은 너무 춥지도 덥지도 않기 때문이다.	37 like	38 ②

01 ②, ④는 명사에 -ly가 붙어 형용사가 된 것이고, 나머지는 형용사에 -ly가 붙어 부사가 된 것이다.

02 • 전망이 좋은 방을 주시면 좋겠군요.
• 그는 우리를 맞이하기 위해 문에 나와 있었다.
• 그는 그 장소를 어려움 없이 찾았다.
• 그가 또 다른 말은 뭐라고 했나요?

03 반의어 관계이다. 따뜻한 : 서늘한 = 높은 : 낮은

04 be good for: ~에 좋다

05 나무들이 함께 가까이 자라는 넓은 지역: forest(삼림, 숲)

06 당신은 어떤 영화를 좋아하나요? / 그것 때문에 나는 약간 바보 같은 기분이 들었다.

07 give it a try: 시도하다, 한번 해 보다

08 B가 2층에 있다고 말했으므로 남성용 셔츠가 있는 위치 (where)를 물었을 것이다.

09 Welcome to ~.: ~에 오신 것을 환영합니다.

10 Can[May] I help you?: 도와드릴까요?

11 love에 -ly를 붙이면 형용사형이 된다.

12 'every+단수명사'가 주어이면 단수동사로 받는다.

13 상반되는 내용의 두 개의 절을 연결하므로 but이 알맞다.

14 give it a try: 한번 시도해 보다

15 ④ 방에 왜 침대가 없는지는 알 수 없다.

16 B가 스마트폰을 찾고 있다고 대답했으므로 도움을 제안하는 표현이 자연스럽다.

17 과거에서 지금까지의 경험을 나타내는 문장이므로 현재완료 (have+p.p.) 시제로 써야 한다.

18 each는 단수 동사로 받는다. some of+복수 명사는 복수 동사로 받는다.

19 계속을 나타내는 현재완료이다.

20 '서로'를 뜻하는 each other는 복수형을 쓰지 않는다.

21 ③ last week라는 특정 과거 시점이 있으므로 현재완료가 아니라 과거시제로 써야 한다. (have climbed → climbed)

22 ⑤는 앞에 almost가 있으므로 전체의 의미를 강조하는 every가 들어가야 한다. each는 개별성을 강조하므로 almost가 있는 문장에 쓸 수 없다.

23 have[has] gone to ~: ~에 갔다(그래서 여기 없다) / 결과를 나타내는 현재완료이다.

24 보기, ② 경험 ①, ④ 계속 ③ 완료 ⑤ 결과

25 ③ each 뒤에는 관사나 대명사의 소유격이 올 수 없다. Each of the students나 Each student로 고쳐야 한다.

26 ① ~ ago라는 과거 시점이 있으므로 과거시제 went가 맞다.

27 each 다음에는 복수 명사나 대명사가 올 수 없다.

28 ⓐ, ② 경험 ①, ④ 계속 ③ 완료 ⑤ 결과

29 have[has]가 있는 문장을 there is[are]를 쓴 문장과 바꿔 쓸 수 있다.

30 cover A with B: B로 A를 덮다

31 누군가 또는 무언가가 다치거나 손상되지 않도록 막다: protect(보호하다)

32 ⑤ 동물들이 보통 집 지붕 위에서 사료를 먹는다는 말은 언급되지 않았다.

33 for a long time: 오랫동안

34 in this place(이곳의)는 weather를 수식하는 형용사구이다.

35 not A or B: A도 B도 아닌

37 look like+명사: ~처럼 보이다

38 ⓐ, ② 대략, 약(부사) ①, ④ ~에 관하여(전치사) ③ ~의 여기 저기에(전치사) ⑤ 여기저기(부사)

단원별 예상문제

p.98~101

01 ④	02 ②	03 third	04 ④
05 upside down		06 ④	07 ②
08 ④	09 ③	10 ③	11 ②, ③
12 ③	13 ⑤	14 has lived	15 before
16 ④	17 ④	18 ③	19 ③
20 ①	21 easily	22 ③	23 ②
24 (1) 지붕을 재빨리 철거했다 (2) 돌을 다시 쌓아올려 지붕을 만들었다.		25 ③	26 ④, ⑤	27 둥근 지붕들
28 ④		29 themselves	

01 ④는 유의어 관계이고 나머지는 반의어 관계이다.

02 be fond of: ~을 좋아하다 / out of: ~ 밖으로

03 서수 first, second, third는 기수와 형태가 달라진다.

04 ④는 jeans(바지, 청바지)의 영영풀이이다.

05 upside down: 거꾸로

06 대화 내용상 찾고자 하는 물건의 위치를 확인하는 것이다.

07 미래에 뭐가 되고 싶은지를 물었는데 ② '나는 차를 마실 거야.' 라고 대답하는 것은 어색하다.

08 ④ What으로 물었으므로 yes나 no로 대답할 수 없다.

09 대화의 흐름상 '~을 찾고 있다'는 의미인 'I'm looking for ~.' 가 알맞다.

10 '그것은 2층에 있다.'는 'It's on the second floor.'로 표현한다.

11 ② You're right.: 네 말이 옳아. ③ That's fine with me.: 나는 좋아.

12 현재완료의 경험 용법이 사용된 문장에서 빈도부사 never는 has와 been 사이에 위치해야 한다.

13 each는 단수 동사로 받는다. all of+복수 명사는 복수 동사로 받는다.

14 since 이하가 과거에서 현재에 이르는 기간을 말하므로 현재완료의 계속 용법이 필요하다.

15 B after A = A before B

16 each hand / Both of us / All of the milk / Every word

17 '시계를 잃어버려 현재 가지고 있지 않다는 것을 나타낸다. 결과를 나타내는 현재완료이다.

18 ③ both는 복수 동사로 받는다. looks → look

19 ③의 has gone은 '~에 가고 없다'는 의미의 현재완료 결과 용법이다. 나머지는 모두 현재완료 경험 용법으로 쓰였다.

20 문맥상 상반의 접속사 but이 알맞다.

21 동사를 수식하므로 부사형이 되어야 한다.

22 문맥상 '더 낮은 세금'이 되어야 알맞다.

23 by -ing: ~함으로써(이때의 by는 수단을 나타냄)

15

25 from the sky: 하늘에서(이때의 from은 기점을 나타냄)

26 선행사가 사물이고 주격이므로 that이나 which가 알맞다.

27 They는 인칭대명사로 앞에 나온 복수 명사를 받는다.

28 과거에서 현재까지 계속된 일이므로 현재완료를 쓴다.

29 목적어가 주어 자신이므로 재귀대명사를 써야 한다.

서술형 실전문제 p.102~103

01 Excuse　02 What　03 problem

04 (C)–(D)–(A)–(B)

05 (1) Peter has lived in Peking since 2010.

　(2) Tom has been in hospital for a week.

　(3) My mother has gone shopping.

06 (1) I ate breakfast each day during my stay in
　London.

　(2) There is a tree on both sides of the gate.

　(3) Every day seems the same to him.

07 (1) has been → went

　(2) have you seen → did you see

　(3) have often played → often played

08 gate　09 houses → house

10 fourth　11 They are on the first floor.

12 in　13 which[that]

14 cafeteria　15 visited → have visited

창의사고력 서술형 문제 p.104

|모범답안|

01 (1) I want to see a movie.

　(2) Yes, I do.

02 Where can I buy them? / Where can I get them? 등

03 (1) Each of the films was very wonderful.

　(2) Every student has passed the exam.

　(3) Each room has a TV.

　(4) All friends of mine are very kind.

단원별 모의고사 p.105~108

01 ④　　02 ②　　03 ④

04 collector　05 up　　06 ⑤　　07 ⑤

08 find / get / buy　09 ②, ③　10 정원이

보이는 방이 있습니까?　11 have no　12 ①

13 ④　　14 ④　　15 ②, ⑤　16 ①

17 ③　　18 have lost　19 Everyone in the boat

has to work together as a team.　20 ③

21 ③　　22 ②　　23 to　　24 ④

25 have built → built　26 without　27 ①

28 ③　　29 have built　30 on the grass roofs

---

01 Excuse me.: (모르는 사람에게 말을 걸 때) 죄송합니다, 실례
합니다.

02 What kind of ~?: 어떤 종류의 ~?

03 No problem.: 괜찮아요.

04 실례합니다. 여자 청바지는 어디에 있나요? - 2층에서 찾을 수 있
어요. 엘리베이터 옆에 있어요. - 감사합니다. - 천만에요.

05 현재완료(have+p.p.)를 이용해 문장을 완성한다. (1) 현재완료
의 계속 용법 (2) 현재완료의 계속 용법 (3) 현재완료의 결과 용법

07 (1) 과거 시점을 나타내는 last year가 있으므로 과거시제로 쓴다.
　(2) 의문사 when으로 시작하므로 과거시제로 쓴다. (3) when
이하의 절이 과거의 특정 시점을 나타내므로 과거시제로 쓴다.

08 들판, 정원 또는 건물의 구내에 들어가는 입구로 사용되는 문과
같은 구조물: gate(대문, 정문)

09 each 다음에는 단수 명사가 온다.

10 four의 서수는 fourth이다.

11 주방은 1층에 있다고 언급되었다.

12 '~에'의 뜻으로 도시 앞에는 전치사 in을 쓴다.

13 선행사가 사물이고 주격이므로 which나 that을 쓸 수 있다.

14 당신이 카운터에서 음식을 선택하고 그것을 지불한 후에 테이블
로 가져가는 레스토랑: cafeteria(구내식당)

15 과거의 일정한 때부터 지금까지 계속된 일이므로 현재완료형을
써야 한다.

---

01 take down: (구조물을 해체하여) 치우다

02 땅에서 자라며 줄기, 잎, 그리고 뿌리를 가지고 있는 살아 있는 것:
식물, 초목(plant)

03 floor: (건물의) 층 / else 또[그 밖의] 다른, 다른

04 '동사 : 행위자' 관계이다. 그리다 : 화가 / 수집하다 : 수집가

05 pile up: ~을 층층이 쌓다 / walk up: 걸어 올라가다

06 이봐, 사진 속의 이 독특한 집을 봐. 집이 거꾸로 있어.- 아, 재미
있어 보이지만, 좀 이상한 것 같아. - 넌 어떤 집에서 살고 싶어?
- 나는 음악을 좋아해서 피아노 모양의 집에서 살 고 싶어.

07 ⑤에서 여성화를 찾고 있다는 말에 어떻게 거기에 가야 하느냐
고 묻는 것은 어색하다.

08 Where can I find ~?는 상점의 위치를 묻는 표현으로 find 대
신 get이나 buy를 쓸 수 있다.

09 상점 등에서 점원이 손님에게 하는 말은 관용적으로 정해져 있다.

10 view: 경관, 전망

11 'There is[are] ~' 구문은 have 동사를 써서 바꿔 쓸 수 있다.

12 next to: ~ 옆에

13 ④ 남자는 바닥 위에서 한번 자 보겠다고 말했다.

14 완료를 나타내는 현재완료의 부정문이다.

15 뒤에 단수 명사 student가 온 것으로 보아 '각각의'라는 뜻의
each와 '모든'이라는 뜻의 every가 적절하다.

16 ① ~ ago라는 과거 시점이 있으므로 과거시제 went가 맞다.

17 ③에서 'each of+복수 대명사'는 단수 취급하므로 have를 has 로 고쳐야 한다.

18 시계를 잃어버린 결과가 현재까지 영향을 미치므로 현재완료의 <결과> 용법으로 나타낸다.

19 주어는 everyone, 술어동사는 has to work이다. in the boat / together / as a team 등의 수식어구는 각각 주어, 동사에 연관시켜 배열한다.

20 과거에서 지금까지의 경험을 나타내는 문장이므로 현재완료 (have+p.p.) 시제로 써야 한다.

21 계절 앞에는 전치사 in을 쓴다.

22 ⓑ, ② ~을 가진, ~이 있는(소유) ① ~에 ③ ~으로(수단). ④ ~와 함께(동반) ⑤ ~으로(원인)

23 give는 수여동사로 간접목적어를 직접목적어 뒤로 보낼 때 전 치사 to를 붙인다.

24 세금 징수원들이 마을에 왔을 때 일어난 일이므로 세금 징수원 들이 떠난 후의 일을 서술하는 문장 앞에 와야 한다.

25 부사구 long ago가 있으므로 현재완료를 쓸 수 없다.

26 문맥상 '지붕이 없는 집'이 되어야 한다.

27 문맥상 '높은 세금을 피하기 위해'가 알맞다.

28 ⓐ in harmony with: ~와 조화를 이루어 ⓒ cover A with B: B로 A를 덮다

29 현재완료의 계속적 용법이다. build - built - built

30 장소 부사 there는 on the grass roofs를 가리킨다.

My Travel, My Way

시험대비 실력평가
p.112

01 ②	02 ②	03 ④	04 decision
05 ③	06 (c)hance	07 check	08 ②

01 ①, ③, ④, ⑤는 날씨와 관련된 단어이고, ②는 날씨와 관련이 없다.

02 a lot of: 많은 / get into: ~에 들어가다, ~을 타다

03 보통 옥외에서 물건을 사고파는 장소: 시장(market)

04 동사-명사의 관계이다. 충고하다 : 충고 = 결정하다 : 결정

05 a few: 소수의, 약간의

06 어떤 것이 일어날 가능성: chance(가능성)

07 check: 살피다, 점검하다

08 be full of: ~으로 가득 차다 / think of: ~을 생각하다

서술형 시험대비
p.113

01 (1) snowy   (2) cool   (3) creator
02 (1) at last   (2) a little   (3) stay indoors
03 (1) anything   (2) mostly   (3) pack   (4) different
04 (1) actually   (2) amazing   (3) mysterious
05 (1) right now   (2) get to
   (3) is full of   (4) catch a cold
06 (1) (a)dmire   (2) (d)rawing   (3) (f)ood

01 (1) 명사 - 형용사 (2) 반의어 관계 (3) 동사 - 행위자 관계

02 (1) at last: 마침내 (2) a little: 조금 (3) stay indoors: 집안 에 머물러 있다

03 (1) anything: 무엇, 아무것, 무엇이든 (2) mostly: 주로, 일반적 으로 (3) pack: 짐을 싸다, 챙기다 (4) different: 각각 다른, (각 양) 각색의

04 (1) actually: 사실, 실제로, 정말로 (2) amazing: 놀라운 (3) mysterious: 신비한

05 (1) right now: 지금, 당장 (2) get to: ~에 도착하다 (3) be full of: ~으로 가득하다 (4) catch a cold: 감기에 걸리다

06 (1) admire: 존경하다 (2) drawing: 그림, 데생 (3) food: 음 식, 식량

Conversation

p.114~115

핵심 Check

1 (1) Have, read / have   (2) Have, eaten / haven't
2 (1) How, weather / snowy   (2) What's, like / hot
  (3) How's / raining

교과서 대화문 익히기

Check(√) True or False   p.116

1 F 2 T 3 F 4 T 5 T 6 F

교과서 확인학습   p.118~119

Listen & Speak 1 A. Listen and Check

1 Have, tired / have, tried / How / but
2 ever, jumping / haven't, about / When, tried / Wasn't / liked, want

Listen & Speak 2 A. Listen and Answer

1 weather, need / outside, check / going / don't
2 Good, welcome, forecast, sunny, but, rain, home, forecast, Have

Communicate A~B

A been, before / have, lived, for / weather, going, vacation / time, visit, autumn / planning, relax / often, may / take, pack / idea, great
B been, places / have, last / How, weather / mostly, changed

Progress Check

1 ridden / have, about / haven't, was / fun, little
2 weather / quite, check / Thanks / going
3 Good, welcome, raining, but, sunny, leave, without

시험대비 기본평가   p.120

01 What's, like
02 ③   03 ④   04 ③

01 날씨를 물을 때는 How is[How's] the weather?나 What is[What's] the weather like?의 표현을 쓴다.
02 '~에 가 본 적 있니?'라고 경험을 물을 때는 Have you been ~?

표현을 사용한다. '전에'는 before로 쓴다.
03 현재의 바깥 날씨를 묻는데 미래 시제로 답하는 것은 적절하지 않다.
04 현재완료로 경험을 묻는 말에 부정으로 답할 때는 No, I haven't.라고 한다.

시험대비 실력평가   p.121~122

01 ②   02 Have, ever / have   03 ③
04 ④   05 ①   06 ⑤   07 ②, ⑤
08 나는 뉴질랜드를 방문했을 때 번지 점프를 한 번 해 보았어.
09 bungee jumping
10 ④   11 Actually   12 What's, like
13 relax   14 ①

01 What's the weather like outside?(바깥 날씨 어떤가요?)처럼 날씨가 어떤지 물을 때는 비인칭 주어 it을 사용하여 「It's+날씨.」의 형태를 써서 답한다.
02 경험을 묻는 현재완료를 쓴다.
03 엄마, 오늘 날씨 어때요? - 바깥 날씨가 꽤 흐려. 일기예보를 확인해 볼게. - 고마워요, 엄마. - 음, 오후에 비가 올 거야.
04 영화를 본 경험이 있는지 묻는 말에 본 적이 없다고 답하며 '너는 봤니?'라고 상대방에게 되묻는 표현이다. 대화의 흐름상 현재완료형으로 물어야 하므로 Have you (seen it)?의 ④가 적절하다.
05 A가 선글라스를 써야겠다고 했으므로 빈칸에는 날씨가 화창하다는 대답이 와야 한다. ⑤는 특정 지역의 가을 날씨를 묻는 질문에 적절한 대답이다.
06 경험을 묻는 현재완료이므로 'have+과거분사'의 형태가 알맞다.
07 How[What] about you?: 너는 어때?
08 try: 시도해 보다 / once: 한 번
09 it은 인칭대명사로 앞에 나온 단수 명사를 받을 수 있다.
10 have been to: ~에 다녀오다, ~에 가 본 적이 있다 / have gone to: ~에 갔다(그래서 지금 여기 없다)
11 문장 전체를 수식하는 부사가 되어야 한다.
12 날씨를 나타낼 때는 How's the weather?나 What's the weather like?의 표현을 쓴다.
13 특히 일이 끝난 후 쉬거나 즐거운 일을 하면서 시간을 보내다
14 ① Ann이 언제 호주에 갔는지는 위 대화를 통해 알 수 없다.

서술형 시험대비   p.123

01 like, It   02 Have, haven't
03 (B) – (C) – (D) – (A)   04 weather
05 cloudy   06 forecast   07 welcome
08 sunny   09 비가 좀 내릴 것으로 예상된다.

01 It은 날씨를 나타내는 비인칭 용법이다.

02 경험을 나타내는 현재완료 문장이다.

03 너 인도 음식을 먹어 본 적이 있니? - 응, 있어, 하지만 인도 카레만 먹어 봤어. - 어땠어? - 정말 매웠지만, 아주 좋았어.

04 날씨를 묻는 표현이다.

05 cloud의 형용사형이 와야 한다.

06 특히 특별한 사건이나 상황에 관련하여 미래에 일어날 것으로 기대되는 것에 대한 언급: forecast(예측, 예보)

07 welcome to: ~에 오신 것을 환영합니다

08 sun의 형용사형이 와야 한다.

교과서
Grammar

핵심 Check   p.124~125

1 (1) to go   (2) to help   (3) to write with
   (4) cold to drink
2 (1) to understand   (2) It   (3) to exercise   (4) of   (5) for

시험대비 기본평가   p.126

01 (1) to visit   (2) to do   (3) It   (4) of   (5) for
02 (1) to exercise   (2) to finish   (3) It   (4) of   (5) for
03 (1) to change   (2) to visit   (3) to read

01 (1), (2) 형용사적 용법의 to부정사가 필요하다. (3) 가주어 It이 필요하다. (4) 형용사가 kind이므로 의미상의 주어는 'of+목적격'을 쓴다. (5) 형용사가 hard이므로 의미상의 주어는 'for+목적격'을 쓴다.

02 (1), (2) 가주어 It이 있는 구문이므로 밑줄 친 부분을 to부정사로 바꾼다. (3) 가주어는 It으로 나타낸다. (4) 형용사가 brave이므로 의미상의 주어는 'of+목적격'을 쓴다. (5) 형용사가 easy이므로 의미상의 주어는 'for+목적격'을 쓴다.

시험대비 실력평가   p.127~129

01 ③   **02** ④   **03** ③   **04** to write
05 It, to   **06** ①   **07** ①   **08** Do you want anything to eat? [Do you want to eat anything?]
09 ④   **10** ④   **11** It is difficult to fix the machine.   **12** ②   **13** ①   **14** to
15 ①   **16** ⑤   **17** sit → sit on[in]
18 ③   **19** ①   **20** ③   **21** It is

---

pleasant to listen to music.   **22** ⑤   **23** going → to go

01 가주어 It의 진주어로 to부정사가 필요하다.

02 부정대명사 anything을 수식하는 형용사적 용법의 to부정사가 와야 한다.

03 ③은 부사적 용법의 to부정사이다. '~하기 위해'로 해석한다. 나머지는 모두 형용사적 용법이다.

04 '써야 할 편지들'이라는 뜻으로 명사 letters를 수식하는 to부정사의 형용사적 용법이다.

05 주어로 쓰인 to부정사가 긴 경우, 이를 뒤로 보내고 그 자리에 가주어 it을 쓴다.

06 가주어 – 진주어 구문으로 「It is+형용사+to부정사」 형태가 적절하다.

07 <보기>의 to read는 앞에 나온 명사 books를 수식하는 형용사적 용법의 to부정사이다. ① 형용사적 용법 ② 명사적 용법 ③ 부사적 용법 ④ 명사적 용법 ⑤ 부사적 용법

08 부정대명사를 수식하는 to부정사의 형용사적 용법을 쓴다.

09 ④ to going 대신 time을 수식하는 형용사적 용법의 to부정사가 필요하다.

10 ④의 it은 인칭대명사이고 나머지는 가주어 it[It]이다.

11 '그 기계를 고치는 것은'은 to fix the machine으로 나타낸다.

12 첫 문장은 형용사가 kind이므로 의미상의 주어는 'of+목적격'을 쓴다. 두 번째 문장은 형용사가 natural이므로 의미상의 주어는 'for+목적격'을 쓴다.

13 honest와 wise는 의미상의 주어로 'of+목적격'을 쓴다.

14 don't have to: ~할 필요가 없다 / reason to be angry at: ~에게 화낸 이유

15 It이 가주어이므로 진주어인 to부정사가 와야 한다.

16 ①, ④ 진주어로 쓰인 to부정사 ② hopes는 to부정사를 목적어로 취한다. ③ enough to+동사원형: ~하기에 충분히 …한 ⑤ 사역동사의 목적격보어는 동사원형이 와야 한다.

17 to부정사의 수식을 받는 명사가 전치사의 목적어일 경우 뒤에 전치사가 온다.

18 to부정사의 수식을 받는 명사가 전치사의 목적어일 경우 to부정사 뒤에 전치사를 쓴다. ③은 to talk with라고 해야 옳다.

19 ①은 '때'를 나타내는 비인칭 주어이다. 나머지는 가주어 it으로 쓰였다.

20 ③은 앞의 명사 house를 꾸며주는 형용사적 용법의 to부정사이고, 나머지는 모두 명사적 용법으로 쓰였다.

21 to부정사로 쓰인 주어가 길거나 의미를 강조하고 싶을 때 가주어 it을 주어 자리에 쓰고 진주어인 to부정사를 문장 뒤로 보낸다.

22 time을 수식하는 to부정사와 「don't have to+동사원형」의 형태가 필요하다.

23 진주어로 to부정사가 와야 한다.

01 It, to   02 to

03 (1) It is easy to bake cookies.

   (2) He bought a magazine to read on the train.

04 to receive

05 (1) It wasn't easy to visit him every weekend.

   (2) It is an exciting experience to live in another country.

06 (1) She has a strong desire to be a singer.

   (2) I will make every effort to solve this problem.

   (3) We had something to talk about.

   (4) I want a sheet[piece] of papeer to write on.

   (5) Please give me something hot to drink.

07 (1) It   (2) on   (3) with   (4) to

08 (1) play → to play

   (2) of → for

09 to visit   10 for you   11 It, to learn 12 to

13 (1) for → of

   (2) of → for

14 It's a place to sell many things for 24 hours.

01 가주어 it을 문장 앞에 두고 진주어 to부정사구를 뒤로 보낸다.

02 앞의 명사를 수식하는 형용사적 용법의 to부정사가 필요하다.

03 (1) 가주어-진주어 구문으로 「It is + 형용사 + to부정사」 어순이 되어야 한다. (2) '읽을 잡지'이므로 to부정사의 형용사적 용법을 쓴다.

04 가주어인 It의 진주어에 해당하는 to부정사구가 되어야 하므로 to receive로 쓴다.

05 (1) '주말마다 그를 방문하는 것은'는 to visit him every weekend로 나타낸다. (2) '다른 나라에서 사는 것은'는 to live in another country로 나타낸다.

06 (1), (2), (3) to부정사의 형용사적 용법을 이용해 「명사+to부 정사」의 형태로 쓴다. (4) to부정사의 목적어가 있고 to부정사의 동사가 자동사일 때는 전치사가 필요하다. (5) -thing으로 끝나는 부정대명사는 「-thing+형용사+to부정사」의 어순을 따른다.

07 (1) 가주어 it이 필요하다. (2) '~ 위에' 쓰는 것이므로 전치사 on이 필요하다. (3) '칼을 가지고 로프를 자르는' 것이므로 전치사 with가 필요하다. (4) 형용사적 용법의 to부정사가 온다.

08 (1) time을 수식하는 to부정사로 바꾼다. (2) important는 의미상의 주어로 'for+목적격'을 쓴다.

09 명사 places를 수식하는 to부정사의 형용사적 용법이다.

10 important는 의미상 주어로 「for+목적격」을 쓴다.

11 to learn to ride a bike가 주어인 문장으로, 가주어 it이 앞에 온다. to ride는 learn의 목적어로 쓰인 to부정사이다.

12 가주어인 It의 진주어에 해당하는 to부정사와 「don't have to+동사원형」의 형태가 필요하다.

13 (1) 형용사가 stupid이므로 의미상의 주어는 'of+목적격'을 쓴다. (2) 형용사가 necessary이므로 의미상의 주어는 'for+목적격'을 쓴다.

14 to부정사의 형용사적 용법(a place to sell ~)을 이용한다.

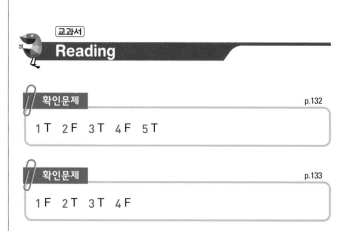

교과서
Reading

📎 **확인문제**   p.132

1 T   2 F   3 T   4 F   5 T

📎 **확인문제**   p.133

1 F   2 T   3 T   4 F

교과서 확인학습 A   p.134~135

01 live   02 week, vacation

03 trip, journal   04 way, special

05 set, mysterious, Earth   06 drive, finally

07 amazing, ring   08 stones, thousands

09 for   10 guess, mystery

11 perfect   12 colors   13 In, around

14 started, so   15 popular, stay 16 like

17 invited   18 full, and

19 busy, admiring

20 much, anything   21 draw, like

22 stop   23 visited   24 become, since

25 movies, else, dinner   26 also, who

27 When, outside, walked   28 touched, get

29 said, smile, portrait   30 Create

31 journal, much

교과서 확인학습 B   p.136~137

1 Hi, I am Lucy Hunter, and I live in London.

2 Last week, my family went on a vacation for three days.

3 During our trip, I made simple drawings in my journal.

4 That was a great way to capture all the special moments.

5 At last, we set foot at Stonehenge, one of the

most mysterious places on Earth.

6 After a two-hour drive from our home in London, we finally got to Stonehenge.

7 It was just amazing to see the ring of huge stones.

8 How did those huge stones get there thousands of years ago?

9 What were they for?

10 Don't try to make a perfect drawing.

11 A few colors will be enough.

12 I guess Stonehenge will remain a mystery for a long time.

13 In the morning, we walked around the Cotswolds.

14 It started to rain in the afternoon, so we decided to stay indoors at our B&B.

15 A B&B is a popular place to stay in England.

16 It feels more like a home than a hotel.

17 The owner invited us for afternoon tea today.

18 The dining table was full of cookies, cake, bread, and cheese.

19 While I was busy eating, Mom was admiring the beautiful cups and plates.

20 I ate too much, so I couldn't eat anything for dinner.

21 It is O.K. to draw everyday objects like cups and plates in your journal.

22 Our last stop was Oxford.

23 We first visited Christ Church College.

24 It has become a world famous place to visit since it appeared in the Harry Potter movies.

25 In the movies, Harry and everyone else eat dinner at the Hall of Christ Church.

26 We also saw portraits of famous people who graduated from the college.

27 When we were outside the building, I walked to the famous olive tree and touched it.

28 "Because I touched this tree," I said, "I will get into Oxford University!"

29 Then, my brother said to me with a smile, "I can't wait to see your portrait on the wall."

30 Create your own avatar.

31 Your drawing journal will become much more interesting.

시험대비 실력평가
p.138~141

01 ① 02 ④ 03 일기에 간단한 그림을 그리는 것 04 특별한 순간을 모두 포착할 수 있다.
05 ③ 06 ② 07 (m)ystery 08 ②

09 ④ 10 ③ 11 ⑤ 12 ②
13 ④ 14 because[as] 15 ④
16 ④ 17 Christ Church College 18 ⑤
19 We also saw portraits of famous people who graduated from the college.
20 ③ 21 ① 22 famous 23 ①, ③
24 ④ 25 ② 26 ② 27 market
28 traditional 29 외국에서 새로운 일들을 해 보는 것
30 ②

01 go on a vacation: 휴가를 가다

02 for+수사가 붙은 기간을 나타내는 명사 / during+특정 기간을 나타내는 명사

03 That은 지시대명사로 앞에 나온 문장을 받는다.

05 What were they for?의 they는 those huge stones를 받으므로 이 문장 앞에 와야 한다.

06 get to: ~에 도착하다

07 이해되거나 알려지지 않은 어떤 것

08 colors가 복수형이고 문맥상 '약간의, 몇 개의'라는 뜻이 필요하므로 A few가 알맞다.

09 거대한 돌의 고리가 무슨 용도로 쓰였는지는 알 수 없다.

10 주어진 문장의 It은 A B&B를 받으므로 B&B를 설명하는 문장 다음에 와야 한다.

11 ⑤는 '그것'의 뜻으로 특정한 명사를 받는 인칭대명사이고 나머지는 모두 비인칭 용법으로 쓰였다.

12 be full of: ~으로 가득 차다

13 while: ~하는 동안

14 이유를 나타내는 접속사가 와야 하므로 because 외에 as나 since도 올 수 있다.

15 ④ 주인이 왜 그들을 초대했는지는 언급되지 않았다.

16 그 장소가 Harry Potter 영화에 등장해서 유명해졌다는 문장 다음에 와야 한다.

17 It은 인칭대명사로 앞에 나온 단수 명사를 받는다.

18 '~한 이래로'의 뜻으로 현재완료에 쓰이는 접속사는 since이다.

19 graduate는 자동사이기 때문에 목적어 앞에 전치사 from이 필요하다.

20 ③ Christ Church College가 영국에서 가장 인기 있는 관광지 중의 하나인지는 언급되지 않았다.

21 '~했을 때'의 뜻으로 때를 나타내는 접속사 when이 알맞다.

22 아주 잘 알려져 있는: famous(유명한)

23 비교급을 강조할 때는 much, far, even, a lot 등을 쓸 수 있다.

24 ④ Lucy의 초상화는 벽에 걸려 있지 않다.

25 Then이 있으므로 야시장에 갔다는 문장 다음에 와야 한다.

26 temples가 복수 명사이므로 much는 쓸 수 없다.

27 대개는 옥외에서 물건을 사고파는 장소: market(시장)

28 명사 food을 수식하므로 형용사형으로 고쳐야 한다.

29 It은 가주어로 진주어인 to try 이하를 받는다.

30 민수가 왜 절을 방문했는지는 언급되지 않았다.

서술형 시험대비

p.142~143

01 foot **02** After **03** amazing **04** at Stonehenge **05** 완벽한 그림을 그리기 위해 노력하지 말라는 것이다. **06** on **07** During **08** That was a great way to capture all the special moments. **09** to stay **10** like **11** owner **12** with **13** nothing → anything **14** 당신의 일기에 컵과 접시 같은 일상적인 물건들을 그려도 괜찮습니다. **15** She was admiring the beautiful cups and plates. **16** to **17** 그토록 많은 아름다운 섬들을 보는 것 **18** forget

01 사람이 그 위에 서 있거나 다리 끝에 있는 신체 부분: foot(발)

02 after a two-hour drive from ~: ~에서 두 시간 동안 운전한 후에

03 사물이 사람을 놀라게 하는 것이므로 현재분사형의 형용사를 쓴다.

04 there는 앞에 언급된 장소를 가리키는 부사이다.

06 go on a vacation: 휴가를 가다

07 for+수사가 붙은 일정한 기간 / during+특정한 기간

08 'all the+복수 명사'의 어순을 취한다.

09 decide는 to부정사를 목적어로 취한다.

10 feel like+명사: ~처럼 느껴지다

11 own: 소유하다 / owner: 소유자, 주인

12 be full of = be filled with: ~으로 가득 차다

13 앞에 not이 있기 때문에 nothing을 쓸 수 없다.

14 like: ~와 같은

16 go on a field trip to: ~으로 현장 학습을 가다

17 It은 가주어로 진주어인 to see ~의 내용을 나타낸다.

18 문맥상 '잊지 않을 것이다'가 되어야 한다.

영역별 핵심문제

p.145~149

01 ④	**02** ③	**03** different	**04** ③
05 ⑤	**06** ②	**07** guess	**08** ③
09 ③	**10** ②	**11** (B)–(C)–(A)–(D)	
12 ④	**13** ②	**14** ④	**15** won't
16 No, he doesn't.		**17** ①	**18** ④
19 ②	**20** it is	**21** ③	**22** ②
23 ②	**24** write → write with		**25** ⑤
26 anything to make myself look slimmer			**27** It, to
28 ④	**29** ①, ⑤	**30** to visit	**31** ③
32 ④	**33** have	**34** ②, ③	**35** ①
36 ②, ④	**37** ③	**38** finally	
39 이상한 거북들을 보는 것			

01 ④는 '명사 - 형용사' 관계인데, 나머지는 '형용사 - 부사'의 관계이다.

02 • 저런 걸 들은 적이 있어요? • 제가 들어갈 만한 충분한 공간이 있나요? • 그가 또 다른 말은 뭐라고 했나요? • 넌 정말 내가 너를 믿으리라고 기대하니?

03 반의어 관계이다. 추운 : 더운 = 같은 : 다른

04 get into: ~에 들어가다 / watch out: 조심하다

05 육지에 완전히 둘러싸인 땅: island(섬)

06 at last: 마침내(=finally)

07 guess: 추측하다

08 ③은 '집에 갔니?'라고 결과를 묻는 표현이고, 나머지는 경험을 묻는 표현이다.

09 B가 비가 오고 있다고 말하고 있고, Yes나 No로 답하지 않았으므로 의문사를 이용한 날씨를 묻는 질문이 와야 알맞다.

10 It was very tasty.(그것은 매우 맛있었어.)라는 말로 보아 긍정의 대답이 들어가야 한다. Have you ever ~?의 긍정의 대답은 Yes, I have.이다.

11 너 말을 타본 적 있니? - 응, 있어. 너는 언제? - 아니, 난 없어. 말 타는 거 어땠어? - 재미있었지만, 조금 무섭기도 했어.

12 How about Seoul?은 서울의 날씨는 어떠냐는 의미이다. ④는 날씨를 묻는 말에 대한 응답으로 적절하지 않다.

13 주어진 문장은 일기예보를 확인해 보겠다는 문장이므로 우산이 필요하냐고 묻는 문장 다음에 와야 한다.

14 날씨를 묻는 표현은 How is the weather?와 What is the weather like?가 있다.

15 be going to는 will을 써서 바꿔 쓸 수 있다.

17 가주어 It을 설명하는 진주어 to부정사가 필요하다.

18 -thing으로 끝나는 부정대명사를 수식하는 to부정사가 필요하다.

19 형용사가 stupid와 clever이므로 의미상의 주어는 'of+목적격'을 쓴다.

20 뒤에 진주어인 to부정사구가 왔으므로 빈칸에는 가주어인 it과 be동사가 와야 한다.

21 -thing으로 끝나는 부정대명사는 「-thing+형용사+to부정사」의 어순을 취한다.

22 <보기>와 나머지는 모두 형용사적 용법이고 ②는 부사적 용법이다.

23 ②는 날씨를 나타내는 비인칭 주어 it이고, 나머지는 to부정사구를 진주어로 하는 가주어 it이다.

24 to부정사의 수식을 받는 명사가 전치사의 목적어일 경우 뒤에 전치사가 온다.

25 형용사적 용법의 to부정사는 명사나 대명사를 뒤에서 수식하여 형용사처럼 쓰인다. 또한, food는 보통 단수로 쓰인다.

26 anything: 어떤 것이든

27 To finish this work이 주어인 문장으로, 가주어 it이 앞에 온다.

28 주어진 문장은 외국에서 새로운 일들을 시도하는 것이 즐거웠다는 뜻이므로 여러 가지 일들을 했다는 문장 다음에 와야 한다.

29 a lot of는 '많은'의 뜻인데 뒤에 복수명사가 오므로 much는 쓸 수 없다.

30 명사 a chance를 꾸며 주는 to부정사의 형용사적 용법이다

31 ③ 민수가 쇼핑을 했다는 말은 언급되지 않았다.

32 부사절 since ~가 있으므로 계속을 나타내는 현재완료가 온다.

33 eat[have] dinner: 저녁을 먹다

34 선행사가 사람이고 주격이므로 who나 that을 쓴다.

35 이유를 나타내는 접속사로 because나 as를 쓸 수 있다.

36 비교급을 강조하는 부사(구)는 much, even, far, a lot 등이다.

37 ③ Christ Church College를 누가 졸업했는지는 언급되지 않았다.

38 final의 부사형은 finally이다.

39 It은 가주어로 진주어인 to watch ~의 내용을 받는다.

단원별 예상문제   p.150~153

01 ④	02 ②	03 creation	04 else
05 ⑤	06 ①, ④	07 ④	08 been

09 나는 해변에서 시간을 좀 보내고 햇빛을 쬐며 휴식을 취할 계획이야.

	10 ⑤	11 write → write on	
12 ②	13 ④	14 It, to	15 ⑤
16 ①	17 ⑤	18 ④	19 ②
20 ②	21 ⑤	22 ②	

23 thousand → thousands   24 ③   25 to make   26 ④, ⑤   27 그토록 아름다운 많은 섬들을 보는 것은 아주 놀라웠다. 28 They went there last month.

01 ④는 유의어 관계이고 나머지는 반의어 관계이다.

02 appear: 나타나다 / show up: 나타나다

03 동사 - 명사의 관계이다.

04 else: 또 다른, 다른

05 ⑤는 pack(짐을 싸다)의 영영풀이이다.

06 날씨를 묻는 표현에는 How's the weather today?, What's the weather like today? 등이 있다

07 No, I haven't.로 답했으므로 현재완료를 이용해서 경험을 묻는 질문이 와야 알맞다.

08 be의 과거분사는 been이다.

09 be planning to: ~할 계획이다

10 4월에는 비가 자주 온다고 언급되었다.

11 to부정사의 수식을 받는 명사가 전치사의 목적어일 경우 뒤에 전치사가 온다.

12 첫 문장은 형용사가 wise이므로 의미상의 주어는 'of+목적격'을 쓴다. 두 번째 문장은 형용사가 impossible이므로 의미상의 주어는 'for+목적격'을 쓴다.

13 It이 가주어이므로 진주어인 to부정사가 와야 한다.

14 To solve this puzzle이 주어인 문장으로, 가주어 it이 앞에 온다.

15 <보기>와 ⑤의 It은 가주어이다. ①, ④ 비인칭 주어, ②, ③ 인칭대명사

16 ①에서 sit은 자동사이므로 chair를 목적어로 취하기 위해서는 전치사 in이나 on이 필요하다.

17 many places to visit(방문할 많은 장소)에서 to visit은 형용사적 용법의 to부정사로 명사인 many places를 수식한다.

18 ④는 to부정사의 형용사적 용법이고, 나머지는 모두 '~하기 위해서'라는 목적을 나타내는 부사적 용법이다.

19 for+수사가 붙은 기간

20 ⓐ, ② 형용사적 용법 ①, ⑤ 명사적 용법 ③, ④ 부사적 용법

21 at last=in the long run: 결국, 마침내

22 get to=arrive at=reach: ~에 도착하다

23 thousand 뒤에 of가 와서 '수천의, 수많은'의 뜻을 나타낼 때는 복수형을 취한다.

24 remain: 계속[여전히] ~이다, 남아 있다

25 try+to부정사: ~하기 위해 애쓰다 / try+-ing: 시험 삼아 ~해 보다

27 It은 to see 이하를 받는 가주어이다.

28 지난달에 남해에 갔다고 언급되었다.

서술형 실전문제   p.154~155

01 gone → been   02 What, like

03 but   04 (A) – (C) – (B) – (D)

05 (1) It isn't easy to keep a diary every day.

(2) I like the photographs which my little[younger] brother takes.

06 (1) It is difficult for me to park a car.

(2) It is safe to ride a bike with a helmet.

(3) It is an exciting experience to live in another country.

07 (1) to go to school

(2) to have lunch

(3) to play on the playground

(4) to do my homework

08 because[as]   09 A B&B

10 of   11 anything

12 They walked around the Cotswolds.   13 many

14 나는 다시 라오스를 방문할 기회를 갖기를 바란다.

15 He or she went to Laos with his or her family.

01 have gone to: ~에 갔다(그래서 여기 없다) / have been to: ~에 가 본 적이 있다, ~에 다녀왔다

02 날씨를 묻는 표현에는 How's the weather today?, What's the weather like today? 등이 있다.

03 상반되는 내용을 연결하는 접속사 but이 알맞다.

04 (A) 엄마, 오늘 날씨 어때요? - (C) 바깥 날씨가 꽤 흐려. 일기예보를 확인해 볼게. - (B) 고마워요, 엄마. - (D) 음, 오후에 비가 올 거야.

05 (1) 「It ~ to부정사」 구문을 이용하여 문장을 완성한다. (2) 관계대명사 which를 이용하여 선행사 the photographs를 수식하도록 한다.

06 to부정사가 이끄는 구가 주어로 오는 경우, to부정사 주어를 문장 뒤로 보내고 그 자리에 It을 쓴다.

07 to부정사의 형용사적 용법을 이용하여 문장을 완성한다.

08 결과의 접속사 so는 이유를 나타내는 접속사를 써서 바꿔 쓸 수 있다. because나 as 대신 since를 쓸 수도 있다.

09 It은 인칭대명사로 앞에 나온 단수 명사를 받는다.

10 be full of: ~으로 가득 차다

11 something은 긍정문, anything은 부정문에서 쓰인다.

12 그들은 코츠월드 언덕을 돌아다녔다고 언급되었다.

13 temples가 복수 명사이기 때문에 much는 쓸 수 없다.

14 to visit는 chance를 수식하는 형용사적 용법이다.

창의사고력 서술형 문제 p.156

|모범답안|

01 (1) I need something to drink
   (2) I need a chair to sit on[in].
   (3) He needs friends to talk with

02 (1) It is kind of her to help the poor.
   (2) It is difficult for us to win the game.
   (3) It is stupid of you to agree to the proposal.
   (4) It is possible for you to finish the work on time.
   (5) It is necessary for foreigners to learn Korean.

03 (1) a movie to watch
   (2) a baseball game to watch
   (3) a piano lesson to take
   (4) four comic books to read

01 앞의 명사를 꾸며주는 to부정사의 형용사적 용법을 이용한다.

02 「It is ~ for[of]+목적어+to부정사」의 가주어, 진주어 구문을 이용한다.

03 to부정사의 형용사적 용법을 이용하여 내용에 맞도록 빈칸을 채운다.

단원별 모의고사 p.157~160

01 ④	02 ③	03 ④	
04 decision	05 up	06 ②	07 ③
08 ⑤	09 ①, ③	10 ④	11 ④
12 ③	13 ③	14 to finish	15 ③
16 ⑤	17 ②	18 ⑤	19 ⓐ to find ⓑ to find
22 ①, ②	23 ④	24 ③	20 ④
26 ①			21 ④

19 ⓐ to find ⓑ to find

20 ④ 21 ④

25 portrait

27 그 올리브 나무에 손을 대면 옥스퍼드 대학에 들어가기 때문이다.

28 ② 29 many

30 ④

01 어떤 것이 일어나거나 존재하게 하다: create(창조하다)

02 right now: 지금, 당장

03 be full of: ~으로 가득 차다 / be fond of: ~을 좋아하다

04 '동사 : 명사'의 관계이다.

05 show up: 나타나다 / clean up: ~을 청소하다

06 Have you ever+과거분사 ~?에 대한 응답은 Yes, I have. / No, I haven't.이다. 빈칸 다음의 말로 보아 부정의 대답이 와야 한다.

07 대답이 No, I haven't.이므로 경험을 묻는 표현인 ③ '넌 곰을 본 적이 있니?'가 알맞다.

08 A가 날씨를 물었으므로 춥고 때때로 눈이 많이 내린다는 응답이 가장 적절하다.

09 How[What] about you?: 너는 어때?

10 Bill이 두려워서 번지 점프를 하지 않는다는 말은 언급되지 않았다.

11 명사 things를 수식하는 형용사적 용법의 to부정사가 와야 한다.

12 문맥상 '함께 여행할 친구를 찾고 있다'는 흐름이 자연스러우므로, 빈칸에는 '~와 함께'에 해당하는 with가 알맞다.

13 기숙사에서 사는 것이므로 live 다음에 전치사 in이 필요하다.

14 it은 가주어이고, 진주어는 형용사 뒤에 to부정사 형태로 와야 한다.

15 <보기>의 to eat는 형용사적 용법의 to부정사이다. ①, ②, ⑤ 부사적 용법 ③ 형용사적 용법 ④ 명사적 용법

16 ⑤ -thing이나 -body로 끝나는 부정대명사의 경우 형용사와 to부정사의 수식을 동시에 받으면 「부정대명사+형용사+to부정사」의 순서로 써야 한다. something important to tell

17 ②의 경우, 두 개의 동사(is, skate)가 같이 쓰일 수는 없다. 가주어 it과 진주어 to부정사구(to skate ~)의 구문으로 만든다.

18 to부정사의 형용사적 용법이다.

19 가주어 It의 진주어로 to부정사 형태가 필요하다.

20 other → else

21 현재완료형에서 '~한 이후로'의 뜻으로 부사절을 이끄는 접속사는 since이다.

22 선행사가 사람이고 주격이므로 who나 that을 쓴다.

23 ④ Harry Potter가 Christ Church College의 학생이라는 말은 언급되지 않았다.

24 ⓐ에는 때를 나타내는 접속사, ⓑ에는 이유를 나타내는 접속사가 와야 한다.

25 어떤 특정한 사람을 그린 그림이나 찍은 사진: portrait(초상화)

26 very는 비교급을 수식할 수 없다.

28 Then이 있으므로 Vientiane의 야시장에 갔다는 문장 다음에 와야 한다.

29 a lot of: 많은

30 ④ 그들의 전통 음식이 무엇인지는 언급되지 않았다.

교과서 다시보기

Lesson 1

01 진정한, 진짜의	02 이, 치아, 이빨	03 유일무이한, 독특한
04 투표하다	05 틀린, 잘못된	06 대통령, 회장
07 만화가	08 재활용[재생]하다	09 위험
10 엎드려 팔굽혀펴기		11 우스운, 웃기는
12 남편	13 문지기, 수위	14 우스개, 농담
15 줄넘기를 하다	16 듣는 사람, 청자	
17 불안해[초조해/두려워] 하는		18 한 번, 언제가
19 성격, 등장인물	20 ~이 되다	21 슈퍼히어로
22 어떤 사람, 누군가		23 연습하다
24 공원[삼림] 관리원		
25 흐린, 구름이 잔뜩 낀		26 활동
27 함께 일하는 사람, 동료		
28 모험심이 강한, 모험을 즐기는		
29 결정하다, 결심하다		
30 경탄할 만한, 엄청난		31 기량, 기술
32 물수제비뜨다	33 기분 좋게, 쾌활하게	
34 연설, 담화	35 ~을 잘하다	
36 ~을 행복하게 만들다		37 (~을) 잘하다
38 잠들다	39 거저 주다, 나누어 주다	
40 ~에 좋다	41 ~에게 안부 전하다	
42 ~와 같은	43 ~을 두려워하는	

01 skill	02 actually	03 real
04 tooth	05 travel	06 unique
07 superhero	08 president	09 skip stones
10 vote	11 speech	12 wrong
13 practice	14 danger	15 enough
16 novel	17 adventurous	18 janitor
19 decide	20 funny	21 cartoonist
22 recycle	23 husband	24 super
25 jump rope	26 cheerfully	27 nervous
28 drawing	29 joke	30 outside
31 per	32 ranger	33 cookbook

34 coworker　　35 such as　　36 be good for

37 Guess what?　38 be good at　39 be afraid of

40 fall asleep　　41 at last　　42 take a look at

43 watch out

1 joke, 농담, 우스개　　2 danger, 위험

3 speaker, 연사, 말[이야기]하는 사람　4 janitor, 문지기, 수위

5 attend, 참석하다　6 tooth, 이, 이빨

7 cartoonist, 만화가　8 pause, (말이나 행동 등의) 멈춤

9 speech, 연설, 담화　10 nervous, 불안해[초조해] 하는

11 novel, 소설　12 scooter, 스쿠터(소형 오토바이)

13 second, (시간 단위인) 초　14 cafeteria, 카페테리아,
구내식당　15 coworker, 함께 일하는 사람, 동료

16 recycle, 재활용[재생]하다

Listen & Speak 1 A. Listen and Check

1 are, doing / making, out of / good at recycling /
like recycling, good for

2 to be, class, listener, try to help, good at planning,
work hard, vote for, for listening

Listen & Speak 2 A. Listen and Check

1 is, wrong / have to, in front of, nervous / Don't, good
speaker, sure, do a good job / feel much better

2 my mom's, should, for / Why don't you, good at
baking / idea, will like / I'm sure, will love

Communicate A. Listen and Answer

1 are, doing / drawing cartoons / Can, take, at / not
yet / not, can't you / guess / Awesome, good at
drawing / think so, to be, drawing skill, enough /
funny, unique characters, sure, cartoonist / made

2 don't, good at / like to, acting, dancing / Don't,
teach you, fast, join us / think about

Progress Check

1 What, doing / making pizza / good at

2 Is, wrong / give a speech, nervous / worry, in front
of, good job, / try

3 is good at, Some, Other, are, good at

Listen & Speak 1 A. Listen and Check

1 B: What are you doing, Nami?

G: I'm making a smart phone case out of my old
jeans.

B: Wow! You're good at recycling old things.

G: Thanks. I like recycling. It's fun, and it's also good
for our Earth.

2 B: Hello, everyone. I'm Kim Yujin. I want to be your
class president. I'm a good listener and always
try to help others. I'm also good at planning fun
school activities. I'll work hard for our class, so
please vote for me. Thank you for listening!

Listen & Speak 2 A. Listen and Check

1 B: Hi, Cindy. Is something wrong?

G: I have to give a speech in front of the whole
school. I'm so nervous.

B: Don't worry. You're a very good speaker. I'm sure
you'll do a good job.

G: Thanks, Minho. I feel much better now.

2 G: Tomorrow is my mom's birthday. What should I
do for her?

B: Why don't you bake a cake for her? You're good
at baking.

G: That's a good idea. I hope my mom will like my
cake.

B: I'm sure your mom will love it.

Communicate A. Listen and Answer

1 Yuri: What are you doing, Jaden?

Jaden: I'm drawing cartoons.

Yuri: Really? Can I take a look at them?

Jaden: No, not yet.

Yuri: Why not? You can show me a few, can't you

Jaden: Well, I guess so.

Yuri: (pause) Ha, ha, ha! Awesome! I like your
cartoons. You're really good at drawing.

Jaden: Do you think so? I want to be a cartoonist,
but I don't think my drawing skills are good
enough.

Yuri: Your cartoons are really funny, and you have
unique characters. I'm sure you'll be a great
cartoonist.

Jaden: Thank you, Yuri. You just made my day.

2 A: Why don't you join our musical theater club?
You're good at singing.

B: Well, I'd like to, but I don't think I'm good at
acting or dancing.

A: Don't worry. We can teach you. I'm sure you'll learn fast. Just join us.

B: O.K. I'll think about it.

Progress Check

1 B: What are you doing?

G: I'm making pizza for dinner.

B: Wow! You're really good at cooking!

G: Thanks.

2 B: Is something wrong?

G: I have to give a speech in English. I'm so nervous.

B: Don't worry. Practice your speech in front of your family. I'm sure you'll do a good job.

G: Thank you. I'll try.

3 W: Everybody is good at something. Some people are good at drawing. Other people are good at singing. What are you good at?

본문 TEST Step 1 p.09~10

01 My, like, novels

02 While, walking, saw

03 looked, cool, unique

04 going, said, suddenly   05 but, asked

06 course, answered

07 see, cafeteria every

08 Suprisingly, of, workers

09 different outside, thought

10 should, graphic, her

11 After, got, began   12 In, superhero

13 rides, super, that

14 saves, danger around

15 per second, away

16 few, later, graphic

17 Awesome, superhero, cool

18 Guess, on, workers   19 my, to

20 loved, too

21 also, coworkers, talents

22 another, won dancing

23 janitor, adventurous, ranger

24 like, superhero, think, asked

25 course, cheerfully   26 go, hello, our

본문 TEST Step 2 p.11~12

01 My name, graphic novels

02 While, walking home, saw, on

---

03 lookesd, cool, unique

04 going home, said, suddenly   05 but, asked

06 course, answered   07 at, every day

08 Surprisingly, one of, workers

09 looks, different, thought   10 should, write

11 After, got home, graphic novel   12 In, superhero

13 rides, can fly   14 saves, around the world

15 per second, gives, away

16 few days later, showed, to

17 Awesome, cool, all my

18 Guess, modeled, on, one of, workers

19 showed, to   20 loved, too

21 also, coworkers, special talents

22 another, worker, won

23 janitor, once, adventurous, ranger

24 like to write, think, asked

25 Of course, cheerfully

26 Let's, say hello to

본문 TEST Step 3 p.13~14

1 내 이름은 호진이고, 만화 소설 쓰는 것을 좋아한다.

2 지난주에 학교에서 집으로 걸어가던 중에 스쿠터에 탄 여자를 보았다.

3 그녀는 정말 멋져 보였고 그녀의 스쿠터는 매우 독특했다.

4 "호진아, 너 집에 가는 중이니?" 그녀가 갑자기 나에게 말했다.

5 "네, 그런데 저를 아시나요?" 나는 물었다.

6 "물론이지," 그녀가 대답했다.

7 "난 매일 학교 식당에서 너를 본단다."

8 놀랍게도, 그녀는 학교 식당 직원 중 한 명이었다.

9 "놀라워! 그녀는 학교 밖에서는 아주 달라 보여."라고 나는 생각했다.

10 "그녀에 대한 만화 소설을 써야겠다."

11 집에 도착한 후, 나는 〈런치 레이디 탄생하다〉라는 새로운 만화 소설을 쓰기 시작했다.

12 그 소설에서 런치 레이디는 슈퍼히어로이다.

13 그녀는 날 수 있는 슈퍼 스쿠터를 탄다.

14 그녀는 전 세계의 위험에 빠진 사람들을 구한다.

15 그녀는 또한 1초에 100개의 쿠키를 만들어 배고픈 아이들에게 나누어 준다.

16 며칠 후에 나는 나의 만화 소설을 친구들에게 보여 주었다.

17 "멋져! 나는 이 슈퍼히어로가 너무 좋아. 그녀는 아주 멋져." 라고 내 모든 친구들이 말했다.

18 "있잖아, 나는 그녀를 우리 식당 직원 중 한 명인 이 여사를 모델로 했어."라고 나는 친구들에게 말했다.

19 나는 이 여사에게 내 책을 보여 주었다.

20 그녀도 그것을 아주 좋아했다.

21 그녀는 또한 나에게 특별한 재능을 가진 그녀의 동료들에 대해 말해 주었다.

22 또 다른 식당 직원인 박 여사는 댄스 경연대회에서 우승했다.

23 우리 학교의 관리인인 김 선생님은 한때 모험적인 공원 관리원이었다.

24 "저는 그들에 대한 슈퍼히어로 이야기를 쓰고 싶어요. 그분들이 그걸 좋아할 것 같아요?" 나는 이 여사한테 물어보았다.

25 "물론 그럴 거야."라고 그녀가 기분 좋게 말했다.

26 "가서 우리의 새 슈퍼히어로 친구들에게 인사하자."

adventurous park ranger.

24 "I'd like to write superhero stories about them. Do you think they'll like that?" I asked Ms. Lee.

25 "Of course they will," she said cheerfully.

26 "Let's go and say hello to our new superhero friends."

본문 TEST Step 4-Step 5 p.15~18

1 My name is Hojin, and I like to make graphic novels.

2 While I was walking home from school last week, I saw a woman on a scooter.

3 She looked really cool, and her scooter was very unique.

4 "Are you going home, Hojin?" she said to me suddenly.

5 "Yes, but do I know you?" I asked.

6 "Of course," she answered.

7 "I see you at the school cafeteria every day."

8 Surprisingly, she was one of the cafeteria workers at school.

9 "Amazing! She looks so different outside the school," I thought.

10 "I should write a graphic novel about her."

11 After I got home, I began to write a new graphic novel, Lunch Lady Begins .

12 In it, Lunch Lady is a superhero.

13 She rides a super scooter that can fly

14 She saves people from danger around the world.

15 She also makes 100 cookies per second and gives them away to hungry children.

16 A few days later, I showed my graphic novel to my friends.

17 "Awesome! I love this superhero. She's so cool," said all my friends.

18 "Guess what? I modeled her on Ms. Lee, one of our cafeteria workers," I told them.

19 I showed my book to Ms. Lee.

20 She loved it, too.

21 She also told me about her coworkers who had special talents.

22 Ms. Park, another cafeteria worker, won a dancing contest.

23 Mr. Kim, the janitor at our school, was once an

구석구석지문 TEST Step 1 p.19

Language Arts

1. studying, library

2. is, fire

3. can't, out

4. flies, saves

Write

1. aunt, role

2. smart, adventurous

3. In, traveled, different

4. While, traveling, over

5. be, afraid, trying, like

Culture Project - Share

1. who, real, in

2. At, moved to, husband

3. attends, famous

4. While, decided to

5. became, hit

구석구석지문 TEST Step 2 p.20

Language Arts

1. Two boys are studying in a library.

2. There is a fire.

3. The boys can't get out

4. Lunch Lady flies on her scooter and saves them.

Write

1. My aunt is my role model.

2. She is smart, strong, and adventurous.

3. In her 30s, she traveled to 70 different countries.

4. While she was traveling, she made friends from all over the world.

5. I want to be someone who is not afraid of trying new things just like her.

Culture Project - Share

1. Julia Child was a person who found her real talent in her 30s.

2. At age 36, she moved to Paris with her husband.

3. She attends a famous cooking school there.
4. While she was studying, she decided to write a cookbook.
5. That book became a big hit.

단어 TEST Step 1
p.21

01 바람	02 미세먼지	03 때때로, 가끔
04 짓다, 건설[건축]하다		05 염소
06 결정하다, 결심하다		07 ~부터[이후]
08 또[그 밖의] 다른, 다른		
09 남쪽[남부]에 위치한		10 입구, 문
11 숲, 삼림	12 동굴	13 신선한
14 비행기 모양의	15 ~이 되다	16 문, 정문
17 100년, 세기	18 연습하다	19 돌
20 조화, 화합	21 원뿔, 원뿔형 물체	22 정보
23 식사, 끼니	24 종류	
25 사랑스러운, 아름다운		26 여행, 관광
27 적	28 저장, 보관	29 낮은
30 나무로 된, 목재의	31 피아노 모양의	32 쇼핑몰, 쇼핑 센터
33 식당	34 대양, 바다	35 ~을 찾다
36 ~을 두려워하다	37 ~을 조심하다	
38 시도하다, 한번 해 보다		39 거꾸로, 뒤집혀
40 ~와 조화를 이루어		41 쌓아 올리다
42 (구조물을 해체하여) 치우다		43 ~을 잘하다

단어 TEST Step 2
p.22

01 cafeteria	02 cover	03 design
04 nature	05 fifth	06 floor
07 welcome	08 avoid	09 ocean
10 thousand	11 without	12 enemy
13 pay	14 collector	15 plant
16 view	17 guesthouse	18 protect
19 restroom	20 round	21 shaped
22 tax	23 unique	24 grass
25 village	26 fine dust	27 sometimes
28 goat	29 forest	30 cave
31 entrance	32 storage	33 wooden
34 harmony	35 look at	36 next to
37 watch out for	38 in harmony with	
39 be good at	40 pile up	41 upside down
42 take down	43 give it a try	

단어 TEST Step 3
p.23

1 thousand, 1,000, 천　2 wooden, 나무로 된, 목재의

3 enemy, 나무로 된, 목재의　4 cave, 동굴

5 information, 정보　6 century, 100년, 세기

7 collector, 징수원　8 forest, 숲, 삼림　9 wind, 바람

10 cafeteria, 카페테리아, 구내식당

11 protect, 보호하다, 지키다　12 restroom, 화장실, 세면실

13 tax, 세금　14 avoid, 방지하다, 피하다

15 guesthouse, 게스트하우스　16 plant, 식물, 초목

대화문 TEST Step 1 p.24~25

Listen & Speak 1 A. Listen and Check

1 look at, looks like / unique, to live in / What kind, live in, want to, airplane–shaped

2 Excuse, there / kind, would, like / like Chinese / There, on, fifth floor

Listen & Speak 2 A. Listen and Writ

1 Excuse, where, find / second floor, next to / Thank / welcome

2 Can, help / looking for, can I find / on, third, next to / you

Communicate A. Listen and Answer

Welcome to, May I help, like, for / kind of, like / with, view, lovely / Every, has, view, are no / have to, floor / do / give, try, have breakfast / can, dining room, next to / see / in, Here's, key / Thank

Progress Check

1 unique, upside, down / looks interesting, kind, strange / What kind of, live in / so, in, piano–shaped

2 Excuse, women's jeans / can find, second floor, next to / Thank / welcome

3 where, find / on the second floor / next to / Thank / welcome

Work -Act

What kind, to build / two–story, looks like / Where, kitchen / on the second floor

대화문 TEST Step 2 p.26~27

Listen & Speak 1 A. Listen and Check

1 B: Hey, look at this house in the picture. It looks like a big shoe!

G: Oh, it's very unique, but I don't want to live in a shoe.

B: What kind of house do you want to live in?

G: Well, I want to live in an airplane–shaped house.

2 M: Excuse me, is there a restaurant in this mall?

W: Yes. What kind of food would you like?

M: I'd like Chinese food.

W There is a great restaurant on the fifth floor.

M: Thank you.

Listen & Speak 2 A. Listen and Write

1 W: Excuse me, where can I find women's shoes?

M: You can find them on the second floor. They're next to the elevator.

W: Thank you.

M: You're welcome.

2 W: Can I help you?

M: I'm looking for watches. Where can I find them?

W: They're on the third floor, next to the restroom.

M: Thank you.

Communicate A. Listen and Answer

Woman: Welcome to Jeonju Hanok Guesthouse. May I help you?

Man: Yes, I'd like a room for two nights.

Woman: Well, what kind of room would you like?

Man: Do you have a room with a garden view? You have a lovely garden.

Woman: Yes, we do. Every room in our house has a garden view, but there are no beds in the rooms.

Man: Do I have to sleep on the floor?

Woman: Yes, you do.

Man: O.K. I'll give it a try. Where can I have breakfast?

Woman: You can have breakfast in the dining room, next to the kitchen.

Man: I see.

Woman: O.K. You're in the Nabi room. Here's your key.

Man: Thank you.

Progress Check

1 B: Hey, look at this unique house in the picture. It's upside down.

G: Oh, it looks interesting, but I think it's kind of strange.

B: What kind of house do you want to live in?

G: I like music, so I want to live in a piano–shaped house.

2 W: Excuse me, where can I find women's jeans?

M: You can find them on the second floor. They're next to the elevator.

W: Thank you.

M: You're welcome.

3 M: Excuse me, where can I find men's hats?

W: You can find them on the second floor. They're next to the elevator.

M: Thank you
W: You're welcome.

Work -Act

A: What kind of house do you want to build?
B: I want to build a two-story house that looks like a boat.
A: Where is the kitchen?
B: It's on the second floor.

---

01 Have, seen roof
02 In, see, on   03 large forests
04 harmony, nature, wooden
05 build, cover, with
06 protect, from, winds
07 Somtimes, out, roofs, meals
08 essential, ago, built, down
09 Centuries, southern, without, paid
10 avoid, taxes, cone-shaped, pilling
11 When, collectors, took, down   12 tax, left, piled
13 From, part, southern, like
14 roofs, round, people
15 have, like, about, themselves
16 only, without, on
17 Each, enough, whole
18 usually, stories
19 storage, second, living, fourth

---

01 Have, seen, on the roof
02 In, can, on roofs   03 has, forests
04 In harmony with, have built, for
05 To build, cover, with
06 protect, from, cold, strong
07 grow out of, enjoy, meals
08 Essential part, long ago, take, down
09 Centuries ago, who, paid, taxes
10 To avoid, some, built, piling up
11 tax collectors, took, down
12 After, left, piled up
13 From, southern, round roofs, look like
14 roofs, big round houses
15 have lived, thousand years, protect, from
16 only, without, first floor

---

17 Each, big enough, whole village
18 usually, four stories
19 first, storage, second, living rooms, third, fourth

---

1 여러분은 집의 지붕 위에 있는 염소를 본 적이 있는가?
2 노르웨이에서, 우리는 지붕 위에 있는 동물들을 볼 수 있다.
3 노르웨이는 큰 숲을 가지고 있다.
4 자연과 조화를 이루면서, 사람들은 오랫동안 나무로 집을 지었다.
5 강하고 따뜻한 집을 만들기 위해, 그들은 지붕을 잔디로 덮는다.
6 잔디 지붕은 길고 추운 겨울과 강한 바람으로부터 그들을 보호한다.
7 때때로, 나무나 식물들이 잔디 지붕에서 자라며, 어떤 동물들은 거기서 식사를 즐긴다.
8 지붕은 집의 필수적인 부분이지만, 오래 전에 어떤 사람들은 오직 지붕을 쉽게 철거하기 위해 지었다.
9 수세기 전 남부 이탈리아에서는 지붕 없는 집을 가진 사람들이 더 적은 세금을 냈다.
10 그들의 집에 부과되는 높은 세금을 피하기 위해, 어떤 사람들은 돌을 쌓아 올려 원뿔 모양의 지붕을 만들었다.
11 세금 징수원들이 마을에 오면, 사람들은 재빨리 지붕을 철거했다.
12 세금 징수원들이 떠난 후 그들은 다시 돌을 쌓아 올렸다.
13 중국 남부의 일부 지역의 하늘에서 보면, 여러분은 큰 도넛처럼 생긴 둥근 지붕들을 볼 수 있다.
14 그것들은 하카족의 크고 둥근 집들의 지붕이다.
15 그들은 적으로부터 스스로를 보호하기 위해 약 천 년 동안 이런 집에서 살아왔다.
16 그 집들에는 1층에 창문이 하나도 없고 문이 하나만 있다.
17 각각의 집은 전체 마을이 들어갈 만큼 크다.
18 그 집은 보통 4개의 층을 가지고 있다.
19 1층에는 주방, 2층에는 창고, 3층과 4층에는 거실과 침실이 있다.

---

1 Have you ever seen a goat on the roof of a house?
2 In Norway, we can see animals on roofs.
3 Norway has large forests.
4 In harmony with nature, people have built wooden houses for a long time.
5 To build strong and warm houses, they cover their roofs with grass.

6 The grass roofs protect them from the long cold winters and strong winds.

7 Sometimes, trees or plants grow out of the grass roofs, and some animals enjoy their meals there.

8 A roof is an essential part of a house, but long ago some people built roofs only to take them down easily.

9 Centuries ago in southern Italy, people who had a house without a roof paid lower taxes.

10 To avoid high taxes on their houses, some people built cone-shaped roofs by piling up stones.

11 When tax collectors came to the town, people took their roofs down quickly.

12 After the tax collectors left, they piled up the stones again.

13 From the sky in a part of southern China, you can see round roofs that look like big doughnuts.

14 They are the roofs of the big round houses of the Hakka people.

15 They have lived in houses like these for about a thousand years to protect themselves from enemies.

16 The houses have only one gate without any windows on the first floor.

17 Each house is big enough for a whole village.

18 It usually has four stories.

19 It has kitchens on the first floor, storage rooms on the second floor, and living rooms and bedrooms on the third and fourth floors.

구석구석지문 TEST Step 1   p.38

Link
1. because of, these days
2. about making, roof
3. Find dust, been
4. designed, that, with, other
5. give, fresh

Write
1. National, in
2. four-story, looks like
3. about, second, floors, top
4. opened in
5. Since, visited, unique

Culture Project
1. In, lived, for
2. weather, hot, cold

---

3. too, cave

구석구석지문 TEST Step 2   p.39

Link
1. I can't open windows because of the fine dust these days.
2. How about making a small garden on the roof?
3. Fine dust has been a big problem in the spring.
4. We designed a roof that has a small garden with trees and many other plants.
5. This garden will give us fresh air.

Write
1. Sejong National Library is in Sejong, Korea.
2. It is a four-story building that looks like an open book.
3. It has about 400 thousand books on the first and second floors and a large cafeteria on the top floor.
4. It opened un 2013.
5. Since then, many people have visited this unique building.

Culture Project
1. In Granada, Spain, some people have lived in cave houses for a long time.
2. The weather in this place is very hot in the summer and cold in the winter.
3. It's not too cold or hot in cave houses.

단어 TEST Step 1 p.40

01 완전한 02 놀라운

03 ~(해)지다, ~이 되다

04 잡다, 포착하다,담아내다 05 해산물

06 여행; 여행하다 07 간단한, 단순한 08 번지 점프

09 예측, 예보 10 지구, 땅 11 또 다른, 다른

12 유명한 13 초상화 14 마침내

15 식량, 음식 16 졸업하다 17 가능성, 기회

18 섬 19 남다, 남아 있다 20 날씨

21 추측하다, 짐작하다 22 시장

23 외국의 24 수수께끼, 미스터리

25 꽁꽁 얼게[너무나] 추운 26 실제로, 정말로

27 예상[기대]하다 28 일기 29 무서운, 겁나는

30 실내에, 집안에 31 창조[창작/창출]하다

32 대학교 33 방학, 휴가

34 나타나다, 출연하다 35 ~에 도착하다

36 ~으로 가득 차다 37 ~에 들어가다, ~에 타다

38 지금, 당장 39 많은 40 ~와 같은

41 ~에 발을 들여놓다 42 좀, 약간, 약간의

43 나타나다

단어 TEST Step 2 p.41

01 touch 02 plate 03 check

04 cloudy 05 pack 06 decide

07 during 08 foreign 09 around

10 drive 11 windy 12 invite

13 huge 14 avatar 15 field trip

16 object 17 college 18 weather

19 moment 20 relax 21 drawing

22 trip 23 turtle 24 market

25 admire 26 diary 27 perfect

28 expect 29 capture 30 graduate

31 freezing 32 scary 33 simple

34 island 35 a few 36 right now

37 get to 38 be full of 39 at last

40 show up 41 set foot at[in] 42 get into

43 such as

단어 TEST Step 3 p.42

1 food, 식량, 음식 2 chance, 가능성

3 island, 섬 4 market, 시장 5 admire, 존경하다

6 drawing, 그림, 소묘 7 amazing, 놀라운

8 beach, 해변, 바닷가 9 create, 창조[창작/창출]하다

10 invite, 초대하다 11 mystery, 수수께끼, 미스터리

12 strange, 이상한, 낯선 13 travel, 여행하다

14 decide, 결정하다 15 relax, 휴식을 취하다

16 pack, (짐을) 싸다

대화문 TEST Step 1 p.43~44

Listen & Speak 1 A. Listen and Check

1 Have, tried / have, only tried / How it / hot, but

2 have, gone / No, haven't, How about / When, visited, tried once / Wasn't, scary / want to, again

Listen & Speak 2 A. Listen and Answer

1 how's weather, need / cloudy outside, check, forecast / Thank / going to rain / don't need

2 welcome to, sunny outside, expectiong, Don't leave, without, weather forecast, Have

Communicate A~B

A have, been to / have, lived, for / How's, there, going to, on vacation / to visit, autumn / planning to spend, relax / often rains, may, sunny days / take, pack, too / good idea, Have

B Have, been to, places / have, went to, last, with / How, weather / mostly sunny, changed

Progress Check

1 Have, ridden / have, How about / haven't, How / fun, a little, too

2 weather / cloudy outside, check, forecast / going to rain

3 welcome to, raining right now, expecting, leave, without

대화문 TEST Step 2 p.45~46

Listen & Speak 1 A. Listen and Check

1 G: Have you ever tried Indian food?

B: Yes, I have, but I've only tried Indian curry.

G: How was it?

B: It was really hot, but I loved it.

2 G: Bill, have you ever gone bungee jumping?

B: No, I haven't. How about you, Katie?

G: When I visited New Zealand, I tried bungee jumping

once.

B: Wasn't it scary?

G: No, I liked it. I want to do it again.

1 B: Mom, how's the weather today? Do I need an umbrella?

W: It's quite cloudy outside. I'll check the weather forecast.

B: Thank you, Mom.

W: Well, it's not going to rain today.

B: Good! Then, I don't need an umbrella today.

2 W: Good morning, and welcome to the weather forecast. It's sunny outside, but we're expecting some rain in the afternoon. Don't leave home without your umbrella. That's the weather forecast for today. Have a nice day.

A Suho: Anna, have you been to Australia before?

Anna: Yes, I have. Actually, I lived in Sydney for a year.

Suho: Great! How's the weather there in April? I'm going to visit Sydney on vacation next week.

Anna: April is a great time to visit Sydney. In April, it's autumn in Australia.

Suho: Good. I'm planning to spend some time on the beach and relax in the sun.

Anna: Well, it often rains in April, but you may have some sunny days.

Suho: I'll take my hat and pack an umbrella, too

Anna: That's a good idea. Have a great time.

B A: Have you been to any special places in Korea?

B: Yes, I have. I went to Ulleungdo last summer with my family.

A: How was the weather there?

B: It was mostly sunny, but the weather changed often.

1 G: Have you ever ridden a horse?

B: Yes, I have. How about you?

G: No, I haven't. How was it?

B: It was fun, but it was a little scary, too.

2 B: Mom, how's the weather today?

W: It's quite cloudy outside. I'll check the weather forecast.

B: Thanks, Mom.

W: Well, it's going to rain in the afternoon.

3 M: Good evening, and welcome to the weather forecast. It's raining right now, but we're expecting a sunny day tomorrow. Don't leave home tomorrow without your hat.

본문 TEST Step 1   p.47~48

01 am, live in
02 Last, on, for
03 During, simple, journal
04 way, capture, special
05 last, set, mysterious
06 After, drive, finally
07 amazing, ring, huge
08 stones, thousands, ago   09 What, for
10 guess, remain, mystery   11 try, perfect
12 few, enough   13 In, around
14 started, so, decided   15 popular, stay
16 like, than   17 invited, for
18 dining, full, and
19 busy, admiring, plates
20 much, anything
21 draw, like, journal   22 Our, stop
23 visited, College
24 become, since, appeared
25 movies, else, dinner
26 also, portraits, graduated
27 outside, walked, touched
28 Because, touched, get
29 said, smile, wait   30 Create, own
31 drawing, much, interesting

본문 TEST Step 2   p.49~50

01 am, live in   02 Last week, went on, for
03 During, drawings, journal
04 to capture, special moments
05 set foot at, one of, places
06 After, drive from, got to   07 amazing, ring
08 huge stones, thousands, ago   09 What, for
10 guess, remain, for
11 Don't try, perfect   12 A few, enough
13 In, walked around
14 to rain, decided to stay
15 popular, stay in
16 feels, like, than   17 owner, invited
18 dining, was full of
19 busy eating, admiring, plates

20 ate, so, couldn't eat
21 to draw, like, journal   22 last stop
23 first visited
24 has become, famous place, since
25 everyone, eat dinner
26 saw portraits, graduated from
27 When, outside, walked to, touched
28 Because, touched, get into
29 with a smile, can't wait to   30 Create, avatar
31 drawing journal, much more

보았다.

27 우리가 건물 밖으로 나왔을 때, 나는 유명한 올리브 나무로 걸어가서 그것을 만졌다.

28 "이 나무를 만졌기 때문에, 난 옥스퍼드 대학교에 들어갈 거야!" 라고 말했다.

29 그러자 오빠가 웃으면서 "벽에 걸린 네 초상화가 빨리 보고 싶어."라고 말했다.

30 여러분 자신의 아바타를 만드세요.

31 그림일기가 훨씬 더 재미있을 거예요.

본문 TEST Step 3   p.51~52

1 안녕, 나는 Lucy Hunter이고 런던에 살아요

2 지난주에 우리 가족은 3일 동안 휴가를 갔습니다.

3 여행 중에 나는 일기에 간단한 그림을 그렸어요.

4 그것은 모든 특별한 순간을 포착하는 훌륭한 방법이었어요.

5 마침내, 우리는 지구에서 가장 불가사의한 장소 중 하나인 스톤헨지에 발을 디뎠다.

6 런던에 있는 집에서 차로 두 시간을 달려서 우리는 마침내 스톤헨지에 도착했다.

7 원형으로 둘러서 있는 거대한 돌들을 보는 것은 정말 놀라웠다.

8 어떻게 그 거대한 돌들이 수천 년 전에 그곳에 도착했을까?

9 그것들은 무엇을 위한 것이었을까?

10 완벽한 그림을 그리려고 하지 마세요.

11 몇 가지 색깔이면 충분할 것입니다.

12 스톤헨지는 오랫동안 미스터리로 남을 것 같다.

13 아침에 우리는 코츠월드 언덕을 돌아다녔다.

14 오후에 비가 오기 시작해서, 우리는 B&B의 실내에서 머물기로 결정했다.

15 B&B는 영국에서 체류하는 곳으로 인기가 있다.

16 그것은 호텔이라기보다는 집처럼 느껴진다.

17 주인은 오늘 오후의 다과회에 우리를 초대했다

18 식탁에는 쿠키, 케이크, 빵, 그리고 치즈가 가득했다.

19 내가 먹느라 바쁠 때, 엄마는 아름다운 컵과 접시를 감탄하며 바라보고 계셨다.

20 나는 너무 많이 먹어서 저녁으로 아무것도 먹을 수 없었다.

21 당신의 일기에 컵과 접시 같은 일상적인 물건들을 그려도 괜찮습니다.

22 우리가 마지막으로 머문 곳은 옥스퍼드였다.

23 우리는 먼저 Christ Church College를 방문했다.

24 이곳은 해리포터 영화에 등장한 이후 방문해야 할 세계적으로 유명한 장소가 되었다.

25 영화에서 Harry와 다른 모든 사람들이 Christ Church의 회관에서 저녁을 먹는다.

26 우리는 또한 그 대학을 졸업한 유명한 사람들의 초상화를

본문 TEST Step 4- Step 5   p.53~56

1 Hi, I am Lucy Hunter, and I live in London.

2 Last week, my family went on a vacation for three days.

3 During our trip, I made simple drawings in my journal.

4 That was a great way to capture all the special moments.

5 At last, we set foot at Stonehenge, one of the most mysterious places on Earth.

6 After a two-hour drive from our home in London, we finally got to Stonehenge.

7 It was just amazing to see the ring of huge stones.

8 How did those huge stones get there thousands of years ago?

9 What were they for?

10 Don't try to make a perfect drawing.

11 A few colors will be enough.

12 I guess Stonehenge will remain a mystery for a long time.

13 In the morning, we walked around the Cotswolds.

14 It started to rain in the afternoon, so we decided to stay indoors at our B&B.

15 A B&B is a popular place to stay in England.

16 It feels more like a home than a hotel.

17 The owner invited us for afternoon tea today.

18 The dining table was full of cookies, cake, bread, and cheese.

19 While I was busy eating, Mom was admiring the beautiful cups and plates.

20 I ate too much, so I couldn't eat anything for dinner.

21 It is O.K. to draw everyday objects like cups and plates in your journal.

22 Our last stop was Oxford.

23 We first visited Christ Church College.

24 It has become a world famous place to visit

since it appeared in the Harry Potter movies.

25 In the movies, Harry and everyone else eat dinner at the Hall of Christ Church.

26 We also saw portraits of famous people who graduated from the college.

27 When we were outside the building, I walked to the famous olive tree and touched it.

28 "Because I touched this tree," I said, "I will get into Oxford University!"

29 Then, my brother said to me with a smile, "I can't wait to see your portrait on the wall."

30 Create your own avatar.

31 Your drawing journal will become much more interesting.

2. We visited a lot of beautiful temples and went to the night market in Vientiane.

3. Then, we moved to Vang Vieng and went river tubing.

4. We also enjoyed their traditional food.

5. It was a lot of fun to try new things in a foreign country.

6. I hope I will have a chance to visit Laos again.

Culture Project

1. September 15, 1835

2. We finally arrived on this island.

3. There are many animals to study here.

4. Today, I saw some strange turtles.

5. It was amazing to watch them.

구석구석지문 TEST Step 1   p.57

Link - Share

1. went on, last

2. It, amazing, islands

3. also visitied, Village

4. never forget

Write

1. Last winter, went, with

2. lot, temples, market

3. moved to, went

4. enjoyed, traditional

5. lot of, to try, foreign

6. chance to visit

Culture Project

1. September

2. arrived on

3. are, to study

4. asw, strange

5. amazing, watch

구석구석지문 TEST Step 2   p.58

Link - Share

1. We went on a field trip to Namhae last month.

2. It was just amazing to see so many beautiful islands.

3. We also visited Namhae German Village.

4. We'll never forget that trip.

Write

1. Last winter, I went to Laos with my family.

적중 100
영어 기출 문제집

정답 및 해설

미래 | 최연희